Chemical Building Blocks: Teacher's Edition

Contents in Brief

Teacher's Edition

See Program Component List on page ii

Student Edition

UNIVERSITY OF TOLEDO LIBRARIES

D1511233

Prentice Hall Science Explorer

Series Tables of Contents

The Nature of Science and Technology

1. What Is Science?
2. The Work of Scientists
3. Technology and Engineering

Life Science

From Bacteria to Plants

1. Living Things
2. Viruses and Bacteria
3. Protists and Fungi
4. Introduction to Plants
5. Seed Plants

Animals

1. Sponges, Cnidarians, and Worms
2. Mollusks, Arthropods, and Echinoderms
3. Fishes, Amphibians, and Reptiles
4. Birds and Mammals
5. Animal Behavior

Cells and Heredity

1. Cell Structure and Function
2. Cell Processes and Energy
3. Genetics: The Science of Heredity
4. Modern Genetics
5. Changes Over Time

Human Biology and Health

1. Bones, Muscles, and Skin
2. Food and Digestion
3. Circulation
4. Respiration and Excretion
5. Fighting Disease
6. The Nervous System
7. The Endocrine System and Reproduction

Environmental Science

1. Populations and Communities
2. Ecosystems and Biomes
3. Living Resources
4. Land, Water, and Air Resources
5. Energy Resources

Earth Science

Inside Earth

1. Plate Tectonics
2. Earthquakes
3. Volcanoes
4. Minerals
5. Rocks

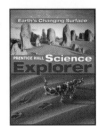

Earth's Changing Surface

1. Mapping Earth's Surface
2. Weathering and Soil Formation
3. Erosion and Deposition
4. A Trip Through Geologic Time

Earth's Waters

1. Earth: The Water Planet
2. Freshwater Resources
3. Ocean Motions
4. Ocean Zones

Weather and Climate

1. The Atmosphere
2. Weather Factors
3. Weather Patterns
4. Climate and Climate Change

Astronomy

1. Earth, Moon, and Sun
2. Exploring Space
3. The Solar System
4. Stars, Galaxies, and the Universe

Physical Science

Chemical Building Blocks

1. Introduction to Matter
2. Solids, Liquids, and Gases
3. Elements and the Periodic Table
4. Exploring Materials

Chemical Interactions

1. Atoms and Bonding
2. Chemical Reactions
3. Acids, Bases, and Solutions
4. Carbon Chemistry

Motion, Forces, and Energy

1. Motion
2. Forces
3. Forces in Fluids
4. Work and Machines
5. Energy
6. Thermal Energy and Heat

Electricity and Magnetism

1. Magnetism
2. Electricity
3. Using Electricity and Magnetism
4. Electronics

Sound and Light

1. Characteristics of Waves
2. Sound
3. The Electromagnetic Spectrum
4. Light

Teacher's Edition

Chemical Building Blocks

PRENTICE HALL Science Explorer

PEARSON
Prentice
Hall

Needham, Massachusetts
Upper Saddle River, New Jersey

Copyright © 2005 by Pearson Education, Inc., publishing as Pearson Prentice Hall, Upper Saddle River, New Jersey 07458.
All rights reserved. Printed in the United States of America. This publication is protected by copyright, and permission should be obtained from the publisher prior to any prohibited reproduction, storage in a retrieval system, or transmission in any form or by any means, electronic, mechanical, photocopying, recording, or likewise. For information regarding permission(s), write to: Rights and Permissions Department.

Pearson Prentice Hall™ is a trademark of Pearson Education, Inc.
Pearson® is a registered trademark of Pearson plc.
Prentice Hall® is a registered trademark of Pearson Education, Inc.
Lab zone™ is a trademark of Pearson Education, Inc.

Planet Diary® is a registered trademark of Addison Wesley Longman, Inc.

Discovery Channel School® is a registered trademark of Discovery Communications, Inc., used under license.
The Discovery Channel logo is a trademark of Discovery Communications, Inc.

SciLinks® is a trademark of the National Science Teachers Association. The SciLinks® service includes copyrighted materials and is owned and provided by the National Science Teachers Association. All rights reserved.

Science News® is a registered trademark of Science Services, Inc.

ISBN 0-13-181130-4   1 2 3 4 5 6 7 8 9 10   08 07 06 05 04

Pacing Options

PRENTICE HALL
TeacherEXPRESS™
Plan • Teach • Assess

Lab zone™

SCIENCE EXPLORER offers many aids to help you plan your instruction time, whether regular class periods or block scheduling. Section-by-section lesson plans for each chapter include suggested times for Student Edition activities. TeacherExpress™ and the Lab zone™ Easy Planner CD-ROM will help you manage your time electronically.

Pacing Chart

	PERIODS	BLOCKS		PERIODS	BLOCKS
Careers: From Plants to Chemicals	1–2	1/2–1	**Chapter 3 Elements and the Periodic Table**		
Chapter 1 Introduction to Matter			Chapter 3 Project *Survey Properties of Metals*	Ongoing	Ongoing
Chapter 1 Project *Design and Build a Density-Calculating System*	Ongoing	Ongoing	1 Introduction to Atoms	2–3	1–1 ¹/₂
			2 Organizing the Elements	2–3	1–1 ¹/₂
1 Describing Matter	3–4	1 ¹/₂–2	3 Metals	3–4	1 ¹/₂–2
2 Measuring Matter	2–3	1–1 ¹/₂	4 Nonmetals and Metalloids	3–4	1 ¹/₂–2
3 Changes in Matter	2–3	1–1 ¹/₂	5 Integrating Astronomy: Elements From Stardust	1–2	¹/₂–1
4 Integrating Physics: Energy and Matter	2–3	1–1 ¹/₂			
Chapter 1 Review and Assessment	1–2	¹/₂–1	Chapter 3 Review and Assessment	1–2	¹/₂–1
Chapter 2 Solids, Liquids, and Gases			**Chapter 4 Exploring Materials**		
Chapter 2 Project *A Story of Changes in Matter*	Ongoing	Ongoing	Chapter 4 Project *Material Profiles*	Ongoing	Ongoing
			1 Tech & Design: Polymers and Composites	3–4	1 ¹/₂–2
1 States of Matter	2–3	1–1 ¹/₂	2 Metals and Alloys	2–3	1–1 ¹/₂
2 Changes of State	3–4	1 ¹/₂–2	3 Ceramics and Glass	1–2	¹/₂–1
3 Gas Behavior	2–3	1–1 ¹/₂	4 Radioactive Elements	3–4	1 ¹/₂–2
4 Integrating Mathematics: Graphing Gas Behavior	2–3	1–1 ¹/₂	Chapter 4 Review and Assessment	1–2	¹/₂–1
Chapter 2 Review and Assessment	1–2	¹/₂–1	Interdisciplinary Exploration: Gold—The Noble Metal	2–3	1–1 ¹/₂

Research-Based and Proven to Work

As the originator of the small book concept in middle school science, and as the nation's number one science publisher, Prentice Hall takes pride in the fact that we've always listened closely to teachers. In doing so, we've developed programs that effectively meet the needs of your classroom.

As we continue to listen, we realize that raising the achievement level of all students is the number one challenge facing teachers today. To assist you in meeting this latest challenge, Prentice Hall has combined the very best author team with solid research to create a program that meets your high standards and will ensure that no child is left behind.

With Prentice Hall, you can be confident that your students will not only be motivated, inspired, and excited to learn science, but that they will also achieve the success needed in today's environment of the No Child Left Behind (NCLB) legislation and testing reform.

On the following pages, you will read about the key elements found throughout *Science Explorer* that truly set this program apart and ensure success for you and your students.

> As we continue to listen, we realize that raising the achievement level of all students is the number one challenge facing teachers today.

A Science Program Backed by Research

In developing Prentice Hall *Science Explorer*, we used research studies as a central, guiding element. Research on *Science Explorer* indicated key elements of a textbook program that ensure students' success: support for reading and mathematics in science, consistent opportunities for inquiry, and an ongoing assessment strand. This research was conducted in phases and continues today.

1. Exploratory: Needs Assessment

Along with periodic surveys concerning state and national standards as well as curriculum issues and challenges, we conducted specific product development research, which included discussions with teachers and advisory panels, focus groups, and quantitative surveys. We explored the specific needs of teachers, students, and other educators regarding each book we developed in Prentice Hall *Science Explorer*.

2. Formative: Prototype Development and Field-Testing

During this phase of research, we worked to develop prototype materials. Then we tested the materials by field-testing with students and teachers and by performing qualitative and quantitative surveys. In our early prototype testing, we received feedback about our lesson structure. Results were channeled back into the program development for improvement.

3. Summative: Validation Research

Finally, we conducted and continue to conduct long-term research based on scientific, experimental designs under actual classroom conditions. This research identifies what works and what can be improved in the next revision of Prentice Hall *Science Explorer*. We also continue to monitor the program in the market. We talk to our users about what works, and then we begin the cycle over again. The next section contains highlights of this research.

A Science Program With Proven Results

In a year-long study in 2000–2001, students in six states using Prentice Hall *Science Explorer* outscored students using other science programs on a nationally normed standardized test.

The study investigated the effects of science textbook programs at the eighth-grade level. Twelve eighth-grade science classes with a total of 223 students participated in the study. The selected classes were of similar student ability levels.

Each class was tested at the beginning of the school year using the TerraNova CTBS Basic Battery Plus, and then retested at the end of the school year. The final results, shown in the graph, show a significant improvement in test scores from the pre-test to the post-test evaluation.

• All tests were scored by CTB/McGraw-Hill, the publisher of the TerraNova exam. Statistical analyses and conclusions were performed by an independent firm, Pulse Analytics, Inc.

In Japan, Lesson Study Research has been employed for a number of years as a tool for teachers to improve their curriculum. In April 2003, Prentice Hall adapted this methodology to focus on a lesson from this edition. Our goal was to test the effectiveness of lesson pedagogy and improve it while in the program development stage. In all three classrooms tested, student learning increased an average of 10 points from the pre- to the post-assessment.

• Detailed results of these studies can be obtained at **www.PHSchool.com/research.**

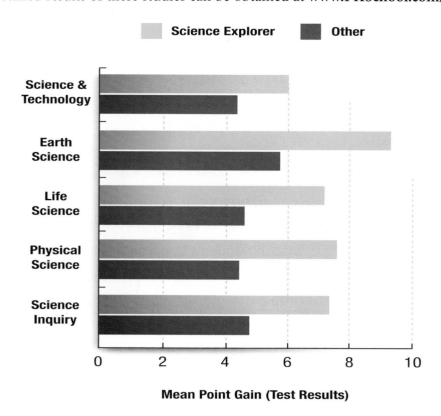

Foundational Research: Inquiry in the Science Classroom

"How do I know if my students are inquiring?" "If students are busy doing lots of hands-on activities, are they using inquiry?" "What is inquiry, anyway?" If you're confused, you are not alone. Inquiry is the heart and soul of science education, with most of us in continuous pursuit of achieving it with our students!

Defining Science Inquiry

What is it? Simply put, inquiry is the intellectual side of science. It is thinking like a scientist—being inquisitive, asking why, and searching for answers. The National Science Education Content Standards define inquiry as the process in which students begin with a question, design an investigation, gather evidence, formulate an answer to the original question, and communicate the investigative process and results. Since it is often difficult to accomplish all this in one class period, the standards also acknowledge that at times students need to practice only one or two inquiry components.

Understanding Inquiry

The National Research Council in Inquiry and the National Science Education Standards (2000) identified several "essential features" of classroom inquiry. We have modified these essential features into questions to guide you in your quest for enhanced and more thoughtful student inquiry.

1. **Who asks the question?** In most curricula, these focusing questions are an element given in the materials. As a teacher you can look for labs that, at least on a periodic basis, allow students to pursue their own questions.

2. **Who designs the procedures?** To gain experience with the logic underlying experimentation, students need continuous practice with designing procedures. Some labs in which the primary target is content acquisition designate procedures. But others should ask students to do so.

3. **Who decides what data to collect?** Students need practice in determining the data to collect.

4. **Who formulates explanations based upon the data?** Students should be challenged to think—to analyze and draw conclusions based on their data, not just copy answers from the text materials.

5. **Who communicates and justifies the results?** Activities should push students not only to communicate but also to justify their answers. Activities also should be thoughtfully designed and interesting so that students want to share their results and argue about conclusions.

Making Time for Inquiry

One last question—Must each and every activity have students do all of this? The answer is an obvious and emphatic "No." You will find a great variety of activities in *Science Explorer*. Some activities focus on content acquisition, and thus they specify the question and most of the procedures. But many others stress in-depth inquiry from start to finish. Because inquiry is an intellectual pursuit, it cannot merely be characterized by keeping students busy and active. Too many students have a knack for being physically but not intellectually engaged in science. It is our job to help them engage intellectually.

Michael J. Padilla, Ph.D.
Program Author of *Science Explorer*
Professor of Science Education
University of Georgia
Athens, Georgia

"Because inquiry is an intellectual pursuit, it cannot merely be characterized by keeping students busy and active."

Evaluator's Checklist

Does your science program promote inquiry by—

✔ Enabling students to pursue their own questions

✔ Allowing students to design their own procedures

✔ Letting students determine what data are best to collect

✔ Challenging students to think critically

✔ Pushing students to justify their answers

Inquiry in *Science Explorer*

Science Explorer offers the most opportunities to get students to think like a scientist. By providing inquiry opportunities throughout the program, *Science Explorer* enables students to enhance their understanding by participating in the discovery.

Student Edition Inquiry

Six lab and activity options are included in every chapter, structured from directed to open-ended—providing you the flexibility to address all types of learners and accommodate your class time and equipment requirements. As Michael Padilla notes, some activities focus on content acquisition, and thus the question and most of the procedures are specified. But many others stress in-depth inquiry from start to finish. The graph below shows how, in general, inquiry levels are addressed in the Student Edition.

Science Explorer encourages students to develop inquiry skills across the spectrum from teacher-guided to open-ended. Even more opportunities for real-life applications of inquiry are included in Science & Society, Science & Technology, Careers in Science, and Interdisciplinary Exploration features.

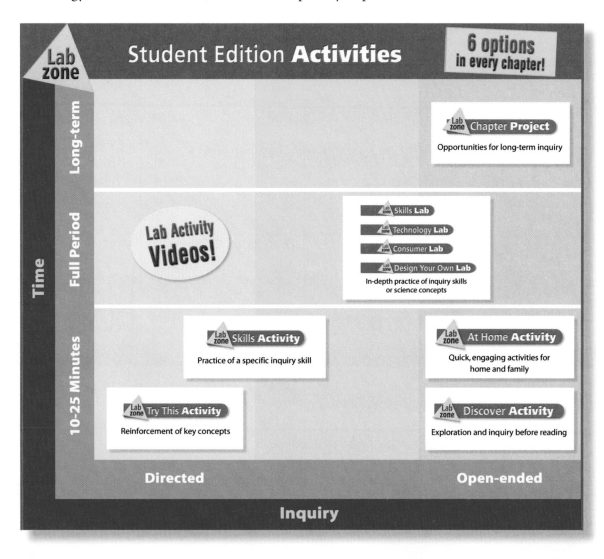

Inquiry Skills Chart

SCIENCE EXPLORER provides comprehensive teaching, practice, and assessment of science skills, with an emphasis on the process skills necessary for inquiry. This chart lists the skills covered in the program and cites the page numbers where each skill is covered.

Basic Process SKILLS				
	Student Text: Projects and Labs	Student Text: Activities	Student Text: Caption and Review Questions	Teacher's Edition: Extensions
Observing	34–35, 73, 96–97	102, 118, 137	11	8, 9, 50, 88, 121, 135, 136
Inferring	34–35, 54, 106–107	24, 31, 55, 74, 80, 88, 135, 142	27, 38, 60, 95, 114, 134, 138, 145, 150	
Predicting	54, 66–67	91	47, 53, 64, 65, 70, 87, 95, 114, 136, 146	82, 86
Classifying	96–97, 106–107, 117	82, 98	7, 15, 23, 33, 38, 65, 89, 95, 114, 125, 150	7, 44, 77, 89, 92
Making Models	34–35, 147	79		11, 26, 44, 46, 56, 58, 76, 78, 94, 110, 119, 140, 143
Communicating	5, 21, 34–35, 41, 54, 66–67, 73, 96–97, 106–107, 117, 126–127, 147	27, 33, 47, 53, 65, 77, 79, 87, 95, 111, 113, 123, 125, 134, 138, 146, 149		13, 17, 23, 25, 43, 49, 57, 59, 83, 91, 93, 95, 101, 103, 105, 109, 111, 119, 123, 131, 133, 145
Measuring	21	16		18, 61
Calculating	5	12, 19, 27, 57, 120, 142	17, 20, 38, 61, 63, 70, 71, 150	17, 18, 19
Creating Data Tables	21, 66–67, 147	131		
Graphing	66–67, 126–127, 147	27, 52, 91, 131	70	26, 62, 63, 64, 65
Advanced Process SKILLS				
Posing Questions	41		52, 94	
Developing Hypotheses		48, 108, 130	26, 111	
Designing Experiments	21, 35, 54, 66–67, 73, 117			144

Advanced Process SKILLS (continued)

	Student Text: Projects and Labs	Student Text: Activities	Student Text: Caption and Review Questions	Teacher's Edition: Extensions
Controlling Variables	21, 96–97			
Forming Operational Definitions	41	6, 42		
Interpreting Data	34–35, 54, 66–67, 106–107, 147	8, 27, 50, 52, 91, 131	18, 38, 70, 86, 87, 102, 134, 150	
Drawing Conclusions	21, 66–67, 96–97, 107	16, 22, 30, 46, 52, 62, 139	15, 32, 47, 114, 125	

Critical Thinking SKILLS

Comparing and Contrasting	73, 117	27	20, 45, 47, 53, 65, 79, 87, 99, 105, 114, 134, 146, 150	17, 19, 51, 91, 99, 103, 141, 143
Applying Concepts	5	33, 47, 65, 79, 95, 111, 134, 138, 146	8, 15, 27, 29, 31, 47, 49, 53, 61, 70, 75, 79, 95, 104, 105, 109, 111, 114, 121, 131, 138, 146, 150	
Interpreting Diagrams, Graphs, Photographs, and Maps		27, 52, 91, 131	13, 24, 38, 51, 53, 56, 71, 78, 81, 83, 119, 125, 141, 146, 150	25, 63
Relating Cause and Effect			33, 47, 53, 61, 65, 70, 79, 114, 146	
Making Generalizations			33, 79, 87, 90, 101, 105, 111, 132	
Making Judgments		129	15, 27, 29, 38, 53, 125	
Problem Solving	126–127		15, 20, 27, 29, 38	

Informational Organizational SKILLS

Concept Maps			37, 113	11, 27, 36, 47, 53, 68, 79, 89, 112, 148
Compare/Contrast Tables			69, 149	9, 77, 105, 134
Venn Diagrams				45
Flowcharts				137
Cycle Diagrams				

The *Science Explorer* program provides additional teaching, reinforcement, and assessment of skills in the *Inquiry Skills Activities Book* and the *Integrated Science Laboratory Manual*.

A National Look at Science Education

Project 2061 was established by the American Association for the Advancement of Science (AAAS) as a long-term project to improve science education nationwide. A primary goal of Project 2061 is to define a "common core of learning"—the knowledge and skills we want all students to achieve. Project 2061 published *Science for All Americans* in 1989 and followed this with *Benchmarks for Science Literacy* in 1993. Benchmarks recommends what students should know and be able to do by the end of grades 2, 5, 8, and 12. Project 2061 clearly states that *Benchmarks* is not a curriculum but a tool for designing successful curricula.

The National Research Council (NRC) used *Science for All Americans* and *Benchmarks* to develop the National Science Education Standards (NSES), which were published in 1996. The NSES are organized into six categories (Content, Teaching, Assessment, Professional Development, Program, and System) to help schools establish the conditions necessary to achieve scientific literacy for all students.

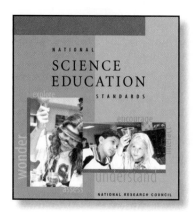

Michael Padilla, the program author of *Science Explorer,* guided one of six teams of teachers whose work led to the publication of *Benchmarks.* He also was a contributing writer of the National Science Education Standards. Under his guidance, *Science Explorer* has implemented these standards through its inquiry approach, a focus on student learning of important concepts and skills, and teacher support aligned with the NSES teaching standards.

Neither *Benchmarks* nor the NSES requires a single, uniform national curriculum, and in fact there is a great diversity nationwide in science curricula. The correlations that follow are designed to help you use the *Science Explorer* program to meet your particular curriculum needs.

Meeting the National Science Education Standards

INTRODUCTION TO MATTER

Science as Inquiry (Content Standard A)

● **Design and conduct a scientific investigation** Students investigate the relationship between the density of a material and its volume. *(Skills Lab)*

● **Develop descriptions, explanations, predictions, and models using evidence** Students investigate how electrical energy can be used to isolate copper. *(Skills Lab)*

● **Use mathematics in all aspects of scientific inquiry** A ratio compares two numbers. You can determine the density of a sample by dividing its mass by its volume. *(Chapter Project; Describing Matter; Measuring Matter; Skills Lab)*

● **Understandings about scientific inquiry** Scientists use the International System of Units to measure the properties of matter. *(Measuring Matter)*

Physical Science (Content Standard B)

● **Properties and changes of properties in matter** Every form of matter has physical properties and chemical properties. A physical change alters the form or appearance of matter but does not make any substance in the matter into a different substance; a chemical change produces one or more new substances.

(Describing Matter; Changes in Matter)

● **Transfer of energy** When atoms combine, they form a chemical bond. Every chemical or physical change in matter includes a change in energy. Forms of energy related to changes in matter include kinetic, potential, chemical, electromagnetic, electrical, and thermal energy. *(Describing Matter; Changes in Matter; Energy and Matter; Skills Lab)*

Science and Technology (Content Standard E)

● **Design a solution or product** Students design and build a density-calculating system. *(Chapter Project)*

Science in Personal and Social Perspectives (Content Standard F)

● **Science and technology in society** Students analyze the issues of transporting hazardous chemicals. *(Science and Society)*

SOLIDS, LIQUIDS, AND GASES

Science as Inquiry (Content Standard A)

● **Use appropriate tools and technology to gather, analyze, and interpret data** Students investigate how surrounding temperature affects the rate at which ice melts. *(Skills Lab—Melting Ice)*

A National Look at Science Education *(continued)*

● **Develop descriptions, explanations, predictions, and models using evidence** Students investigate the relationship between pressure and volume of a gas. *(Skills Lab—It's a Gas)*

● **Communicate scientific procedures and explanations** Students create a skit or cartoon to communicate how particles of matter behave as they change state. *(Chapter Project)*

● **Use mathematics in all aspects of scientific inquiry** A graph is a diagram that tells how two variables are related. *(Graphing Gas Behavior; Skills Lab—It's a Gas)*

Physical Science (Content Standard B)

● **Properties and changes of properties in matter** A solid has a definite shape and volume; a liquid has a definite volume but not a definite shape; a gas has neither definite shape nor definite volume. Matter can change state through melting, freezing, vaporization, condensation, and sublimation. When working with a gas, it is helpful to know its volume, temperature, and pressure. *(Chapter Project; States of Matter; Changes of State; Skills Lab—Melting Ice; Gas Behavior; Skills Lab—It's a Gas)*

● **Transfer of energy** A substance changes state when its thermal energy increases or decreases sufficiently. Temperature is a measure of the average energy of motion of the particles of a substance. *(Chapter Project; Changes of State; Gas Behavior)*

ELEMENTS AND THE PERIODIC TABLE

Science as Inquiry (Content Standard A)

● **Design and conduct a scientific investigation** Students investigate the properties of metallic elements. *(Chapter Project)*

● **Develop descriptions, explanations, predictions, and models using evidence** Students classify elements based on their properties and infer the position of the elements on a periodic table. *(Skills Lab—Alien Periodic Table)*

● **Think critically and logically to make the relationships between evidence and explanations** Students investigate the properties of elements to determine their uses. *(Skills Lab—Copper or Carbon: That Is the Question)*

Physical Science (Content Standard B)

● **Properties and changes of properties in matter** An element can be identified by the number of protons in the nucleus of its atoms. Many properties of an element can be predicted by its position in the periodic table. The physical properties of metals include shininess, malleability, ductility, and conductivity. A nonmetal is an element that lacks most of the properties of a metal; metalloids have some properties of both metals and nonmetals. The plasma state of matter consists of a gas-like mixture of free electrons and atoms stripped of electrons. *(Introduction to Atoms; Organizing the Elements; Metals; Nonmetals and Metalloids; Elements From Stardust)*

● **Transfer of energy** Nuclear fusion is a process in which two atomic nuclei combine to form a larger nucleus, releasing huge amounts of energy in the process. *(Elements From Stardust)*

History and Nature of Science (Content Standard G)

● **History of science** For over two centuries, scientists have created models of atoms in an effort to understand why matter behaves as it does. Mendeleev discovered a set of patterns that applied to all elements, which he used to create the periodic table. *(Science and History; Organizing the Elements)*

EXPLORING MATERIALS

Science as Inquiry (Content Standard A)

● **Develop descriptions, explanations, predictions, and models using evidence** Students model the way a sample of radioactive waste decays to a nonhazardous level. *(Skills Lab)*

Physical Science (Content Standard B)

● **Properties and changes of properties in matter** A polymer is a large, complex molecule built from smaller molecules joined together in a repeating pattern. An alloy is a substance made of two or more elements that has the properties of metal. Ceramics are hard, crystalline solids made by heating clay and other mineral materials to high temperatures; glass is a clear, solid material with no crystal structure. *(Chapter Project; Polymers and Composites; Metals and Alloys; Ceramics and Glass)*

● **Transfer of energy** Radioactivity is the spontaneous emission of radiation by an unstable atomic nucleus. *(Radioactive Elements; Skills Lab)*

Science and Technology (Content Standard E)

● **Design a solution or product** Students design and build a package made of polymers that will protect breakable items during shipping. *(Technology Lab)*

● **Evaluate completed technological designs or products** Students explore the properties of different types of materials. *(Chapter Project)*

● **Understandings about science and technology** Many polymers are synthesized from simpler materials. A great variety of synthetic polymers have been created over the years. Alloys are used much more than pure metals because they are generally stronger and less likely to react with air or water. The properties of ceramics and glass make them useful for many purposes. The decay of radioactive isotopes makes them useful in many ways. *(Chapter Project; Polymers and Composites; Tech & Design in History; Metals and Alloys; Ceramics and Glass; Radioactive Elements)*

Science in Personal and Social Perspectives (Content Standard F)

● **Science and technology in society** Plastics increase the volume of trash. Students weigh the impact of making and using polyester fleece. *(Polymers and Composites; Technology and Society)*

History and Nature of Science (Content Standard G)

● **History of science** Henri Becquerel and Marie and Pierre Curie pioneered the study of radioactive elements. *(Radioactive Elements)*

Note: To see how the benchmarks are supported by *SCIENCE EXPLORER,* go to **PHSchool.com.**

Reading

Reading Comprehension in the Science Classroom

Q&A

Q: Why are science texts often difficult for students to read and comprehend?

A: In general, science texts make complex literacy and knowledge demands on learners. They have a more technical vocabulary and a more demanding syntax, and place a greater emphasis on inferential reasoning.

Q: What does research say about facilitating comprehension?

A: Studies comparing novices and experts show that the conceptual organization of experts' knowledge is very different from that of novices. For example, experts emphasize core concepts when organizing knowledge, while novices focus on superficial details. To facilitate comprehension, effective teaching strategies should support and scaffold students as they build an understanding of the key concepts and concept relationships within a text unit.

Q: What strategies can teachers use to facilitate comprehension?

A: Three complementary strategies are very important in facilitating student comprehension of science texts. First, guide student interaction with the text using the built-in strategies. Second, organize the curriculum in terms of core concepts (e.g., the **Key Concepts** in each section). Third, develop visual representations of the relationships among the key concepts and vocabulary that can be referred to during instruction.

Nancy Romance, Ph.D.
Professor of Science Education
Florida Atlantic University
Fort Lauderdale, Florida

"Effective teaching strategies should support and scaffold students as they build an understanding of the key concepts and concept relationships within a text unit."

Reading Support in *Science Explorer*

The latest research emphasizes the importance of activating learners' prior knowledge and teaching them to distinguish core concepts from less important information. These skills are now more important than ever, because success in science requires students to read, understand, and connect complex terms and concepts.

Before students read—
Reading Preview introduces students to the key concepts and key terms they'll find in each section. The **Target Reading Skill** is identified and applied with a graphic organizer.

During the section—
Boldface Sentences identify each key concept and encourage students to focus on the big ideas of science.

Reading Checkpoints reinforce students' understanding by slowing them down to review after every concept is discussed.

Caption Questions draw students into the art and photos, helping them connect the content to the images.

After students read—
Section Assessment revisits the **Target Reading Skill** and encourages students to use the graphic organizer.

Each review question is scaffolded and models the way students think, by first easing them into a review and then challenging them with increasingly more difficult questions.

Evaluator's Checklist

Does your science program promote reading comprehension with—

✔ Text structured in an outline format and key concepts highlighted in boldface type

✔ Real-world applications to activate prior knowledge

✔ Key concepts, critical vocabulary, and a reading skill for every section

✔ Sample graphic organizers for each section

✔ Relevant photos and carefully constructed graphics with questions

✔ Reading checkpoints that appear in each section

✔ Scaffolded questions in section assessments

Math in the Science Classroom

Why should students concern themselves with mathematics in your science class?

Good science requires good data from which to draw conclusions. Technology enhances the ability to measure in a variety of ways. Often the scientist must measure large amounts of data, and thus an aim of analysis is to reduce the data to a summary that makes sense and is consistent with established norms of communication—i.e., mathematics.

Calculating measures of central tendency (e.g., mean, median, or mode), variability (e.g., range), and shape (graphic representations) can effectively reduce 500 data points to 3 without losing the essential characteristics of the data. Scientists understand that a trade-off exists between precision and richness as data are folded into categories, and so margins of error can be quantified in mathematical terms and factored into all scientific findings.

Mathematics is the language used by scientists to model change in the world. Understanding change is a vital part of the inquiry process. Mathematics serves as a common language to communicate across the sciences. Fields of scientific research that originated as separate disciplines are now integrated, such as happened with bioengineering. What do the sciences have in common? Each uses the language of mathematics to communicate about data and the process of data analysis. Recognizing this need, *Science Explorer* integrates mathematics practice throughout the program and gives students ample opportunity to hone their math skills.

Clearly, mathematics plays an important role in your science classroom!

William Tate, Ph.D.
Professor of Education and
Applied Statistics and
Computation
Washington University
St. Louis, Missouri

> "Mathematics is the language used by scientists to model change in the world."

Integrated Math Support

In the Student Edition

The math instruction is based on principles derived from Prentice Hall's research-based mathematics program.

Sample Problems, Math Practice, Analyzing Data, and a Math Skills Handbook all help to provide practice at point of use, encouraging students to Read and Understand, Plan and Solve, and then Look Back and Check.

Color-coded variables aid student navigation and help reinforce their comprehension.

In the Teacher's Edition

Math teaching notes enable the science teacher to support math instruction and math objectives on high-stakes tests.

In the Guided Reading and Study Workbook

These unique worksheets help students master reading and enhance their study and math skills. Students can create a record of their work for study and review.

Evaluator's Checklist

Does your science program promote math skills by—

✔ Giving students opportunities to collect data

✔ Providing students opportunities to analyze data

✔ Enabling students to practice math skills

✔ Helping students solve equations by using color-coded variables

✔ Using sample problems to apply science concepts

Technology and Design

Technology and Design in the Science Classroom

Much of the world we live in is designed and made by humans. The buildings in which we live, the cars we drive, the medicines we take, and often the food we eat are products of technology. The knowledge and skills needed to understand the processes used to create these products should be a component of every student's basic literacy.

Some schools offer hands-on instruction on how technology development works through industrial arts curricula. Even then, there is a disconnect among science (understanding how nature works), mathematics (understanding data-driven models), and technology (understanding the human-made world). The link among these fields of study is the engineering design process—that process by which one identifies a human need and uses science knowledge and human ingenuity to create a technology to satisfy the need. Engineering gives students the problem-solving and design skills they will need to succeed in our sophisticated, three-dimensional, technological world.

As a complement to "science as inquiry," the National Science Education Standards (NRC, 1996) call for students at all age levels to develop the abilities related to "technology as design," including the ability to identify and frame a problem and then to design, implement, and evaluate a solution. At the 5–8 grade level, the standards call for students to be engaged in complex problem-solving and to learn more about how science and technology complement each other. It's also important for students to understand that there are often constraints involved in design as well as trade-offs and unintended consequences of technological solutions to problems.

As the *Standards for Technological Literacy* (ITEA, 2000) state, "Science and technology are like conjoined twins. While they have separate identities they must remain inextricably connected." Both sets of standards emphasize how progress in science leads to new developments in technology, while technological innovation in turn drives advances in science.

Ioannis Miaoulis, Ph.D.
President
Museum of Science
Boston, Massachusetts

"Engineering gives students the problem-solving and design skills they will need to succeed in our sophisticated, three-dimensional, technological world."

Evaluator's Checklist

Does your science program promote technology and design by—

✔ Incorporating technology and design concepts and skills into the science curriculum

✔ Giving students opportunities to identify and solve technological design problems

✔ Providing students opportunities to analyze the impact of technology on society

✔ Enabling students to practice technology and design skills

Technology and Design

Technology and Design in *Science Explorer*

How often do you hear your students ask: "Why do I need to learn this?" Connecting them to the world of technology and design in their everyday life is one way to help answer this question. It is also why so many state science curricula are now emphasizing technology and design concepts and skills.

Science Explorer makes a special effort to include a technology and design strand that encourages students to not only identify a need but to take what they learned in science and apply it to design a possible solution, build a prototype, test and evaluate the design, and/or troubleshoot the design. This strand also provides definitions of technology and engineering and discusses the similarities and differences between these endeavors and science. Students will learn to analyze the risks and benefits of a new technology and to consider the tradeoffs, such as safety, costs, efficiency, and appearance.

In the Student Edition

Integrated Technology & Design Sections

Sections throughout *Science Explorer* specifically integrate technology and design with the content of the text. For example, students not only learn how seismographs work but also learn what role seismographs play in society and how people use the data that are gathered.

Technology Labs

These labs help students gain experience in designing and building a device or product that meets a particular need or solves a problem. Students follow a design process of Research and Investigate, Design and Build, and Evaluate and Redesign.

Chapter Projects

Chapter Projects work hand-in-hand with the chapter content. Students design, build, and test based on real-world situations. They have the opportunity to apply the knowledge and skills learned to building a product.

Special Features

This technology and design strand is also reflected in Technology & Society and Science & Society features as well as Technology & History timelines. These highly visual features introduce a technology and its impact on society. For example, students learn how a hybrid car differs from a traditional car.

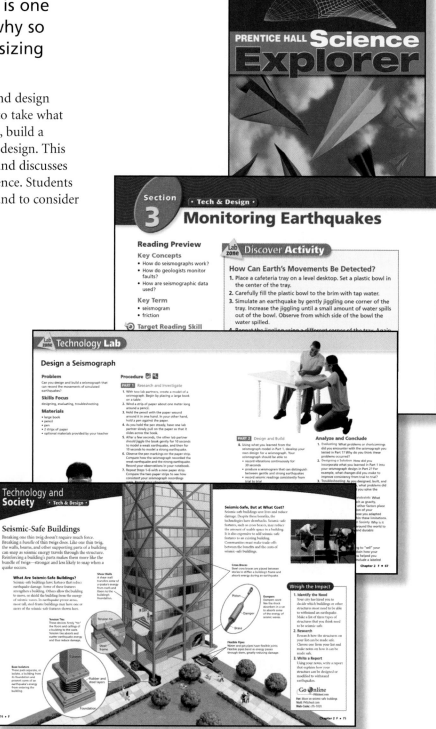

Assessment in the Science Curriculum

No Child Left Behind clearly challenges school districts across the nation to raise expectations for all students with testing of student achievement in science beginning in 2007–2008.

A primary goal of NCLB is to provide classroom teachers with better data from scientifically valid assessments in order to inform instructional planning and to identify students who are at risk and require intervention. It has been a common practice to teach a science lesson, administer a test, grade it, and move on. This practice is a thing of the past. With the spotlight now on improving student performance, it is essential to use assessment results as a way to identify student strengths and challenges. Providing student feedback and obtaining student input is a valuable, essential part of the assessment process.

Assessment is a never-ending cycle, as is shown in the following diagram. Although you may begin at any point in the assessment cycle, the basic process is the same.

An important assessment strategy is to ensure that students have ample opportunities to check their understanding of skills and concepts before moving on to the next topic. Checking for understanding also includes asking appropriate, probing questions with each example presented. This enables students and teachers to know whether the skills or concepts being introduced are actually understood.

Eileen Depka
Supervisor of Standards
and Assessment
Waukesha, Wisconsin

"Meeting the NCLB challenge will necessitate an integrated approach to assessment with a variety of assessment tools."

Use a variety of assessment tools to gain information and strengthen student understanding.

Implement the plan with a focus on gathering and using assessment information throughout.

Analyze assessment results to create a picture of student strengths and challenges.

Identify strategies to achieve the target, create a plan for implementation, and choose assessments tools.

Choose a target to create a focused path on which to proceed.

IMPLEMENT · ASSESS · ANALYZE · STRATEGIZE · TARGET

Evaluator's Checklist

Does your science program include assessments that—

✔ Are embedded before, during, and after lesson instruction
✔ Align to standards and to the instructional program
✔ Assess both skill acquisition and understanding
✔ Include meaningful rubrics to guide students
✔ Mirror the various formats of standardized tests

Assessment in *Science Explorer*

Science Explorer's remarkable range of strategies for checking progress will help teachers find the right opportunity for reaching all their students.

The assessment strategies in *Science Explorer* will help both students and teachers alike ensure student success in content mastery as well as high-stakes test performance. A wealth of opportunities built into the Student Edition help students monitor their own progress. Teachers are supported with ongoing assessment opportunities in the Teacher's Edition and an easy-to-use, editable test generator linked to content objectives. These integrated, ongoing assessment tools assure success.

Especially to support state and national testing objectives, Prentice Hall has developed test preparation materials that model the NCLB approach.

- **Diagnostic Assessment** tools provide in-depth analysis of strengths and weaknesses, areas of difficulty, and probable underlying causes that can help teachers make instructional decisions and plan intervention strategies.

- **Progress Monitoring** tools aligned with content objectives and state tests provide ongoing, longitudinal records of student achievement detailing individual student progress toward meeting end-of-year and end-of-schooling grade level, district, or state standards.

- **Outcomes** tools that mimic state and national tests show whether individual students have met the expected standards and can help a school system judge whether it has made adequate progress in improving its performance year by year.

Caption Questions enhance critical thinking skills

Reading Checkpoints reinforce students' understanding

Scaffolded Section Assessment Questions model the way students think

Comprehensive Chapter Reviews and Assessment provide opportunities for students to check their own understanding and practice valuable high-stakes test-taking skills

Exam*View*®, Computer Test Bank CD-ROM provides teachers access to thousands of modifiable test questions in English and Spanish

Test Preparation Blackline Masters and Student Workbook include diagnostic and prescription tools, progress-monitoring aids, and practice tests that help teachers focus on improving test scores.

Section 3 Assessment

Target Reading Skill Sequencing Refer to your flowchart about seismographs as you answer Question 1.

Reviewing Key Concepts

1. a. Defining What is a seismogram?
   b. Explaining How can geologists tell apart the different types of seismic waves on a seismogram?
   c. Comparing and Contrasting Two identical seismographs are located 1,000 km and 1,200 km from an earthquake's epicenter. How would the two seismograms for the earthquake compare?
2. a. Reviewing What changes are measured by the instruments used to monitor faults?
   b. Describing How are satellites used to measure movements along a fault?
   c. Inferring A satellite that monitors a fault detects an increasing tilt in the land surface along the fault. What could this change in the land surface indicate?

3. a. Listing What are three ways in which geologists use seismographic data?
   b. Explaining How do geologists use seismographic data to make maps of faults?
   c. Making Generalizations Why is it difficult to predict earthquakes?

Writing in Science

Dialogue Geologists in Alaska have just detected an earthquake and located the earthquake's epicenter. Write a dialogue in which the geologists notify a disaster response team that will help people in the earthquake area.

Chapter 2 F ◆ 65

Standardized Test Prep

Test-Taking Tip
When answering questions about diagrams, read all parts of the diagram carefully, including title, captions, and labels. Make sure that you understand the meaning of arrows and other symbols. Determine exactly what the question asks. Then eliminate those answer choices that are not supported by the diagram.

Practice answering this question.
The diagram shows how stress affects a mass of rock in a process called
   A compression.
   B tension.
   C squeezing.
   D shearing.
The correct answer is **D** because the arrows show rock being pulled in opposite directions.

Choose the letter that best answers the question or completes the statement.

1. In a strike-slip fault, rock masses along the fault move
   A in the same direction.
   B down only.
   C together.
   D sideways past each other.

2. Stress will build until an earthquake occurs if friction along a fault is
   F decreasing.   G high.
   H low.   J changed to heat.

Use the information below and your knowledge of science to answer Questions 3 and 4.

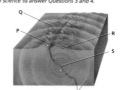

Seismic waves

3. When an earthquake occurs, seismic waves travel
   A from P in all directions.
   B from R to S.
   C from S in all directions.
   D from Q to P.

4. At point R, seismic waves from an earthquake would be
   F weaker than at P.
   G likely to cause little damage.
   H weaker than at Q.
   J likely to cause the most damage.

5. To estimate the total energy released by an earthquake, a geologist should use the
   A Mercalli scale.   B Richter scale.
   C epicenter scale.   D moment magnitude scale.

Constructed Response

6. A geologist discovers a large fault beneath a major city. Why would this information be helpful in determining earthquake risk in the area? What three safety steps should the geologist recommend?

Chapter 2 F ◆ 79

Master Materials List

SCIENCE EXPLORER offers an abundance of activity options in the Student Edition so you can pick and choose those that suit your needs. Prentice Hall has worked with Neo/SCI Corporation to develop Consumable Kits and Nonconsumable Kits that precisely match the needs of the SCIENCE EXPLORER labs. Use this Master Materials List or the Materials Ordering CD-ROM to help order your supplies. For more information on materials kits for this program, contact your local Prentice Hall sales representative or Neo/SCI Corporation at 1-800-526-6689 or **www.neosci.com**.

Neo SCI®
New ideas for teaching science

Consumable Materials

Description	Textbook Section(s)	Quantity per class	Description	Textbook Section(s)	Quantity per class
Aluminum foil, roll	2-2 (TT), 3-3 (DIS)	1	*Ice cube, bag	2-2 (Lab)	1
Antacid tablet	2-1 (DIS)	5	Index card, 3" x 5"	1-4 (Lab), 3-1 (SA)	5
Bag, plastic, sealable	4-2 (DIS)	5	Iodine solution, 1%, 100 mL	4-1 (Lab)	1
Balloon, large	2-1 (DIS)	5	Manganese dioxide, 10 g	3-4 (TT)	1
Battery, 6V	1-4 (Lab)	5	Marshmallow, mini, bag	1-4 (DIS)	1
Battery, dry cell, 1.5-V	3-3 (Lab)	5	Match, pkg	1-4DIS), 3-4 (TT)	1
Bolt, stainless steel	4-2 (DIS)	5	Modeling clay, white, 1 lb	1-2 (Lab), 1-4 (DIS), 2-4 (Lab)	1
Borax, 20 g	4-1 (DIS)	1			
*Bottle, plastic, 1-L	2-1 (DIS)	5	*Nail polish remover, bottle	2-2 (TT)	1
*Box, sealable	3-1 (DIS)	5	Nail, low-carbon steel	4-2 (DIS)	5
Bubble wrap, plastic, ft	2-3 (DIS), 4-1 (Lab)	5	Nail, high-carbon steel	4-2 (DIS)	5
Bulb, flashlight	3-3 (Lab)	5	Oil, vegetable 16 oz	2-1 (TT)	1
Can, coffee	4-4 (DIS)	5	Optical fiber, plastic	4-3 (TT)	5
*Can, soda, empty	1-2 (DIS), 1-4 (DIS), 3-3 (DIS)	10	Paper clip, pkg/100	1-1 (DIS), 1-4 (DIS), 1-4 (Lab)	1
Cardboard, 12" x 12", sheet	4-1 (Lab), 4-3 (TT)	5	*Paper towel, roll	1-2 (Lab), 2-1 (TT), 2-2 (TT), 4-2 (DIS), 4-3 (DIS)	1
Chalk, pkg/12	2-3 (DIS), 1-3 (DIS)	1			
Charcoal, 16 oz	3-4 (DIS)	1	Paper, construction, blue, sheet	3-2 (DIS)	20
Copper chloride, 100 g	1-4 (Lab)	1	Paper, construction, green, sheet	3-2 (DIS)	20
*Crayon	1-2 (Lab)	5	Paper, construction, red, sheet	3-2 (DIS)	20
Cup, paper, 7 oz	4-1 (DIS)	5	Paper, construction, yellow, sheet	3-2 (DIS)	20
Cup, plastic, 10 oz	1-2 (DIS), 4-1 (Lab), 2-2 (Lab), 4-4 (DIS)	110	*Paper, white, ream	1-3 (DIS), 3-4 (DIS), 4-1 (Lab), 4-4 (DIS)	1
Dropper, plastic, pkg/10	1-3 (DIS), 2-2 (TT)	1	Pencil lead, 0.9 mm	3-3 (Lab)	5
Dry cell, 1.5V	3-3 (Lab)	5	*Pencils, colored, pkg/4	4-4 (Lab)	1
*Egg, hard-boiled	4-1 (Lab)	5	Rod, stirring, plastic	2-2 (Lab), 4-1 (DIS)	20
*Flashlight, penlight	4-3 (TT)	5	*Salt water, 250 mL	4-2 (DIS)	1
Foam, plastic, 12"	4-1 (Lab)	5	*Shavings, wood, bag	4-1 (Lab)	1
Gauze, roll	2-2 (TT)	1	Socket, flashlight	3-3 (Lab)	5
Glue, white, 4 oz	4-1 (DIS)	1	Splint, wooden	3-4 (TT)	5
Graph paper, sheet	4-4 (Lab)	5	*Stick, wooden	1-2 (Lab)	5
*Honey, bottle	2-1 (TT)	1	Tape, masking or clear, roll	2-3 (DIS), 3-1 (DIS)	2
Hydrogen peroxide, 8 oz	3-4 (TT)	1			

KEY: CP: Chapter Project; **DIS:** Discover; **SA:** Skills Activity; **TT:** Try This; **Lab:** Skills, Consumer, Design Your Own, & Technology & Design
* items school supplied

Quantities based on five groups of six students per class.

Master Materials List

Consumable Materials (continued)

Description	Textbook Section(s)	Quantity per Class	Description	Textbook Section(s)	Quantity per Class
Tape, packaging, roll	4-1 (Lab)	1	Wax paper, roll	2-3 (DIS)	1
Vinegar, 500 mL	1-3 (DIS)	1	*Wrapping paper, foil, package	3-3 (DIS)	1

Nonconsumable Materials

Description	Textbook Section(s)	Quantity per Class	Description	Textbook Section(s)	Quantity per Class
*Balance	1-2 (DIS), 1-2 (Lab), 4-1 (Lab), 4-3 (DIS)	5	Meter stick, 1/2	1-4 (TT)	5
Ball, tennis	1-4 (TT)	5	Mirror, hand	2-2 (DIS)	5
Basin	4-3 (DIS)	5	Pan, aluminum, 9"	1-4 (DIS), 3-3 (DIS)	10
Battery holder, 1.5V	3-3 (Lab)	5	*Penny	4-4 (Lab)	500
Beaker, 250 mL	3-3 (Lab)	5	Ruler, 15 cm	1-2 (Lab), 3-4 (Lab), 4-4 (DIS)	5
*Book	2-4 (Lab), 4-1 (Lab)	20	*Scissors	4-1 (DIS), 4-1 (Lab), 4-4 (DIS)	5
*Calculator	1-1 (SA)	5	*Spoon, large	5-1 (DIS)	5
Checkers, pkg/24	1-1 (DIS)	1	*Spoon, metal	1-3 (DIS)	5
Cloth, muslin, 12" x 36"	2-2 (DIS), 4-1 (Lab)	5	*Stopwatch	2-2 (Lab), 3-3 (Lab), 4-1 (Lab)	5
Flower pot, glazed	4-3 (DIS)	5	Syringe, plastic, 60 cc	2-4 (Lab)	5
Flower pot, unglazed	4-3 (DIS)	5	Test tube	3-4 (TT)	5
*Fork	3-4 (DIS)	5	Thermometer, alcohol, 12", -10°C–110°C	1-4 (DIS), 2-2 (TT), 2-2 (Lab), 4-1 (Lab)	10
Goggles, safety	1-4 (DIS), 3-4 (TT)	30	Tongs	1-4 (DOS)	5
Graduated cylinder, 100 mL	1-2 (Lab)	5	Wire with alligator clips	1-4 (Lab)	5
Hand lens	4-1 (Lab)	5	Wire, aluminum, 4 oz	3-3 (DIS)	1
*Hot plate	3-3 (Lab), 4-1 (Lab)	5	Wire, copper, non-insulated, 4 oz	3-3 (Lab)	1
*Jar, glass, 250 mL	1-4 (Lab)	5	Wire, copper, insulated, 25 m	3-3 (Lab)	1
Jar, plastic, clear with lid	2-1 (TT), 4-4 (Lab)	10			
Marble, assorted, bag	1-1 (DIS)	1			

KEY: CP: Chapter Project; **DIS:** Discover; **SA:** Skills Activity; **TT:** Try This; **Lab:** Skills, Consumer, Design Your Own, & Technology & Design
   * items school supplied

Quantities based on five groups of six students per class.

Chemical Building Blocks

Book-Specific Resources

Student Edition
Interactive Textbook
Teacher's Edition
All-in-One Teaching Resources
Color Transparencies
Guided Reading and Study Workbook
Student Edition on Audio CD
Discovery Channel Video
Lab Activity Video
Consumable and Nonconsumable Materials Kits

Program Print Resources

Integrated Science Laboratory Manual
Computer Microscope Lab Manual
Inquiry Skills Activity Books
Progress Monitoring Assessments
Test Preparation Workbook
Test-Taking Tips With Transparencies
Teacher's ELL Handbook
Reading in the Content Area

Program Technology Resources

TeacherExpress™ CD-ROM
Interactive Textbook
Presentation Pro CD-ROM
ExamView®, Computer Test Bank CD-ROM
Lab zone™ Easy Planner CD-ROM
Probeware Lab Manual With CD-ROM
Computer Microscope and Lab Manual
Materials Ordering CD-ROM
Discovery Channel DVD Library
Lab Activity DVD Library
Web Site at PHSchool.com

Spanish Print Resources

Spanish Student Edition
Spanish Guided Reading and Study Workbook
Spanish Teaching Guide With Tests

Acknowledgments appear on page 196, which constitutes an extension of this copyright page.

Copyright © 2005 by Pearson Education, Inc., publishing as Pearson Prentice Hall, Upper Saddle River, New Jersey 07458. All rights reserved. Printed in the United States of America. This publication is protected by copyright, and permission should be obtained from the publisher prior to any prohibited reproduction, storage in a retrieval system, or transmission in any form or by any means, electronic, mechanical, photocopying, recording, or likewise. For information regarding permission(s), write to: Rights and Permissions Department.

Pearson Prentice Hall™ is a trademark of Pearson Education, Inc.
Pearson® is a registered trademark of Pearson plc.
Prentice Hall® is a registered trademark of Pearson Education, Inc.

Lab zone™ is a trademark of Pearson Education, Inc.

Planet Diary® is a registered trademark of Addison Wesley Longman, Inc.

Discovery Channel School® is a registered trademark of Discovery Communications, Inc., used under license. The Discovery Channel School logo is a trademark of Discovery Communications, Inc.

SciLinks® is a trademark of the National Science Teachers Association. The SciLinks® service includes copyrighted materials and is owned and provided by the National Science Teachers Association. All rights reserved.

Science News® is a registered trademark of Science Services, Inc.

Cover
Table salt and rock salt are two forms of the compound sodium chloride.

ISBN 0-13-115096-0

2 3 4 5 6 7 8 9 10   08 07 06 05 04

Program Authors

Michael J. Padilla, Ph.D.
Professor of Science Education
University of Georgia
Athens, Georgia

Michael Padilla is a leader in middle school science education. He has served as an author and elected officer for the National Science Teachers Association and as a writer of the National Science Education Standards. As lead author of Science Explorer, Mike has inspired the team in developing a program that meets the needs of middle grades students, promotes science inquiry, and is aligned with the National Science Education Standards.

Ioannis Miaoulis, Ph.D.
President
Museum of Science
Boston, Massachusetts

Originally trained as a mechanical engineer, Ioannis Miaoulis is in the forefront of the national movement to increase technological literacy. As dean of the Tufts University School of Engineering, Dr. Miaoulis spearheaded the introduction of engineering into the Massachusetts curriculum. Currently he is working with school systems across the country to engage students in engineering activities and to foster discussions on the impact of science and technology on society.

Martha Cyr, Ph.D.
Director of K–12 Outreach
Worcester Polytechnic Institute
Worcester, Massachusetts

Martha Cyr is a noted expert in engineering outreach. She has over nine years of experience with programs and activities that emphasize the use of engineering principles, through hands-on projects, to excite and motivate students and teachers of mathematics and science in grades K–12. Her goal is to stimulate a continued interest in science and mathematics through engineering.

Book Authors

David V. Frank, Ph.D.
Head, Department of
Physical Sciences
Ferris State University
Big Rapids, Michigan

John G. Little
Science Teacher
St. Mary's High School
Stockton, California

Steve Miller
Science Writer
State College, Pennsylvania

Contributing Writers

Thomas L. Messer
Science Teacher
Foxborough Public Schools
Foxborough, Massachusetts

Thomas R. Wellnitz
Science Teacher
The Paideia School
Atlanta, Georgia

Consultants

Reading Consultant

Nancy Romance, Ph.D.
Professor of Science
Education
Florida Atlantic University
Fort Lauderdale, Florida

Mathematics Consultant

William Tate, Ph.D.
Professor of Education and
Applied Statistics and
Computation
Washington University
St. Louis, Missouri

Reviewers

Tufts University Content Reviewers

Faculty from Tufts University in Medford, Massachusetts, developed *Science Explorer* chapter projects and reviewed the student books.

Astier M. Almedom, Ph.D.
Department of Biology

Wayne Chudyk, Ph.D.
Department of Civil and Environmental Engineering

John L. Durant, Ph.D.
Department of Civil and Environmental Engineering

George S. Ellmore, Ph.D.
Department of Biology

David Kaplan, Ph.D.
Department of Biomedical Engineering

Samuel Kounaves, Ph.D.
Department of Chemistry

David H. Lee, Ph.D.
Department of Chemistry

Douglas Matson, Ph.D.
Department of Mechanical Engineering

Karen Panetta, Ph.D.
Department of Electrical Engineering and Computer Science

Jan A. Pechenik, Ph.D.
Department of Biology

John C. Ridge, Ph.D.
Department of Geology

William Waller, Ph.D.
Department of Astronomy

Content Reviewers

Paul Beale, Ph.D.
Department of Physics
University of Colorado
Boulder, Colorado

Jeff Bodart, Ph.D.
Chipola Junior College
Marianna, Florida

Michael Castellani, Ph.D.
Department of Chemistry
Marshall University
Huntington, West Virginia

Eugene Chiang, Ph.D.
Department of Astronomy
University of California – Berkeley
Berkeley, California

Charles C. Curtis, Ph.D.
Department of Physics
University of Arizona
Tucson, Arizona

Daniel Kirk-Davidoff, Ph.D.
Department of Meteorology
University of Maryland
College Park, Maryland

Diane T. Doser, Ph.D.
Department of Geological Sciences
University of Texas at El Paso
El Paso, Texas

R. E. Duhrkopf, Ph.D.
Department of Biology
Baylor University
Waco, Texas

Michael Hacker
Co-director, Center for Technological Literacy
Hofstra University
Hempstead, New York

Michael W. Hamburger, Ph.D.
Department of Geological Sciences
Indiana University
Bloomington, Indiana

Alice K. Hankla, Ph.D.
The Galloway School
Atlanta, Georgia

Donald C. Jackson, Ph.D.
Department of Molecular Pharmacology, Physiology, & Biotechnology
Brown University
Providence, Rhode Island

Jeremiah N. Jarrett, Ph.D.
Department of Biological Sciences
Central Connecticut State University
New Britain, Connecticut

David Lederman, Ph.D.
Department of Physics
West Virginia University
Morgantown, West Virginia

Becky Mansfield, Ph.D.
Department of Geography
Ohio State University
Columbus, Ohio

Elizabeth M. Martin, M.S.
Department of Chemistry and Biochemistry
College of Charleston
Charleston, South Carolina

Joe McCullough, Ph.D.
Department of Natural and Applied Sciences
Cabrillo College
Aptos, California

Robert J. Mellors, Ph.D.
Department of Geological Sciences
San Diego State University
San Diego, California

Joseph M. Moran, Ph.D.
American Meteorological Society
Washington, D.C.

David J. Morrissey, Ph.D.
Department of Chemistry
Michigan State University
East Lansing, Michigan

Philip A. Reed, Ph.D.
Department of Occupational & Technical Studies
Old Dominion University
Norfolk, Virginia

Scott M. Rochette, Ph.D.
Department of the Earth Sciences
State University of New York, College at Brockport
Brockport, New York

Laurence D. Rosenhein, Ph.D.
Department of Chemistry
Indiana State University
Terre Haute, Indiana

Ronald Sass, Ph.D.
Department of Biology and Chemistry
Rice University
Houston, Texas

George Schatz, Ph.D.
Department of Chemistry
Northwestern University
Evanston, Illinois

Sara Seager, Ph.D.
Carnegie Institution of Washington
Washington, D.C.

Robert M. Thornton, Ph.D.
Department of Biology
University of California
Davis, California

John R. Villarreal, Ph.D.
College of Science and Engineering
The University of Texas – Pan American
Edinburg, Texas

Kenneth Welty, Ph.D.
School of Education
University of Wisconsin–Stout
Stout, Wisconsin

Edward J. Zalisko, Ph.D.
Department of Biology
Blackburn College
Carlinville, Illinois

Teacher Reviewers

David R. Blakely
Arlington High School
Arlington, Massachusetts

Jane E. Callery
Two Rivers Magnet Middle
    School
East Hartford, Connecticut

Melissa Lynn Cook
Oakland Mills High School
Columbia, Maryland

James Fattic
Southside Middle School
Anderson, Indiana

Dan Gabel
Hoover Middle School
Rockville, Maryland

Wayne Goates
Eisenhower Middle School
Goddard, Kansas

Katherine Bobay Graser
Mint Hill Middle School
Charlotte, North Carolina

Darcy Hampton
Deal Junior High School
Washington, D.C.

Karen Kelly
Pierce Middle School
Waterford, Michigan

David Kelso
Manchester High School Central
Manchester, New Hampshire

Benigno Lopez, Jr.
Sleepy Hill Middle School
Lakeland, Florida

Angie L. Matamoros, Ph.D.
ALM Consulting, INC.
Weston, Florida

Tim McCollum
Charleston Middle School
Charleston, Illinois

Bruce A. Mellin
Brooks School
North Andover, Massachusetts

Ella Jay Parfitt
Southeast Middle School
Baltimore, Maryland

Evelyn A. Pizzarello
Louis M. Klein Middle School
Harrison, New York

Kathleen M. Poe
Fletcher Middle School
Jacksonville, Florida

Shirley Rose
Lewis and Clark Middle School
Tulsa, Oklahoma

Linda Sandersen
Greenfield Middle School
Greenfield, Wisconsin

Mary E. Solan
Southwest Middle School
Charlotte, North Carolina

Mary Stewart
University of Tulsa
Tulsa, Oklahoma

Paul Swenson
Billings West High School
Billings, Montana

Thomas Vaughn
Arlington High School
Arlington, Massachusetts

Susan C. Zibell
Central Elementary
Simsbury, Connecticut

Safety Reviewers

W. H. Breazeale, Ph.D.
Department of Chemistry
College of Charleston
Charleston, South Carolina

Ruth Hathaway, Ph.D.
Hathaway Consulting
Cape Girardeau, Missouri

Douglas Mandt, M.S.
Science Education Consultant
Edgewood, Washington

Activity Field Testers

Nicki Bibbo
Witchcraft Heights School
Salem, Massachusetts

Rose-Marie Botting
Broward County Schools
Fort Lauderdale, Florida

Colleen Campos
Laredo Middle School
Aurora, Colorado

Elizabeth Chait
W. L. Chenery Middle School
Belmont, Massachusetts

Holly Estes
Hale Middle School
Stow, Massachusetts

Laura Hapgood
Plymouth Community
    Intermediate School
Plymouth, Massachusetts

Mary F. Lavin
Plymouth Community
    Intermediate School
Plymouth, Massachusetts

James MacNeil, Ph.D.
Cambridge, Massachusetts

Lauren Magruder
St. Michael's Country
    Day School
Newport, Rhode Island

Jeanne Maurand
Austin Preparatory School
Reading, Massachusetts

Joanne Jackson-Pelletier
Winman Junior High School
Warwick, Rhode Island

Warren Phillips
Plymouth Public Schools
Plymouth, Massachusetts

Carol Pirtle
Hale Middle School
Stow, Massachusetts

Kathleen M. Poe
Fletcher Middle School
Jacksonville, Florida

Cynthia B. Pope
Norfolk Public Schools
Norfolk, Virginia

Anne Scammell
Geneva Middle School
Geneva, New York

Karen Riley Sievers
Callanan Middle School
Des Moines, Iowa

David M. Smith
Eyer Middle School
Allentown, Pennsylvania

Gene Vitale
Parkland School
McHenry, Illinois

Contents

Chemical Building Blocks

Reference Section

VIDEO

Enhance understanding through dynamic video.

Preview Get motivated with this introduction to the chapter content.

Field Trip Explore a real-world story related to the chapter content.

Assessment Review content and take an assessment.

Go Online
Web Links

Get connected to exciting Web resources in every lesson.

SciLINKS NSTA Find Web links on topics relating to every section.

Active Art Interact with selected visuals from every chapter online.

Planet Diary® Explore news and natural phenomena through weekly reports.

Science News® Keep up to date with the latest science discoveries.

Interactive Textbook

Experience the complete textbook online and on CD-ROM.

Activities Practice skills and learn content.

Videos Explore content and learn important lab skills.

Audio Support Hear key terms spoken and defined.

Self-Assessment Use instant feedback to help you track your progress.

Activities

From Plants to Chemicals

Inquiry and Chemical Engineering

Working scientist Dr. Rathin Datta finds ways to get useful chemicals from plants. This article shows how he uses persistence, experimentation, and thinking about things in new ways as key elements of scientific inquiry. While the properties of materials are studied elsewhere in this book, students need not have any previous knowledge of those concepts to understand this real-world application of scientific inquiry.

Build Background Knowledge
Products From Plants
Ask: **What medicines do you know of that come from plants?** *(Sample answer: Aloe, Echinacea, gingko, aspirin, morphine)* **What other products can you think of that come from plants?** *(Sample answer: Cotton, rayon, rubber, cooking oils, lumber, gasohol)*

Introduce the Career

Before students read the article, let them read the title, examine the pictures, and read the captions on their own. Then ask: **What questions came into your mind as you looked at these pictures?** *(Sample questions: Can stretchy fabric really be made from corn? How can corn be made into fuel? How do scientists discover all these products that can be made from corn?)* Point out to students that, just as they had questions about what they were seeing, scientists too have questions about what they observe.

Careers in **Science**

Many products, such as gasohol and plastic bottles, are made from corn-based chemicals.

From Plants to Chemicals

Can you power a car with corn? Can you drink soda from a bottle made from plants? Can you use corn to make chemicals strong enough to remove paint?

You can, thanks to scientists like Rathin Datta. Rathin is a chemical engineer at the Argonne National Laboratory in Illinois. He specializes in finding ways to get useful chemicals from plants. His discoveries will help make the environment cleaner for all of us.

For years, Rathin has been finding ways to make useful products from substances found naturally in plants. He's helped find ways to turn corn into an automobile fuel called gasohol. He's researched plants that can be used to produce powerful medicines. He has even worked on a way to use corn to make a stretchy fabric that athletes wear.

"I've always been interested in the plant and biological side of chemistry," says Rathin, who grew up in northern India. "That's because I've always been concerned about the effect of chemicals on the environment."

x ◆ K

Background

Facts and Figures Chemistry is the study of properties of materials, such as their structure and composition. Chemists also study how different materials interact and how adding or removing energy from materials changes them.

Chemical engineering is related to chemistry. Chemical engineers, like Rathin Datta, design and manage facilities in which chemical reactions take place. The chemical engineer chooses the equipment and processes that are most appropriate for the chemistry involved. Chemical engineers were among the first to introduce automated control processes into industrial design.

Talking With
Dr. Rathin Datta

Are Plant-Based Chemicals Safer?

Chemicals that come from crop plants are called *agrochemicals*, meaning "chemicals from agriculture," Rathin explains. Many agrochemicals are much less dangerous to the environment than chemicals made from petroleum, called *petrochemicals*.

Because agrochemicals are made from plant materials, nature usually recycles them, just as it recycles dead plants. Think of what happens to a tree after it falls to the ground. Tiny microbes work on its leaves and branches until the tree has rotted completely away. Much the same thing happens to products made from agrochemicals. A bag made from corn-based chemicals will break down and disappear after only a few weeks of being buried. In contrast, a plastic bag made from petrochemicals can survive hundreds of years.

Career Path

Rathin Datta was born in India. His interest in science was inspired in part by his father, who was a mathematician. Rathin came to the United States in 1970 to earn a Ph.D. in chemical engineering at Princeton University. He now works at Argonne National Laboratory in Illinois. Rathin and his team at Argonne were winners of the 1998 Presidential Green Chemistry Challenge Award for their work on the technology for the "green" solvent. Rathin plays the sitar, an Indian lute, and enjoys opera.

Converting Carbohydrates

The starting ingredients in many agrochemicals are energy-rich substances called carbohydrates. Sugar and starch are carbohydrates. Rathin converts, or changes, carbohydrates from corn into an agrochemical that can be used to make plastic. To do this, he needs help from tiny organisms—bacteria. First, he puts a special kind of bacteria in a big vat of ground-up corn. The bacteria convert the corn's carbohydrates into acids through a natural process called fermentation. Rathin then uses the acids to make plastic.

"The bacteria do all the work of converting the carbohydrates into useful molecules," says Rathin. "The hardest part for us comes afterward. The fermentation process produces a whole mix of materials. We have to find ways to separate out the one kind of material that we want to use from all the others."

Researchers Rathin Datta (right) and Mike Henry (left) developed a new, low-cost solvent. The clear substance that Rathin holds is the solvent.

K ◆ 1

Explore the Career

Choose from among the teaching strategies on these pages as you help your students explore the practical application of inquiry skills in the real world.

Help Students Read Explain that the prefix *agro-* comes from the Greek word *agros,* meaning "field." Agriculture is the science of cultivating the soil, producing crops, and raising livestock. Agronomy is the application of soil science and plant science to raising crops. Then, explain that the prefix *petro-* comes from the Greek word *petros,* which means "stone or rock." Ask: **How do petrochemicals relate to rock?** *(Sample answer: Petrochemicals are made from petroleum, which is oil found in rock layers beneath Earth's surface.)*

Demonstrate Students can observe fermentation in souring milk. Let a glass jar or beaker of milk sit at room temperature for several days. Invite students to observe the milk daily to monitor changes in odor, texture, and color. Explain that bacteria are changing the sugar in milk, lactose, into lactic acid. In fermentation, bacteria or other simple organisms break down sugar to use as food.

Research Invite interested students to find out why plastic bags made from petroleum-based products do not decompose.

Background

Facts and Figures Scientists usually use the term *fermentation* to refer to chemical reactions caused by microscopic organisms such as bacteria, molds, and yeasts. In the process of fermentation, organisms break down sugar to use as energy for cell processes. It is this process that causes milk to sour and wine to become vinegar.

A product of fermentation has a simpler structure than that of the substance that was fermented. Fermentation of sugars by yeasts produces ethanol, glycerol, and carbon dioxide. Mold fermentation of sugars produces citric acid, antibiotics, and vitamin B12. Bacterial fermentation produces acetone, monosodium glutamate, and acetic acid.

Discuss Determine whether students know what a solvent is. Explain that a solvent is a liquid that helps other substances dissolve. Water is a solvent because many substances, such as table salt and sugar, dissolve in it. Ask: **Why is it important to Dr. Datta to find a corn-based solvent?** *(Because solvents are found everywhere, he is concerned about how widespread use of such chemicals affects the environment and the people who use them.)* **What are disadvantages to petrochemicals?** *(Petrochemicals may be harmful to people, are slow to break down, and the supply of petroleum is limited.)* Remind students that petrochemicals are often less expensive than agrochemicals. Invite a debate by asking: **If you knew that a product you used was not biodegradable and hurt the environment, how much more money would you be willing to pay for an environmentally friendly, biodegradable alternative?** *(Encourage students to express their opinions while respecting those of others.)*

Use Visuals Invite students to follow the process in the diagram that shows how agrichemicals are produced. Ask: **Which part of the process was the most difficult?** *(Recovering and purifying the products of fermentation)* **How did Dr. Datta solve this problem?** *(By developing a new kind of plastic that acts like a very fine filter)* Tell students that in this usage, fine means that the filter is able to separate a mixture of extremely small particles. **What are the advantages of Dr. Datta's new process?** *(His process is less expensive and uses 90 percent less energy.)* **How are the products of Dr. Datta's process used?** *(As biodegradable plastics used for food containers, bottles, and packing peanuts; as solvents such as paint remover and cleansers; and as gasohol, which is car fuel)*

Making Solvents From Corn

Rathin Datta's most recent discovery is a good example of how agrochemicals can replace petrochemicals. He and his team have found a new way to use corn to make powerful solvents. Solvents are used to dissolve other substances.

"Solvents are found everywhere," says Rathin. "For example, factories use them in many processes to clean electronic parts or to remove ink from recycled newspapers. Households use them in grease-cleaning detergents and in paint removers."

Almost 4 million tons of solvents are used in the United States every year. Most are made from petrochemicals and can be very poisonous.

Addressing the Challenge

"Scientists have known for a long time that much safer solvents can be made from agrochemicals," says Rathin. "But the process has been too expensive. It doesn't do any good to make something that is environmentally sound if it costs too much for people to use," says Rathin. "Our challenge as chemical engineers was to think about an old process in an entirely new way. We had to find a less expensive way to make these solvents."

Stretchy fabric, like the material worn by this athlete, is likely to be made from corn.

Products That Can Be Made From Corn

Fermentation

Corn

Discovering a New Process

Rathin needed a new process to separate the solvents he wanted from a mixture. "I started working with a new kind of plastic that acts like a very fine filter. When we pass the fermented corn over this plastic, it captures the acids we want to keep and lets the other material pass through."

After two years of experimenting, Rathin perfected his process of making agrochemical solvents. His process works for less than half the cost of the old method. It also uses 90 percent less energy. Soon, most of the solvents used in the United States could be this cleaner, safer kind made from corn. "It even makes a great fingernail polish remover," says Datta.

2 ◆ K

Background

Facts and Figures Gasohol is a mixture of gasoline and ethanol. Ethanol, an alcohol, can come from coal, organic wastes, wood products, grain, sugar crops, or almost any starchy plant.

Gasoline-alcohol mixtures have been used as petroleum alternatives since the internal-combustion engine was first developed in the 1870s. However, because these mixtures are expensive to produce, they cannot compete successfully with gasoline unless oil shortages raise the price of gasoline. One advantage of gasohol over pure alcohol fuel is that most of a car's fuel system does not have to be modified for the new fuel.

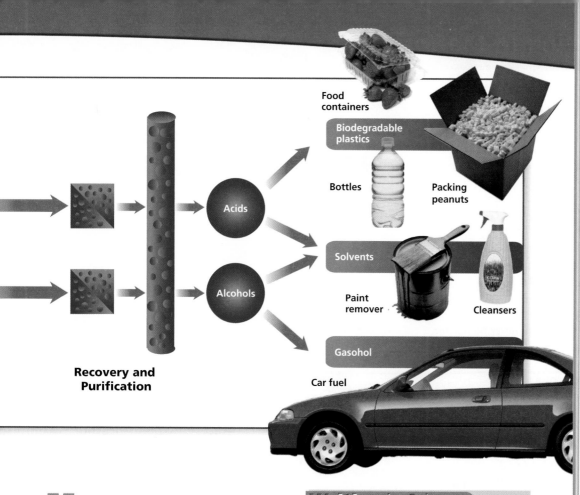

Food containers

Biodegradable plastics

Bottles

Packing peanuts

Acids

Solvents

Paint remover

Cleansers

Alcohols

Gasohol

Car fuel

Recovery and Purification

 **Show Examples** Bring to class several household solvents such as nail polish remover, paint thinner, and cleansers. Invite students to read the warning labels on the back of these products. Ask: **What is the solvent in nail polish remover?** *(Acetone)* **Why would Dr. Datta want to replace it with an alternative?** *(Dr. Datta believes products made from corn are less likely to hurt people.)*

Making a Difference

"It's very satisfying to take a natural product like corn and use it to produce a chemical that will replace a less safe chemical," says Rathin. "It's rare to find a compound that can do everything that this corn solvent can do and still be nonpoisonous and easily break down in the environment." Rathin's projects are long term. But finally a company has formed to manufacture and sell the solvent.

Writing in Science

Career Link After years of research, Rathin and his team discovered how to make a solvent that was safe *and* inexpensive. The product is now being sold by a company. In a paragraph, describe the steps a researcher might follow to get an invention manufactured and sold.

Go Online
PHSchool.com

For: More on this career
Visit: PHSchool.com
Web Code: cgb-1000

K ◆ 3

Writing in Science

Writing Mode Description
Scoring Rubric
4 Exceeds criteria; includes a concise, grammatically correct paragraph with precise details that completely describe the steps a researcher might follow to get an invention manufactured and sold
3 Meets criteria
2 Includes sketchy details and/or minor errors
1 Paragraph is incomplete and/or has serious errors

Go Online
PHSchool.com

For: More on this career
Visit: PHSchool.com
Web Code: cgb-1000

Students can research this career and others that are related to the study of chemistry.

Chapter at a Glance

PRENTICE HALL
Teacher**EXPRESS**™
Plan · Teach · Assess

  Chapter **Project** *Design and Build a Density-Calculating System*

Technology	**Local Standards**

DISCOVERY
CHANNEL
SCHOOL
Video Preview

All in One **Teaching Resources**
- Chapter Project Teacher Notes, pp. 38–39
- Chapter Project Student Overview, pp. 40–41
- Chapter Project Student Worksheets, pp. 42–43
- Chapter Project Scoring Rubric, p. 44

Section 1

4 periods
2 blocks

Describing Matter
K.1.1.1 Identify the properties used to describe matter.
K.1.1.2 Define elements and explain how they relate to compounds.
K.1.1.3 Describe the properties of a mixture.

Go **Online**
*SCi*LINKS™ NSTA

DISCOVERY
CHANNEL
SCHOOL
Video Field Trip

Section 2

2–3 periods
1 1/2 blocks

Measuring Matter
K.1.2.1 Differentiate between weight and mass.
K.1.2.2 Identify the units used to express the amount of space occupied by matter.
K.1.2.3 Describe how the density of a material is determined.

Go **Online**
PHSchool.com

Section 3

2–3 periods
1 1/2 blocks

Changes in Matter
K.1.3.1 Describe what a physical change is.
K.1.3.2 Describe what a chemical change is.
K.1.3.3 Explain how changes in matter are related to changes in energy.

Go **Online**
active art

Go **Online**
PHSchool.com

Section 4

1–2 periods
1 block

Energy and Matter
K.1.4.1 Identify forms of energy that are related to changes in matter.
K.1.4.2 Describe how chemical energy is related to chemical change.

Go **Online**
*SCi*LINKS™ NSTA

Review and Assessment

All in One **Teaching Resources**
- Key Terms Review, p. 76
- Transparency K8
- Performance Assessment Teacher Notes, p. 84
- Performance Assessment Scoring Rubric, p. 85
- Performance Assessment Student Worksheet, p. 86
- Chapter Test, pp. 87–90

DISCOVERY
CHANNEL
SCHOOL
Video Assessment

Go **Online**
PHSchool.com

Test Preparation

Test Preparation Blackline Masters

Chapter Activities Planner

For more activities

LAB ZONE
Easy Planner
CD-ROM

Student Edition	Inquiry	Time	Materials	Skills	Resources
Chapter Project, p. 5	Open-ended	Ongoing (2–3 weeks)	**All in One Teaching Resources** See p. 38	Applying concepts, calculating, communicating	**Lab zone Easy Planner** **All in One Teaching Resources** Support pp. 38–39
Section 1					
Discover Activity, p. 6	Guided	15 minutes	Small objects such as checkers, marbles, and paper clips of different sizes and colors	Forming operational definitions	**Lab zone Easy Planner**
Skills Activity, p. 8	Directed	10 minutes		Interpreting data	**Lab zone Easy Planner**
Section 2					
Discover Activity, p. 16	Guided	15 minutes	Triple-beam balance, objects of different mass, such as rocks, plastic drinking cups, aluminum cans, pencils	Drawing conclusions	**Lab zone Easy Planner**
Skills Lab, p. 21	Open-ended	Prep: 10 minutes Class: 30 minutes	Balance, water, paper towels, metric ruler, 100-mL graduated cylinder, various objects to measure	Drawing conclusions, designing experiments, controlling variables	**Lab zone Easy Planner Lab Activity Video** **All in One Teaching Resources** Skills Lab: *Making Sense of Density*, pp.59–60
Section 3					
Discover Activity, p. 22	Guided	10 minutes	Piece of chalk, sheet of paper, metal spoon, vinegar, dropper	Drawing conclusions	**Lab zone Easy Planner**
Skills Activity, p. 24	Guided	10 minutes		Inferring	**Lab zone Easy Planner**
Section 4					
Discover Activity, p. 30	Guided	15 minutes	Cold water, empty soda can, thermometer, paper clip, modeling clay, aluminum pie pan, mini marshmallow, match, tongs, goggles	Drawing conclusions	**Lab zone Easy Planner**
Try This Activity, p. 31	Guided	10 minutes	Meter stick, tennis ball	Inferring	**Lab zone Easy Planner**
At-Home Activity, p. 33	Guided	Home		Classifying, applying concepts	**Lab zone Easy Planner**
Skills Lab, pp. 34–35	Directed	Prep: 15 minutes Class: 40 minutes	Glass jar, two metal paper clips, 6-volt battery, index card, wires with alligator clips or a battery holder with wires, 100-mL copper chloride solution (0.6 *M*)	Making models, inferring, observing, interpreting data	**Lab zone Easy Planner Lab Activity Video** **All in One Teaching Resources** Skills Lab: *Isolating Copper by Electrolysis*, pp.73–75

Section 1 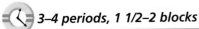 Describing Matter

 3–4 periods, 1 1/2–2 blocks

ABILITY LEVELS
L1 Basic to Average
L2 For All Students
L3 Average to Advanced

Objectives

K.1.1.1 Identify the properties used to describe matter.

K.1.1.2 Define elements and explain how they relate to compounds.

K.1.1.3 Describe the properties of a mixture.

Local Standards

Key Terms

- matter • chemistry • substance • physical property • chemical property
- element • atom • chemical bond • molecule • compound • chemical formula
- mixture • heterogeneous mixture • homogeneous mixture • solution

Preteach

Build Background Knowledge

Students describe properties of an object.

 **Discover Activity** *What Is a Mixture?* L2

Targeted Print and Technology Resources

All in One Teaching Resources

L2 Reading Strategy: *Building Vocabulary*

⊙ **Presentation-Pro CD-ROM**

Instruct

Properties of Matter Lead a discussion about the two kinds of properties of matter.

Elements Use a periodic table to launch a discussion about elements.

Compounds Use the definition of *compound* to initiate a discussion about the relationship between elements and compounds.

Mixtures Use a table to compare and contrast compounds and mixtures.

Targeted Print and Technology Resources

All in One Teaching Resources

L2 Guided Reading, pp. 47–50

L2 Transparency K1

www.SciLinks.org Web Code: scn-1111

⊙ **Student Edition on Audio CD**

Assess

Section Assessment Questions

 Have students use their definitions to answer the questions.

Reteach

Students use flashcards to review the definitions of key terms.

Targeted Print and Technology Resources

All in One Teaching Resources

- Section Summary, p. 46

L1 Review and Reinforce, p. 51

L3 Enrich, p. 52

Section 2 Measuring Matter

 *2–3 periods, 1–1 1/2 blocks*

Objectives

K.1.2.1 Differentiate between weight and mass.

K.1.2.2 Identify the units used to express the amount of space occupied by matter.

K.1.2.3 Describe how the density of a material is determined.

Key Terms

• weight • mass • International System of Units • volume • density

Local Standards

Preteach

Build Background Knowledge

Students observe bars of soap that sink and float.

 **Discover Activity** *Which Has More Mass?* L3

Targeted Print and Technology Resources

 **Teaching Resources**

L2 Reading Strategy Transparency
K2: *Asking Questions*

○ **Presentation-Pro CD-ROM**

Instruct

Weight and Mass Contrast weight and mass in a discussion based on their definitions.

Volume Use the definition of volume and its formula to discuss its units.

Density Use the mathematical formula of density to explain its units.

 Skills Lab *Making Sense of Density* L2

Targeted Print and Technology Resources

 **Teaching Resources**

L2 Guided Reading, pp. 55–56
L2 Transparency K3
L2 Skills Lab: *Making Sense of Density*, pp. 59–60

📼 **Lab Activity Video/DVD**
Skills Lab: *Making Sense of Density*

PHSchool.com Web Code: cgd-1012

○ **Student Edition on Audio CD**

Assess

Section Assessment Questions

Have students use their completed graphic organizers to help answer the questions.

Reteach

Students write the formula for density and describe how to make each measurement.

Targeted Print and Technology Resources

 Teaching Resources

• Section Summary, p. 54
L1 Review and Reinforce, p. 57
L3 Enrich, p. 58

Section 3 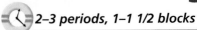 Changes in Matter

 *2–3 periods, 1–1 1/2 blocks*

ABILITY LEVELS
L1 Basic to Average
L2 For All Students
L3 Average to Advanced

Objectives

K.1.3.1 Describe what a physical change is.
K.1.3.2 Describe what a chemical change is.
K.1.3.3 Explain how changes in matter are related to changes in energy.

Local Standards

Key Terms

• physical change • chemical change • law of conservation of mass • energy
• temperature • thermal energy • endothermic change • exothermic change

---

Preteach

Build Background Knowledge

Students describe changes they have observed and later classify them as physical or chemical.

Lab zone Discover Activity *Is a New Substance Formed?* **L2**

Targeted Print and Technology Resources

All in One Teaching Resources

L2 Reading Strategy Transparency
K4: *Relating Cause and Effect*

⊙ **Presentation-Pro CD-ROM**

Instruct

Physical Change Lead a discussion about what happens to a substance in a physical change.

Chemical Change Begin a discussion about how chemical and physical changes differ and diagram two types of chemical changes.

Matter and Thermal Energy Ask questions in a discussion to differentiate between temperature and thermal energy.

Targeted Print and Technology Resources

All in One Teaching Resources

L2 Guided Reading, pp. 63–64
L2 Transparencies K5, K6

PHSchool.com Web Code: cgp-1013

⊙ **Student Edition on Audio CD**

Assess

Section Assessment Questions

🔄 Have students use their completed graphic organizers to answer the questions.

Reteach

Students construct a concept map describing physical and chemical changes.

Targeted Print and Technology Resources

All in One Teaching Resources

• Section Summary, p. 62
L1 Review and Reinforce, p. 65
L3 Enrich, p. 66

Section 4 **Energy and Matter**

 2–3 periods, 1–1 1/2 blocks

Objectives

K.1.4.1 Identify forms of energy that are related to changes in matter.
K.1.4.2 Describe how chemical energy is related to chemical change.

Key Terms

• kinetic energy • potential energy • chemical energy • electromagnetic energy • electrical energy • electrode

Local Standards

Preteach

Build Background Knowledge

Students identify the energy in a ball.

 **Discover Activity** *Where Was the Energy?* **L2**

Targeted Print and Technology Resources

All in One Teaching Resources

L2 Reading Strategy Transparency K7: *Identifying Main Ideas*

 Presentation-Pro CD-ROM

Instruct

Forms of Energy Begin a compare/contrast table to organize information about different forms of energy.

Transforming Energy Ask questions in a discussion about energy changes during chemical changes.

 Skills Lab *Isolating Copper by Electrolysis* **L2**

Targeted Print and Technology Resources

All in One Teaching Resources

L2 Guided Reading, pp. 69–70
L2 Skills Lab: *Isolating Copper by Electrolysis*, pp. 73–75

Lab Activity Video/DVD
Skills Lab: *Isolating Copper by Electrolysis*

www.SciLinks.org Web Code: scn-1114

 Student Edition on Audio CD

Assess

Section Assessment Questions

Have students use their completed graphic organizers to answer the questions.

Reteach

Students diagram forms of energy related to changes in matter.

Targeted Print and Technology Resources

All in One Teaching Resources

• Section Summary, p. 68
L1 Review and Reinforce, p. 71
L3 Enrich, p. 72

Chapter 1 **Content Refresher**

Section 1 **Describing Matter**

Compounds and Molecules The common usage of the words *compound* and *molecule* is often confused. A compound is a substance that can be separated into simpler substances only by a chemical change. A molecule is a discreet, electrically neutral particle made of smaller particles, i.e., atoms, that are bonded together. Molecules may be formed of the same kind of atoms, as in oxygen (O_2). But more often they are formed of different kinds of atoms, as in carbon dioxide (CO_2). In the former, the substance is an element. In the latter, the substance is a compound.

Not all compounds consist of molecules, however. Compounds called ionic compounds are made up of ions—groups of atoms that have a positive or negative charge. An ion forms when an atom or group of atoms loses or gains electrons. For example, sodium chloride is an ionic compound composed of positive ions of sodium and negative ions of chlorine (called chloride ions) that are attracted to each other. Ionic compounds are usually solids at room temperature. They have a structure—called a crystal lattice—in which ions are arranged in a three-dimensional network of alternating positive and negative ions, rather than in discrete groups of particles.

Compounds that do consist of molecules are called molecular compounds. In molecular compounds, the molecules form when atoms share electrons. For example, a molecule of carbon dioxide is made up of one carbon atom that shares two electrons with each of two oxygen atoms. Because no atoms gain or lose electrons, there are no ions in the compound. Most molecular compounds exist as liquids or gases at room temperature. Those that are solids, such as table sugar, do form crystals, but the attractions that hold the molecules together differ from those that hold ions together.

Address Misconceptions

Some students may think that matter such as water, wood, and steel are elements because they are so common. This misconception is addressed in Section 1, *Describing Matter.*

Help Students Read

KWL (Know-Want-Learned)

What I Know/What I Want to Know/What I Learned

Strategy Help students access prior knowledge, set a purpose for reading, recall what has been read, and link new information to prior knowledge. Before students read, have them create a three-column chart with the headings *What I Know, What I Want to Know,* and *What I Learned.* Then, assign students to read Section 1, *Describing Matter.*

Example
1. Pre-reading Have students fill in the first column with information about matter that they already know. Then have them preview the section and generate questions they would like to have answered during the reading.
2. Reading As students read the section, instruct them to fill in the third column of their KWL chart with the answers to their questions, along with information that was new to them.
3. Post-reading Below their KWL chart, have students use the information they have written in the *What I Learned* column to make a list entitled *Information I Expect to Use.*

Go Online
NSTA-PD LINKS
For: Professional development support
Visit: www.SciLinks.org/PDLinks
Web Code: scf-1110
Professional Development

Section 2 Measuring Matter

Standards of Measure The International System of Units is based on the metric system. The metric system was first adopted in France in 1790 in an effort to create a consistent system of units. At that time, each area of the world had its own units of measure that were inherited from earlier times. For example, a foot was the length of a person's foot. A rundlet was equal to 16 gallons in one town, but 18 gallons in another. Because such measurements were not consistent, they could not be reproduced; there was no standard.

Initially, the meter was defined as one ten-millionth of the distance from the equator to the North Pole along the meridian that passes through Paris. The second was defined as 1/86,400 of the average day. The gram was defined as the weight of 1 cubic centimeter of water at 4°C. Over time, these standards were found to be inconsistent: Earth is not a perfect sphere; the average day length slowly changes; and gravity is not constant on all parts of Earth.

These standards have been redefined as scientific measurement techniques and are more precise. The meter is now defined as the distance traveled by light in a vacuum in 1/299,792,458 of a second. The second is defined as the number of cycles of radiation given off by an isotope of cesium. The kilogram is equal to the mass of a cube of platinum-iridium that was cast more than 100 years ago. This kilogram standard is located in a triple bell jar in France. Scientists are working at defining the kilogram in a more precise way. Some are looking at a specific number of atoms. Others are working to define a kilogram in terms of voltage and current with a special kind of balance that uses electromagnetic force.

Section 3 Changes in Matter

Types of Chemical Reactions Chemical reactions are divided into three general types: synthesis, decomposition, and replacement. In a synthesis reaction, two or more substances combine to form a single substance. The reactants can be either elements or compounds, but the product is always a compound.

$$2 K + Cl_2 \rightarrow 2 KCl$$

$$SO_2 + H_2O \rightarrow H_2SO_3$$

Oxidation and tarnishing are both synthesis reactions.

In a decomposition reaction, a single compound is broken down into two or more products.

$$2 HgO + heat \rightarrow 2 Hg + O_2$$

Most decomposition reactions require energy in the form of heat, light, or electricity (electrolysis).

A replacement reaction may be a single replacement or a double replacement. In a single-replacement reaction, one element replaces a second element in a compound.

$$2 K + 2 H_2O \rightarrow 2 KOH + H_2$$

A double-replacement reaction usually occurs only between two ionic compounds that are dissolved in water. In this reaction, the positive ions are exchanged between the two reacting compounds.

$$K_2CO_3 + BaCl_2 \rightarrow 2 KCl + BaCO_3$$

Many chemical reactions are not easily categorized because they may involve complex interactions. Combustion is an example. In combustion, an element or a compound reacts with oxygen, releasing energy in the form of heat and light.

$$CH_4 + 2 O_2 \rightarrow CO_2 + 2 H_2O$$

The above combustion reaction occurs when natural gas is burned. (If not enough oxygen is present, combustion will be incomplete and carbon monoxide, CO, may also be produced.) Although it looks like both a synthesis and a replacement reaction, a chemist would not describe it as either.

Section 4 Energy and Matter

Relativity and the Conservation of Matter and Energy Chemistry, the study of matter, overlaps with physics, the study of motion, forces, and energy because changes in matter are always accompanied by energy transformations. The laws of conservation of matter and energy can be combined to state that matter and energy cannot be created or destroyed, they just change form.

In a sense, Albert Einstein's special theory of relativity, $E = mc^2$, brings these two laws together. According to the special theory of relativity, a very small amount of mass (matter) can be converted to an extremely large amount of energy (as in a nuclear reaction). In other words, mass and energy are two different forms of the same thing. Mass (matter) can be thought of as a very concentrated form of energy. Practically speaking, it is extremely difficult to transform mass into energy, and beyond human ability to transform energy into matter.

Interactive Textbook
- **Complete student edition**
- Video and audio
- Simulations and activities
- Section and chapter activities

Chapter 1

Introduction to Matter

Chapter Preview

❶ Describing Matter
Discover *What Is a Mixture?*
Skills Activity *Interpreting Data*
Math Skills *Ratios*

❷ Measuring Matter
Discover *Which Has More Mass?*
Skills Lab *Making Sense of Density*

❸ Changes in Matter
Discover *Is a New Substance Formed?*
Skills Activity *Inferring*
Active Art *Conserving Matter*
Analyzing Data *Comparing Energy Changes*
Science and Society *Transporting Hazardous Chemicals*

❹ Energy and Matter
Discover *Where Was the Energy?*
Try This *Dropping the Ball*
At-Home Activity *Tracking Energy Changes*
Skills Lab *Isolating Copper by Electrolysis*

Interactive Textbook

This "junk sculpture" of an armadillo is made entirely of metal can lids. ▶

4 ◆ K

Chapter Project L3

Objectives

Students will design and build a device to measure mass and volume in order to calculate the density of powdered solids and liquids. After completing this Chapter Project, students will be able to

- apply chapter concepts to design devices that measure mass and volume
- calculate the density of various substances using data obtained from their devices
- communicate their design and redesign processes

Skills Focus

Applying concepts, calculating, communicating

Project Time Line 2 to 3 weeks

All in One Teaching Resources

- Chapter Project Teacher Notes
- Chapter Project Worksheet 1
- Chapter Project Worksheet 2
- Chapter Project Scoring Rubric

Developing a Plan

To begin, have students research how a balance works. Suggest that they preview Measuring Matter to learn how mass, volume, and density are related. Allow about a week for students to design and build a balance and a container to measure volume. Next, students will need a few days to test and redesign their devices. Then give students time to calculate densities and prepare presentations. On the final day, allow students time to present their data and design-and-build process.

Possible Materials

Balances and containers to measure volume can be made from many different materials. You may have students design their devices using specific materials or materials of their choice. Suitable materials include plastic coat hangers, wooden dowels, string, paper plates, paper cups, and empty yogurt containers. Provide metric weights and a graduated cylinder for calibrating the devices.

Lab zone™ Chapter **Project**

Design and Build a Density-Calculating System

How do you find the density of something if you don't have a balance to measure its mass? Suppose you can't use a graduated cylinder to measure the volume of such items as honey or table sugar. Can you build your own balance and devise a way to find the volume of items that are not easily measured with a ruler?

Your Goal To design and build a device for collecting data that can be used to calculate the density of powdered solids and liquids

To complete the project, you must

- build a device to measure accurately the masses of powdered solids and liquids
- develop a method to measure volume without using standard laboratory equipment
- obtain data you can use to calculate the density of items
- follow the safety guidelines in Appendix A

Plan It! Preview the chapter to find out how mass, volume, and density are related. Research how balances are constructed and how they work. Build a balance out of the materials supplied by your teacher. Then devise a container with a known volume that you can use to find the volumes of your test materials. When your teacher approves your plan, test your system. Redesign and retest your system to improve its accuracy and reliability.

Introduction to Matter

Show the Video Preview to introduce the chapter and provide an overview of chapter content. Discussion question: **What makes seawater undrinkable?** *(It has too much salt.)*

Performance Assessment

The Chapter Project Scoring Rubric will help you evaluate how well students complete the Chapter Project. You may want to share the rubric with your students so they know what is expected. Students will be assessed on

- how well they apply chapter concepts in the design, construction, and modification of their density-calculating systems
- the accuracy and reliability of their balances
- how correctly and accurately they calculate the densities of test materials
- the thoroughness and clarity of their final presentations

Students can keep their design plans and density calculations in their portfolios. **Portfolio**

Possible Shortcuts

Show students various design ideas for the balance, and allow students to choose a design to build.

Launching the Project

Show students a balance and a graduated cylinder. Ask: **What is the balance used for?** *(To measure mass)* **What does the graduated cylinder measure?** *(Volume)* Demonstrate how these devices are used. Measure both a liquid and a powdered solid. Consider allowing students to practice measuring mass and volume. Then explain that students will design their own devices to measure mass and volume and use their measurements to calculate density.

Objectives

After this lesson, students will be able to

K.1.1.1 Identify the properties used to describe matter.

K.1.1.2 Define elements and explain how they relate to compounds.

K.1.1.3 Describe the properties of a mixture.

Target Reading Skill

Building Vocabulary Explain that knowing definitions of key-concept words helps students understand what they read.

Answer

As students read the section, have them write the key terms and their definitions. When they have finished reading, tell students to write another definition for each term using their own words. Then, have them use each term in a sentence, either oral or written.

Preteach

Build Background Knowledge

L2

Describing Matter

Display any object, and invite the class to describe it. Students may describe its shape, size, color, texture, odor, or weight. List these properties on the board as students identify them. Then, play a guessing game in which volunteers describe a common object using descriptions from each category on the list.

Section

1 Describing Matter

Reading Preview

Key Concepts

- What kinds of properties are used to describe matter?
- What are elements, and how do they relate to compounds?
- What are the properties of a mixture?

Key Terms

- matter • chemistry
- substance • physical property
- chemical property • element
- atom • chemical bond
- molecule • compound
- chemical formula • mixture
- heterogeneous mixture
- homogeneous mixture
- solution

🔄 Target Reading Skill

Building Vocabulary
A definition states the meaning of a word or phrase by telling its most important feature or function. After you read the section, use what you have learned to write a definition of each Key Term in your own words.

Lab zone Discover **Activity**

What Is a Mixture?

1. Your teacher will give you a handful of objects, such as checkers, marbles, and paper clips of different sizes and colors.

2. Examine the objects. Then sort them into at least three groups. Each item should be grouped with similar items.

3. Describe the differences between the unsorted handful and the sorted groups of objects. Then make a list of the characteristics of each sorted group.

Think It Over

Forming Operational Definitions The unsorted handful of objects represents a mixture. Your sorted groups represent substances. Using your observations, infer what the terms *mixture* and *substance* mean.

You have probably heard the word *matter* many times. Think about how often you hear the phrases "As a matter of fact, …" or "Hey, what's the matter?" In science, this word has a specific meaning. **Matter** is anything that has mass and takes up space. All the "stuff" around you is matter, and you are matter too. Air, plastic, metal, wood, glass, paper, and cloth—all of these are matter.

▼ Paper, ceramic, wood, metal, and foam are all forms of matter.

Lab zone Discover **Activity**

Skills Focus Forming operational definitions

L2

Materials small objects such as checkers, marbles, and paper clips of different sizes and colors

Time 15 minutes

Tips Encourage students to think about the properties of the objects as they sort them.

Expected Outcome Students will likely group objects of the same type together, for example checkers in one group, paper clips in another.

Think It Over Sample answer: A substance has one set of properties. A mixture is made up of parts that have different properties.

Properties of Matter

Even though air and plastic are both matter, no one has to tell you they are different materials. Matter can have many different properties, or characteristics. Materials can be hard or soft, rough or smooth, hot or cold, liquid, solid, or gas. Some materials catch fire easily, but others do not burn. **Chemistry** is the study of the properties of matter and how matter changes.

The properties and changes of any type of matter depend on its makeup. Some types of matter are substances and some are not. In chemistry, a **substance** is a single kind of matter that is pure, meaning it always has a specific makeup—or composition—and a specific set of properties. For example, table salt has the same composition and properties no matter where it comes from—seawater or a salt mine. On the other hand, think about the batter for blueberry muffins. It contains flour, butter, sugar, salt, blueberries, and other ingredients shown in Figure 1. While some of the ingredients, such as sugar and salt, are pure substances, the muffin batter is not. It consists of several ingredients that can vary with the recipe.

Every form of matter has two kinds of properties— physical properties and chemical properties. A physical property of oxygen is that it is a gas at room temperature. A chemical property of oxygen is that it reacts with iron to form rust. You'll read more about physical and chemical properties in the next two pages.

FIGURE 1
Substances or Not?
Making muffin batter involves mixing together different kinds of matter. The batter itself is not a pure substance. *Classifying Why are salt, sugar, and baking soda pure substances?*

Pure Substances
Table salt, table sugar, and baking soda are pure substances.

Not Substances
Flour, baking powder, milk, eggs, and fruit are not pure substances.

K ◆ 7

Instruct

Properties of Matter

Teach Key Concepts L2
Properties of Matter

Focus Tell students that matter is anything that has mass and takes up space.

Teach Explain that chemistry is the study of the properties of matter and how matter changes. Ask: **What are the two kinds of properties that every form of matter has?** *(Physical and chemical)*

Apply Ask: **Why is melting a physical property, but burning is a chemical property?** *(Sample answer: Melting changes only the form of the substance. When a substance burns, it combines with oxygen from the air to form new substances.)* **learning modality: verbal**

Independent Practice L2

All in One Teaching Resources

• Guided Reading and Study Worksheet: *Describing Matter*

⊙ **Student Edition on Audio CD**

Differentiated Instruction

Special Needs L1
Classifying Matter Give students various food items such as water, juice, sugar, flour, salt, and breakfast cereal. Display the packages from which the samples came so students can refer to the list of ingredients. Challenge students to classify the samples as substances or not substances. *(Water, sugar, and salt are substances. Juice, flour, and breakfast cereal are not.)* Ask: **When is matter not a substance?** *(Sample answer: When it is not made of a single kind of matter.)* **learning modality: logical/ mathematical**

Monitor Progress _____ L2

Writing Have students write the definition of *substance* in their own words.

Answer
Figure 1 Each has a specific composition and set of properties.

Help Students Read

L1

KWL Refer to the Content Refresher in this chapter, which provides guidelines for using the KWL strategy.

Have students make a KWL chart with three columns titled *What I Know, What I Want to Know,* and *What I Learned.* The first two columns should be filled out before reading. The third column should be completed after reading.

Observing Physical Properties

Materials ice cube, 2 paper cups, water

Time 15 minutes

Focus Tell students that a physical property is a characteristic of a pure substance that can be observed without changing it into a different substance.

Teach At the beginning of class, have students freeze some water in a paper cup. Also have them begin to observe an ice cube in a paper cup at room temperature. Ask: **How do you know that water is a pure substance?** *(Sample answer: It is a single kind of matter with its own makeup and properties.)* Later, students can compare the melting ice cube to the cup of frozen water.

Teach Ask: **Why are melting and freezing physical properties?** *(Water has not changed into a different substance; it has only changed forms.)* **learning modality: visual**

FIGURE 2
Physical Properties
The physical properties of matter help you identify and classify matter in its different forms.
Applying Concepts *Why is melting point a physical property?*

▲ **Physical State**
Above 0°C, these icicles of solid water will change to liquid.

◀ **Texture and Color**
Bumpy texture and bright colors are physical properties of this hungry chameleon.

▲ **Flexibility**
Metal becomes a shiny, flexible toy when shaped into a flat wire and coiled.

Skills Activity

Interpreting Data

Melting point is the temperature at which a solid becomes a liquid. Boiling point is the temperature at which a liquid becomes a gas. Look at the data listed below. Identify each substance's physical state at room temperature (approximately 20°C). Is it a gas, a liquid, or a solid? Explain your conclusions.

Substance	Melting Point (°C)	Boiling Point (°C)
Water	0	100
Ethanol	−117	79
Propane	−190	−42
Table salt	801	1,465

Physical Properties of Matter A **physical property** is a characteristic of a pure substance that can be observed without changing it into another substance. For example, a physical property of water is that it freezes at a temperature of 0°C. When liquid water freezes, it changes to solid ice, but it is still water. Hardness, texture, and color are some other physical properties of matter. When you describe a substance as a solid, a liquid, or a gas, you are stating another physical property. Whether or not a substance dissolves in water is a physical property, too. Sugar will dissolve in water, but iron will not. Stainless steel is mostly iron, so you can stir sugar into your tea with a stainless steel spoon.

Physical properties can be used to classify matter. For example, two properties of metals are luster and the ability to conduct heat and electricity. Some metals, such as iron, can be attracted by a magnet. Metals are also flexible, which means they can be bent into shapes without breaking. They can also be pressed into flat sheets and pulled into long, thin wires. Other materials such as glass, brick, and concrete will break into small pieces if you try to bend them or press them thinner.

8 ◆ K

Skills Activity

Skills Focus Interpreting data

Materials none

Time 10 minutes

Tips Make sure students realize that each substance is a solid before its melting point and a liquid between its melting point and boiling point.

Expected Outcome Water—liquid; ethanol—liquid; propane—gas; table salt—solid. A substance is a solid at room temperature if its melting point is greater than 20°C. It's a liquid if its melting point is less than and its boiling point is greater than 20°C. It's a gas if its boiling point is less than 20°C.

Extend Ask students to identify the substances' physical states at −90°C or at 90°C. **learning modality: logical/mathematical**

FIGURE 3
Chemical Properties

The chemical properties of different forms of matter cannot be observed without changing a substance into a new substance.

◀ **New Substances, New Properties**
Gases produced during baking create spaces in freshly made bread.

◀ **Flammability**
Wood fuels a fire, producing heat, gases, and ash.

Ability to React ▶
Iron can form rust, turning a once shiny car into a crumbling relic.

Chemical Properties of Matter Unlike physical properties of matter, some properties can't be observed just by looking at or touching a substance. A **chemical property** is a characteristic of a pure substance that describes its ability to change into different substances. To observe the chemical properties of a substance, you must try to change it to another substance. Like physical properties, chemical properties are used to classify substances. For example, a chemical property of methane (natural gas) is that it can catch fire and burn in air. When it burns, it combines with oxygen in the air and forms new substances, water and carbon dioxide. Burning, or flammability, is a chemical property of methane as well as the substances in wood or gasoline.

One chemical property of iron is that it will combine slowly with oxygen in air to form a different substance, rust. Silver will react with sulfur in the air to form tarnish. In contrast, a chemical property of gold is that it does *not* react easily with oxygen or sulfur. Bakers make use of a chemical property of the substances in bread dough. With the help of yeast added to the dough, some of these substances can produce a gas, which causes the bread to rise.

 Reading Checkpoint What must you do in order to observe a chemical property of a substance?

Chapter 1 K ◆ 9

Use Visuals: Figure 3 L2
Observing Chemical Properties

Focus Point out the examples of chemical properties in Figure 3, and have students read the captions.

Teach For each example of a chemical property in Figure 3, have students identify what the substance was before and what the new substance became. Ask: **When wood burns, what does it combine with?** (*Oxygen in the air*) **What new substances are produced in burning?** (*Carbon dioxide, ash, and water*) **When iron rusts, what does it combine with?** (*Oxygen in the air*) **What new substance is produced?** (*Rust, or iron oxide*)

Apply Ask: **How do chemical properties differ from physical properties?** (*Sample answer: Chemical properties cannot be observed just by looking at a substance. The substance must combine with something else to form a new substance.*) **learning modality: visual**

Monitor Progress _____ L2

Skills Check Have students create a compare/contrast table for physical and chemical properties in which they define and give examples of each.

Students can save their tables in their portfolios. **Portfolio**

Answers
Figure 2 Melting does not change a substance into another substance.

 Reading Checkpoint Try to change the substance to another substance

K ● 9

Elements

Focus Tell students that all matter is made of elements.

Teach Display a large periodic table in the classroom. Explain that all the known elements are in this table. Ask: **What is an element?** *(A pure substance that cannot be broken down into any other substance)* Emphasize that elements are the simplest substances.

Apply Ask: **How can you tell one element from another?** *(Each element can be identified by its specific physical and chemical properties.)* **learning modality: verbal**

Address Misconceptions   L1

Identifying Simple Substances

Focus Students may think that familiar matter such as water, wood, and steel are elements because they are so common.

Teach Remind students that an element cannot be broken down into any other substance. Point out that only the substances listed in the periodic table are elements. Encourage students to use reference materials to identify the make up of familiar kinds of matter.

Apply Ask: **What elements make up water?** *(Hydrogen and oxygen)* **What elements make up carbon dioxide?** *(Carbon and oxygen)* **learning modality: verbal**

Go Online
SciLINKS NSTA

For: Links on describing matter
Visit: www.SciLinks.org
Web Code: scn-1111

Download a worksheet that will guide students' review of Internet sources on matter.

FIGURE 4
Examples of Elements

Some elements have familiar uses. Many elements are solids at room temperature, but some are gases or liquids.

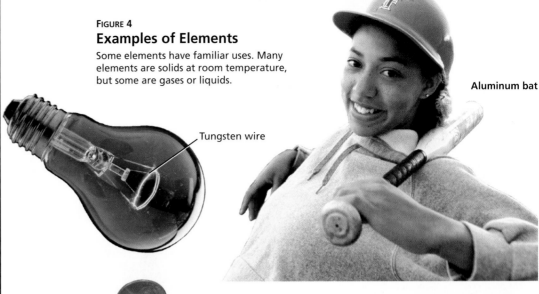

Aluminum bat

Tungsten wire

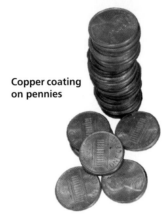

Copper coating on pennies

Go Online
SciLINKS NSTA

For: Links on describing matter
Visit: www.SciLinks.org
Web Code: scn-1111

Elements

What is matter made of? Why is one kind of matter different from another kind of matter? Educated people in ancient Greece debated these questions. Around 450 B.C., a Greek philosopher named Empedocles proposed that all matter was made of four "elements"—air, earth, fire, and water. He thought that all other matter was a combination of two or more of these four elements. The idea of four elements was so convincing that people believed it for more than 2,000 years.

What Is an Element? In the late 1600s, experiments by the earliest chemists began to show that matter was made up of many more than four elements. Now, scientists know that all matter in the universe is made of slightly more than 100 different substances, still called elements. An **element** is a pure substance that cannot be broken down into any other substances by chemical or physical means. **Elements are the simplest substances.** Each element can be identified by its specific physical and chemical properties.

You are already familiar with some elements. Aluminum, which is used to make foil and outdoor furniture, is an element. Pennies are made from zinc, another element. Then the pennies are given a coating of copper, also an element. With each breath, you inhale the elements oxygen and nitrogen, which make up 99 percent of Earth's atmosphere. Elements are often represented by one- or two-letter symbols, such as C for carbon, O for oxygen, and H for hydrogen.

Particles of Elements—Atoms What is the smallest possible piece of matter? Suppose you could keep tearing a piece of aluminum foil in half over and over again. Would you reach a point where you have the smallest possible piece of aluminum? The answer is yes. Since the early 1800s, scientists have known that all matter is made of atoms. An **atom** is the basic particle from which all elements are made. Different elements have different properties because their atoms are different. Experiments in the early 1900s showed that an atom is made of even smaller parts. Look at the diagram of a carbon atom in Figure 5. The atom has a positively charged center, or nucleus, that contains smaller particles. It is surrounded by a "cloud" of negative charge. You will learn more about the structure of atoms in Chapter 3.

When Atoms Combine Atoms of most elements have the ability to combine with other atoms. When atoms combine, they form a **chemical bond**, which is a force of attraction between two atoms. In many cases, atoms combine to form larger particles called **molecules** (MAHL uh kyoolz)—groups of two or more atoms held together by chemical bonds. A molecule of water, for example, consists of an oxygen atom chemically bonded to two hydrogen atoms. Two atoms of the same element can also combine to form a molecule. Oxygen molecules consist of two oxygen atoms. Figure 6 shows models of three molecules. You will see similar models throughout this book.

Reading Checkpoint What is a molecule?

FIGURE 5
Modeling an Atom
Pencil "lead" is made of mostly graphite, a form of carbon. Two ways to model atoms used in this book are shown here for carbon.

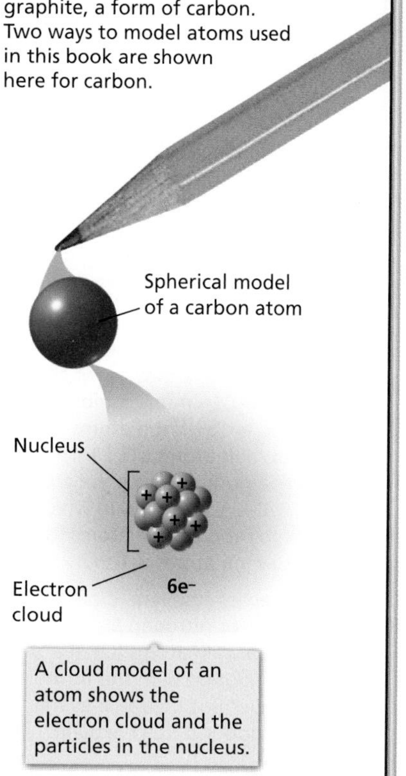

Spherical model of a carbon atom

Nucleus

Electron cloud

6e⁻

A cloud model of an atom shows the electron cloud and the particles in the nucleus.

FIGURE 6
Modeling Molecules
Models of molecules often consist of colored spheres that stand for different kinds of atoms.
Observing How many atoms are in a molecule of carbon dioxide?

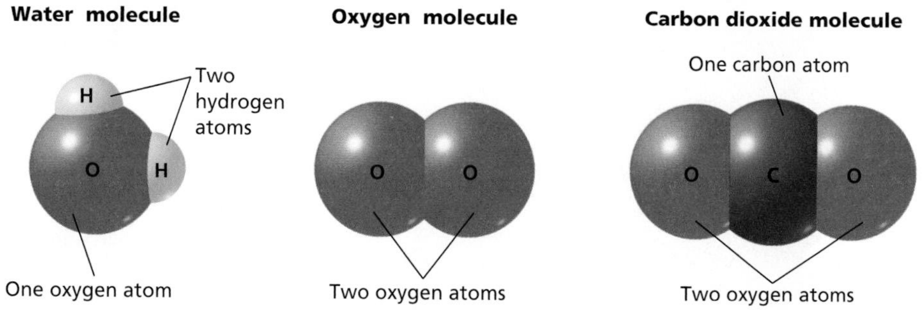

Water molecule

Two hydrogen atoms

H

O   H

One oxygen atom

Oxygen molecule

O   O

Two oxygen atoms

Carbon dioxide molecule

One carbon atom

O   C   O

Two oxygen atoms

Chapter 1 K ◆ 11

Lab zone Build Inquiry L1

Modeling Atoms and Molecules

Materials short bolts, long bolts, hex nuts, square nuts

Time 10 minutes

Focus Remind students that molecules form when atoms combine.

Teach Invite students to assemble different molecules from the four kinds of "atoms."

Apply Ask: **Why can't you make a molecule with only one bolt or one nut?** *(Sample answer: Each bolt or nut represents one atom, and a molecule is made of more than one atom.)* **learning modality: kinesthetic**

Use Visuals: Figure 6 L2
Molecules and Elements

Focus Have students examine the models of the molecules in Figure 6.

Teach Ask: **What does each sphere model?** *(An atom)* Relate atoms to elements. Ask: **What elements make up carbon dioxide?** *(Carbon and oxygen)* Repeat with water and oxygen. Then, ask: **What holds atoms together in molecules?** *(Chemical bonds)*

Apply Ask: **How can oxygen be both an element and a molecule?** *(Sample answer: An oxygen molecule is formed from two atoms of oxygen.)* **learning modality: visual**

All in One Teaching Resources
• Transparency K1

Differentiated Instruction

English Learners/Beginning L1
Vocabulary: Writing Write simple model sentences using the words *element, atom,* and *molecule*. Read the sentences aloud, prompting students to repeat after you. Then invite students to write their own sentences using each term. If necessary, help them find English words to express what they want to write. **learning modality: visual**

English Learners/Intermediate L2
Vocabulary: Writing Expand on the Beginning strategy by adding more key terms for the students to write sentences with. Consider adding the words *matter, substance, compound,* and *mixture*. Write model sentences that use the words, but the sentences may be more complicated. **learning modality: visual**

Monitor Progress L2

Skills Check Students can make a concept map that relates elements, atoms, and molecules.

Answers
Figure 6 3 (1 carbon atom, 2 oxygen atoms)
Reading Checkpoint A particle made up of two or more atoms held together by chemical bonds

K ● 11

Compounds

Teach Key Concepts
L2

Defining Compounds

Focus Explain that most elements in nature are found combined with other elements.

Teach Write the definition of *compound* on the board. Underline the phrases *pure substance*, *chemically combined*, and *set ratio*. Ask: **Why are compounds a kind of pure substance?** (*Compounds are a single type of matter with a specific makeup and specific properties.*) **How are compounds different from the elements that make them up?** (*Compounds have different properties.*) Emphasize that during chemical bonding, the properties of the elements change.

Apply Ask: **Why is the ratio of different atoms in a compound important?** (*Compounds made of the same elements but having different ratios of atoms are different compounds. CO_2 and CO have two different ratios of the same elements, and both are different compounds with different properties.*) **learning modality: verbal**

Math Skills

Math Skill Ratios

Focus Tell students that a ratio compares two different numbers.

Teach Write Fe_2O_3 on the board. Ask: **What is the ratio of atoms of iron (Fe) to atoms of oxygen (O) in this compound?** (*Two to three*) Say that rust has two atoms of iron for every three atoms of oxygen. Demonstrate different ways of expressing the ratio. The ratio of iron to oxygen is 2 to 3, or iron : oxygen = 2 : 3, or 2 Fe : 3 O.

Answer

N_2O_5 contains two nitrogen atoms for every five oxygen atoms. Both N_2O_5 and NO_2 are made up of only nitrogen atoms and oxygen atoms. However, the two compounds are different because NO_2 contains one nitrogen atom for every two oxygen atoms.

Math Skills

Ratios A ratio compares two numbers. It tells you how much you have of one item compared to how much you have of another. For example, a cookie recipe calls for 2 cups of flour to every 1 cup of sugar. You can write the ratio of flour to sugar as 2 to 1, or 2 : 1.

The chemical formula for rust, a compound made from the elements iron (Fe) and oxygen (O), may be written as Fe_2O_3. In this compound, the ratio of iron atoms to oxygen atoms is 2 : 3. This compound is different from FeO, a compound in which the ratio of iron atoms to oxygen atoms is 1 : 1.

Practice Problem What is the ratio of nitrogen atoms (N) to oxygen atoms (O) in a compound with the formula N_2O_5? Is it the same as the compound NO_2? Explain.

Compounds

All matter is made of elements, but most elements in nature are found combined with other elements. A **compound** is a pure substance made of two or more elements chemically combined in a set ratio. A compound may be represented by a **chemical formula,** which shows the elements in the compound and the ratio of atoms. For example, part of the gas you exhale is carbon dioxide. Its chemical formula is CO_2. The number *2* below the symbol for oxygen tells you that the ratio of carbon to oxygen is 1 to 2. (If there is no number after the element's symbol, the number *1* is understood.) If a different ratio of carbon atoms and oxygen atoms are seen in a formula, you have a different compound. For example, carbon monoxide—a gas produced in car engines—has the formula CO. Here, the ratio of carbon atoms to oxygen atoms is 1 to 1.

When elements are chemically combined, they form compounds having properties that are different from those of the uncombined elements. For example, the element sulfur is a yellow solid, and the element silver is a shiny metal. But when silver and sulfur combine, they form a compound called silver sulfide, Ag_2S. You would call this black compound *tarnish.* Table sugar ($C_{12}H_{22}O_{11}$) is a compound made of the elements carbon, hydrogen, and oxygen. The sugar crystals do not resemble the gases oxygen and hydrogen or the black carbon you see in charcoal.

 Reading Checkpoint What information does a chemical formula tell you about a compound?

FIGURE 7
Compounds From Elements
This snail's shell is made mostly of calcium carbonate—a compound made from calcium, carbon, and oxygen.

Mixtures

Elements and compounds are pure substances, but most of the materials you see every day are not. Instead, they are mixtures. A **mixture** is made of two or more substances—elements, compounds, or both—that are together in the same place but are not chemically combined. Mixtures differ from compounds in two ways. **Each substance in a mixture keeps its individual properties. Also, the parts of a mixture are not combined in a set ratio.**

Think of a handful of moist soil such as that in Figure 8. If you look at the soil through a magnifier, you will find particles of sand, bits of clay, maybe even pieces of decaying plants. If you squeeze the soil, you might force out a few drops of water. A sample of soil from a different place probably won't contain the same amount of sand, clay, or water.

Heterogeneous Mixtures A mixture can be heterogeneous or homogeneous. In a **heterogeneous mixture** (het ur uh JEE nee us), you can see the different parts. The damp soil described above is one example of a heterogeneous mixture. So is a salad. Just think of how easy it is to see the pieces of lettuce, tomatoes, cucumbers, and other ingredients that cooks put together in countless ways and amounts.

Homogeneous Mixtures The substances in a **homogeneous mixture** (hoh moh JEE nee us), are so evenly mixed that you can't see the different parts. Suppose you stir a teaspoon of sugar into a glass of water. After stirring for a little while, the sugar dissolves, and you can no longer see crystals of sugar in the water. You know the sugar is there, though, because the sugar solution tastes sweet. A **solution** is an example of a homogeneous mixture. A solution does not have to be a liquid, however. Air is a solution of nitrogen gas (N_2) and oxygen gas (O_2), plus small amounts of a few other gases. A solution can even be solid. Brass is a solution of the elements copper and zinc.

FIGURE 8
Heterogeneous Mixture
Soil from a flowerpot in your home may be very different from the soil in a nearby park.
Interpreting Photographs
What tells you that the soil is a heterogeneous mixture?

FIGURE 9
Homogeneous Mixture
A swimmer blows bubbles of air—a homogeneous mixture of gases.

Chapter 1 K ◆ 13

Mixtures

Teach Key Concepts   L2
Mixtures

Focus Explain that most materials are not elements or compounds.

Teach Begin a table with the column headings *Compounds* and *Mixtures*. Complete the table by asking questions such as: **Is a mixture a pure substance?** *(No)* **How do mixtures differ from compounds?** *(In a mixture, each part keeps its properties, the parts are not combined in a set ratio, and the parts are easy to separate.)*

Apply Invite students to give examples of mixtures and compounds to complete the table. *(Sample answer: Mixtures—soil, salad, sugar water; compounds—water, carbon dioxide, sugar)* **learning modality: visual**

Lab zone **Build Inquiry**   L3

Making Mixtures

Materials paper clips, marbles, 2 paper cups, stir stick, salt, water

Time 10 minutes

Focus Ask: **How do heterogeneous and homogeneous mixtures differ?** *(In a heterogeneous mixture, you can see the parts.)*

Teach Challenge students to make heterogeneous and homogeneous mixtures.

Apply Ask: **Which mixture is a solution?** *(Salt water)* **learning modality: kinesthetic**

Differentiated Instruction

Less Proficient Readers   L1
Vocabulary: Key Terms Have students make an outline of this section using the red headings as the main topics. Then, students can listen to this section on the **Student Edition on Audio CD**. As they listen, they can identify supporting ideas and add them under the appropriate headings in their outline. **learning modality: verbal**

Monitor Progress   L2

Oral Presentation Ask students to differentiate between compounds and mixtures and give examples of each.

Answers
Figure 8 You can see its different parts.

 **Reading Checkpoint** A chemical formula shows the elements in the compound and the ratio of atoms.

K ● 13

Separating Mixtures

Materials magnet, mixture of sand and iron filings, paper

Time 10 minutes

Focus Have students study Figure 10 for ideas about separating a mixture.

Teach Challenge students to separate the mixture of sand and iron filings. You might suggest that students spread the mixture on the paper. Ask: **What physical property are you using to separate this mixture?** (*Magnetism*)

Apply Ask: **How could you separate a mixture of sand and salt?** (*Add water to the mixture to dissolve the salt, then use a filter to separate the sand from the salt solution.*)
learning modality: kinesthetic

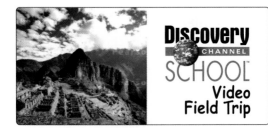

Introduction to Matter

Show the Video Field Trip to let students learn about water purification and understand the differences between mixtures and pure substances. Discussion question: **How does the Catalina plant desalinate seawater?** (*By using reverse osmosis, which uses pressure to separate salts, minerals, and other matter from water*)

FIGURE 10
Separating a Mixture
The different physical properties of iron, sulfur, and table salt help in separating a mixture of these substances.

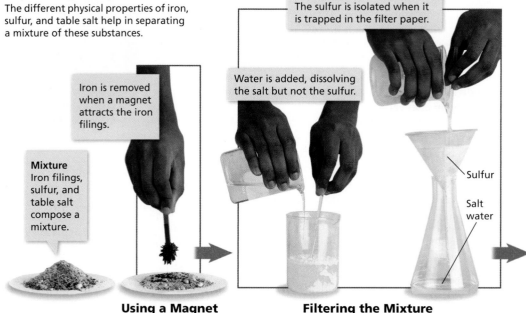

The sulfur is isolated when it is trapped in the filter paper.

Iron is removed when a magnet attracts the iron filings.

Water is added, dissolving the salt but not the sulfur.

Mixture Iron filings, sulfur, and table salt compose a mixture.

Sulfur

Salt water

Using a Magnet   **Filtering the Mixture**

Introduction to Matter

Video Preview
▶ Video Field Trip
Video Assessment

Separating Mixtures Compounds and mixtures differ in yet another way. A compound can be difficult to separate into its elements. But, a mixture is usually easy to separate into its components because each component keeps its own properties. Figure 10 illustrates a few of the ways you can use the properties of a mixture's components to separate them. These methods include magnetic attraction, filtration, distillation, and evaporation.

In the Figure, iron filings, powdered sulfur, and table salt start off mixed in a pile. Iron is attracted to a magnet, while sulfur and salt are not. Salt can be dissolved in water, but sulfur will not dissolve. So, pouring a mixture of salt, sulfur, and water through a paper filter removes the sulfur.

Now the remaining solution can be distilled. In distillation, a liquid solution is boiled. Components of the mixture that have different boiling points will boil away at different temperatures. As most of the water boils in Figure 10, it is cooled and then collected in a flask. Once the remaining salt water is allowed to dry, or evaporate, only the salt is left.

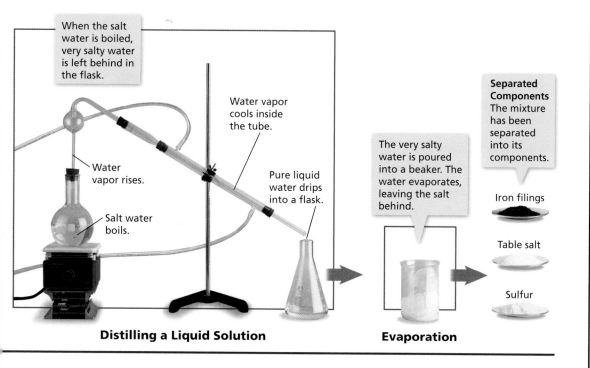

When the salt water is boiled, very salty water is left behind in the flask.

Water vapor cools inside the tube.

Water vapor rises.

Pure liquid water drips into a flask.

Salt water boils.

The very salty water is poured into a beaker. The water evaporates, leaving the salt behind.

Separated Components The mixture has been separated into its components.

Iron filings

Table salt

Sulfur

Distilling a Liquid Solution

Evaporation

Section 1 Assessment

🎯 **Target Reading Skill** Building Vocabulary Use your definitions to help answer the questions.

Reviewing Key Concepts

1. a. Explaining What is the difference between chemical properties and physical properties?
   b. Classifying A metal melts at 450°C. Is this property of the metal classified as chemical or physical? Explain your choice.
   c. Making Judgments Helium does not react with any other substance. Is it accurate to say that helium has no chemical properties? Explain.

2. a. Reviewing How are elements and compounds similar? How do they differ?
   b. Applying Concepts Plants make a sugar compound with the formula $C_6H_{12}O_6$. What elements make up this compound?

3. a. Identifying How does a heterogeneous mixture differ from a homogeneous mixture?
   b. Drawing Conclusions Why is it correct to say that seawater is a mixture?
   c. Problem Solving Suppose you stir a little baking soda into water until the water looks clear again. How could you prove to someone that the clear material is a solution, not a compound?

Math Practice

4. Ratios Look at the following chemical formulas: H_2O_2 and H_2O. Do these formulas represent the same compound? Explain.

Math Practice

Math Skill Ratios

4. No, the formulas H_2O_2 and H_2O represent different compounds because they describe different ratios (2 : 2 and 2 : 1, respectively) of hydrogen and oxygen atoms. (The ratio 2 : 2 may also be expressed in the reduced form 1 : 1.)

Lab zone Chapter Project

Keep Students on Track By now, students should be designing their balances. Encourage them to keep the balance as simple as possible. Key design elements for the balance include a balance point with minimal friction or other impedances and a method for holding the weights and the material to be measured. Simple hooks, pans, or cups will work well. Review student designs, and then permit them to start building.

Reviewing Key Concepts

1. a. Physical properties can be observed without changing pure substances into other substances. Chemical properties can be observed only by changing pure substances into other substances. **b.** Melting point is a physical property because the metal is still the same substance, it is only changing form. **c.** No. The fact that helium does not react with any other substance is a chemical property because it describes helium's ability to change (or not change) into different substances.

2. a. Both elements and compounds are pure substances. While elements are not made of simpler substances, compounds are made up of two or more elements. **b.** $C_6H_{12}O_6$ is made up of the elements carbon, hydrogen, and oxygen.

3. a. You can see the different parts of a heterogeneous mixture, but the substances in a homogeneous mixture are so thoroughly mixed that you cannot see them. **b.** Seawater is a mixture made up of salt, water, and many other substances. **c.** Sample answer: You could put some of the liquid in an open container. When the water in the solution evaporates, solid baking soda would remain.

Reteach L1

Students can use flashcards to review the definitions of key terms.

Performance Assessment L2

Writing Have students write a summary about the ways matter is described.

All in One Teaching Resources

- Section Summary: *Describing Matter*
- Review and Reinforce: *Describing Matter*
- Enrich: *Describing Matter*

Objectives

After this lesson, students will be able to

K.1.2.1 Differentiate between weight and mass.

K.1.2.2 Identify the units used to express the amount of space occupied by matter.

K.1.2.3 Describe how the density of a material is determined.

Target Reading Skill

Asking Questions Explain that changing a head into a question helps students anticipate the ideas, facts, and events they are about to read.

Answer

Sample questions and answers:

How are weight and mass different? (*Weight is a measure of the force of gravity on an object. Mass is a measure of the amount of matter in an object.*)

What is volume? (*The amount of space that matter occupies*) **How is density determined?** (*By dividing the mass of a sample of matter by its volume*)

All in One Teaching Resources

• Transparency K2

Preteach

Build Background Knowledge L2

Sink or Float

Obtain two bars of soap, one that floats and one that does not. Unwrap the soap. Show students the two bars and ask: **What will happen when I place these bars of soap in a pan of water?** (*Sample answer: They will sink.*)

Put the soap in the water. Let students observe the results and try to explain them.

Reading Preview

Key Concepts

• What is the difference between weight and mass?

• What units are used to express the amount of space occupied by matter?

• How is the density of a material determined?

Key Terms

• weight • mass
• International System of Units
• volume • density

Target Reading Skill

Asking Questions Before you read, preview the red headings. In a graphic organizer like the one below, ask a *what* or *how* question for each heading. As you read, write the answers to your questions.

Weight and Mass

Question	Answer
How are weight and mass different?	Weight is a measure of . . .

Lab zone Discover Activity

Which Has More Mass?

1. Your teacher will provide you with some small objects. Look at the objects, but do not touch them.

2. Predict which object is lightest, which is second lightest, and so on. Record your predictions.

3. Use a triple-beam balance to find the mass of each object.

4. Based on the masses, list the objects from lightest to heaviest.

Think It Over

Drawing Conclusions How did your predictions compare with your results. Are bigger objects always heavier than smaller objects? Why or why not?

Here's a riddle for you: Which weighs more, a pound of feathers or a pound of sand? If you answered "a pound of sand," think again. Both weigh exactly the same—one pound.

There are all sorts of ways to measure matter, and you use these measurements every day. Scientists rely on measurements as well. In fact, scientists work hard to make sure their measurements are as accurate as possible.

Weight and Mass

Suppose you want to measure your weight. To find the weight, you step on a scale like the one shown in Figure 11. Your body weight presses down on the springs inside the scale. The more you weigh, the more the springs compress, causing the pointer on the scale to turn farther, giving a higher reading. However, your scale would not indicate the same weight if you took it to the moon and stepped on it. You weigh less on the moon, so the springs of the scale would not be compressed as much by your weight.

FIGURE 11
Measuring Weight
If you stood on this scale on the moon, it would show that your weight there is less than on Earth.

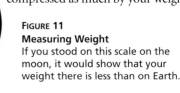

Lab zone Discover Activity

Skills Focus Drawing conclusions **L3**

Materials triple-beam balance, objects of different mass, such as rocks, plastic drinking cups, aluminum cans, pencils

Time 15 minutes

Tips Choose objects that are small but heavy (lead weights, small rocks, bolts, or paperweights), and objects that are larger but lightweight (plastic drinking cups, pieces of plastic foam, or empty aluminum cans).

Think It Over Students may predict that the larger objects are heavier, but should conclude that small objects can be heavier than large objects, depending on density (although students may not yet know the term).

Weight Your **weight** is a measure of the force of gravity on you. On Earth, all objects are attracted toward the center of the planet by the force of Earth's gravity. On another planet, the force of gravity on you may be more or less than it is on Earth. On the moon, you would weigh only about one-sixth of your weight on Earth.

Mass Why do you weigh less on the moon than on Earth? The force of gravity depends partly on the mass of an object. The **mass** of an object is the measurement of the amount of matter in the object. If you travel to the moon, the amount of matter in your body—your mass—does not change. But, the mass of the moon is much less than the mass of Earth, so the moon exerts much less gravitational force on you. **Unlike weight, mass does not change with location, even when the force of gravity on an object changes.** For this reason scientists prefer to measure matter by its mass rather than its weight. The mass of an object is a physical property.

Units of Mass To measure the properties of matter, scientists use a system called the **International System of Units.** This system is abbreviated "SI" after its French name, *Système International*. The SI unit of mass is the kilogram (kg). If you weigh 90 pounds on Earth, your mass is about 40 kilograms. Although you will see kilograms used in this textbook, usually you will see a smaller unit—the gram (g). There are exactly 1,000 grams in a kilogram. A nickel has a mass of 5 grams, and a baseball has a mass of about 150 grams.

✔ **Reading Checkpoint** What is the SI unit of mass?

Go Online
PHSchool.com

For: More on measuring matter
Visit: PHSchool.com
Web Code: cgd-1012

Equating Units of Mass

1 kg = 1,000 g
1 g = 0.001 kg

FIGURE 12
Measuring Mass
A triple-beam balance measures mass in grams. *Calculating How do you convert a mass in grams to the equivalent mass in kilograms? (Hint: Look at the table.)*

A balloon and the air inside it have a combined mass of about 3 g or 0.003 kg.

A pineapple has a mass of about 1,600 g or 1.6 kg.

An average orange has a mass of about 230 g or 0.23 kg.

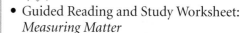

K ◆ 17

Differentiated Instruction

Gifted and Talented L3
Calculating Weight Invite students to calculate their weight as it would be on the moon. Remind them that they would weigh only about one-sixth (0.16) of their weight on Earth. Then challenge them to calculate their weight as it would be on the surfaces of the other planets. The relative gravitational pulls on the surfaces of the

other planets are as follows: Mercury—0.38, Venus—0.91, Mars—0.38, Jupiter—2.54, Saturn—0.93, Uranus—0.8, Neptune—1.2, and Pluto—0.04. Ask: **What is Jupiter's large gravitational pull attributable to?** *(Jupiter has the most mass of any planet in the solar system.)* **learning modality: logical/mathematical**

Weight and Mass

Teach Key Concepts L2
Contrasting Weight and Mass

Focus Tell students that weight and mass measure two different things.

Teach Write the definitions of weight and mass on the board. Ask: **Why do scientists prefer to describe matter by its mass?** *(Unlike weight, mass does not change with location, even when the force of gravity on an object changes.)*

Apply Ask: **What units do scientists use to measure mass?** *(Grams and kilograms)* **learning modality: verbal**

Go Online
PHSchool.com

For: More on measuring matter
Visit: PHSchool.com
Web Code: cgd-1012

Students can review measuring matter in an online activity.

Independent Practice L2

All in One Teaching Resources

• Guided Reading and Study Worksheet: *Measuring Matter*

◉ **Student Edition on Audio CD**

Monitor Progress L2

Writing Have students write definitions for weight and mass in their own words.
Students can save their definitions in their portfolios. 💼 Portfolio

Answer
Figure 12 Divide the mass in grams by 1000 or multiply it by 0.001.

✔ **Reading Checkpoint** The kilogram is the SI unit of mass.

Volume

Teach Key Concepts L2
Units of Volume

Focus Write the definition of volume.

Teach Ask: **What units can be used to express volume?** *(The liter, milliliter, and cubic centimeter)* **What unit is equal to the cubic centimeter?** *(The milliliter)* Write the formula for volume. Show that the units of the measurements are also multiplied.

Apply Ask: **How can you measure the volume of an object with an irregular shape?** *(By placing it in water in a graduated cylinder and finding the difference in the volume of water before and after the object was added)* **learning modality: visual**

Calculating Volume

Materials calculator, graduated cylinder, metric ruler, objects with regular and irregular shapes, water

Time 15 minutes

Focus Write the formula for volume *(Volume = Length × Width × Height)*.

Teach Invite students to measure the volume of various objects, both regular and irregular in shape.

Apply Ask: **How do you convert milliliters to liters?** *(By dividing the volume in milliliters by 1,000)* Have students convert all their volume measurements from milliliters and cubic centimeters to liters. **learning modality: logical/mathematical**

Equating Units of Volume

1 L = 1,000 mL
1 mL = 0.001 L
1 mL = 1 cm³

FIGURE 13
Finding Volume
The volume of a regular solid can be found by measuring its dimensions and multiplying the values.
Interpreting Tables *What volume of water in milliliters would this brick displace if submerged?*

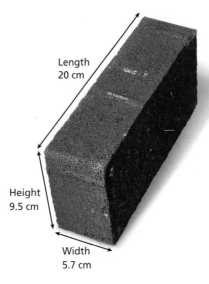

Length
20 cm

Height
9.5 cm

Width
5.7 cm

Volume = 20 cm x 9.5 cm x 5.7 cm
= 1,083 cm³

Volume

You learned in Section 1 that all matter has mass and takes up space. The amount of space that matter occupies is called its **volume.** It's easy to see that solids and liquids take up space. Gases have volume, too. Watch a balloon as you blow into it. You're actually increasing the volume of gas in the balloon with your breath.

Units of Volume Common units of volume include the liter (L), milliliter (mL), and cubic centimeter (cm^3). Some plastic soda bottles hold 1 liter of liquid. Volumes smaller than a liter are usually given in milliliters. A milliliter is one one-thousandth of a liter and is exactly the same volume as 1 cubic centimeter. A teaspoonful of water has a volume of about 5 milliliters, and an ordinary can of soda contains 355 milliliters of liquid. In the laboratory, volumes of liquid are usually measured with a graduated cylinder.

Calculating Volume The volumes of solid objects are usually expressed in cubic centimeters. Suppose you want to know the volume of a rectangular object, such as the brick shown in Figure 13. First, you measure the brick's length, width, and height (or thickness). Then, you multiply these values.

> **Volume = Length × Width × Height**

Measurements always have units. So, when you multiply the three measurements, you must multiply the units as well as the numbers.

> **Units = cm × cm × cm = cm^3**

How can you measure the volume of an irregular object, such as a piece of fruit or a rock? One way is to submerge the object in water in a graduated cylinder. The water level will rise by an amount that is equal to the volume of the object in milliliters.

 Reading Checkpoint How are milliliters related to cubic centimeters?

Density

Samples of two different materials may have the same volume, but they don't necessarily have the same mass. Remember the riddle about the sand and the feathers? A kilogram of sand takes up much less space than a kilogram of feathers. The volumes differ because sand and feathers have different densities—an important property of matter. **Density** relates the mass of a material in a given volume. Often, density is expressed as the number of grams in one cubic centimeter. For example, the density of water at room temperature is stated as "one gram per cubic centimeter (1 g/cm^3)." This value means that every gram of water has a volume of 1 cm^3. Notice that the word *per* is replaced by the fraction bar in the units of density. **The bar tells you that you can determine the density of a sample of matter by dividing its mass by its volume.**

$$\text{Density} = \frac{\text{Mass}}{\text{Volume}}$$

Math — Sample Problem

Calculating Density

A small block of wood floats on water. It has a mass of 200 g and a volume of 250 cm^3. What is the density of the wood?

1 Read and Understand
What information are you given?
Mass of block = 200 g
Volume of block = 250 cm^3

2 Plan and Solve
What quantity are you trying to calculate?
The density of the block = ■

What formula contains the given quantities and the unknown quantity?

$$\text{Density} = \frac{\text{Mass}}{\text{Volume}}$$

Perform the calculation.

$$\text{Density} = \frac{\text{Mass}}{\text{Volume}} = \frac{200 \text{ g}}{250 \text{ cm}^3} = 0.80 \text{ g/cm}^3$$

3 Look Back and Check
Does your answer make sense?
The density is lower than 1.0 g/cm^3, which makes sense because the block can float.

Math — Practice

1. A sample of liquid has a mass of 24 g and a volume of 16 mL. What is the density of the liquid?

2. A piece of solid metal has a mass of 43.5 g and a volume of 15 cm^3. What is the density of the metal?

Differentiated Instruction

Special Needs L1
Comparing Densities Set up a station with a container of water and objects of different densities. Include solid objects as well as liquids. Ask: **If an object is less dense than water, would you expect it to sink or float?** (*Float*) **If it is more dense?** (*Sink*) Invite students to compare the densities of the objects with water. Have them record their observations in a chart with the columns *Less Dense* and *More Dense*. **learning modality: kinesthetic**

Density

Teach Key Concepts   L2
Density

Focus Explain that density is the mass of a material in a given volume.

Teach Write the formula for density on the board. Explain that the units most often used for density are grams per cubic centimeter.

Apply Ask: **What causes some materials to float in water, while others sink?** (*Materials that are less dense than water will float. Materials that are more dense will sink.*) **learning modality: verbal**

Math — Sample Problem

Math Skill Calculating density

Focus Point out that density is a ratio of two quantities, mass and volume.

Teach Ask: **What measurements are given in the problem?** (*Mass and volume*) Show students how to set up the equation and insert the given quantities. Ask: **Do the given quantities have the proper units?** (*Yes*) **Would it be correct to use milliliters as the unit for volume?** (*Yes. One milliliter is equal to one cubic centimeter.*)

All in One Teaching Resources
• Transparency K3

Math — Practice

Math Skill Calculating density
Answers
1. 1.5 g/mL
2. 2.9 g/cm^3

Monitor Progress _____ L2

Skills Check Have students write problems that are solved using the formulas for volume and density. Students can exchange problems and solve them.

Answers
Figure 13 1,083 mL

✓ Reading Checkpoint One milliliter and one cubic centimeter are exactly the same volume.

Answer

✔ **Reading Checkpoint** The oils in salad dressings have densities lower than that of water.

Assess

Reviewing Key Concepts

1. a. Mass is the measure of the amount of matter in an object. **b.** The mass of an object is constant. Its weight, however, can vary from place to place because weight is a measure of the force of gravity on the object.
2. a. Volume **b.** 1,000 milliliters equal one liter. **c.** 620 cm^3 (rounded from 619.65 cm^3)
3. a. Mass and volume **b.** Sample answer: Put the solid substance in water. If it sinks, it is more dense than water. If it floats, it is less dense than water. **c.** Sample answer: Using a balance, measure the mass of an empty balloon. Fill the balloon with air. (Students may suggest using a pump rather than blowing into the balloon because exhaled air differs from atmospheric air.) Measure the mass of the filled balloon. The difference in the two values is the mass of the air. Then measure the volume of the balloon using the water displacement method. Calculate the density of the air by dividing the mass by the volume.

Reteach L1

Have students write the formula for density. They should include the units for each measurement and a description of how each measurement is made.

Performance Assessment L2

Drawing Have students use diagrams to describe how to find the density of a small, irregularly shaped solid.

All in One Teaching Resources

- Section Summary: *Measuring Matter*
- Review and Reinforce: *Measuring Matter*
- Enrich: *Measuring Matter*

FIGURE 14
Density Layers
The density of water is less than corn syrup but greater than vegetable oil.

Labels: Vegetable Oil, Water, Corn Syrup

Sinking or Floating? Suppose you have a solid block of wood and a solid block of iron. When you drop both blocks into a tub of water, you can see right away that the wood floats and the iron sinks. You know the density of water is 1 g/cm^3. Objects with densities greater than that of water will sink. Objects with lesser densities will float. So, the density of this wood is less than 1 g/cm^3. The density of the iron is greater than 1 g/cm^3.

Watch a bottle of oil-and-vinegar salad dressing after it has been shaken. You will see oil droplets rising above the vinegar. Finally, the oil forms a separate layer above the vinegar. What can you conclude? You're right if you said that the oil is less dense than vinegar.

Using Density Density is a physical property of a substance. So, density can be used to identify an unknown substance. For example, suppose you were hiking in the mountains and found a shiny, golden-colored rock. How would you know if the rock was really gold? Later at home, you could look up the density of gold at room temperature. Then measure the mass and volume of the rock and find it density. If the two densities match, you would have quite a find!

✔ **Reading Checkpoint** Why does the oil in some salad dressings rise to the top of the bottle?

Section 2 Assessment

↻ **Target Reading Skill** Asking Questions Use the answers you wrote in your graphic organizer about the headings to answer the questions below.

Reviewing Key Concepts

1. a. Defining What is mass?
   b. Explaining Why is mass more useful than weight for measuring matter?
2. a. Identifying What property of matter is measured in cubic centimeters?
   b. Comparing and Contrasting How are milliliters related to liters?
   c. Calculating A plastic box is 15.3 cm long, 9.0 cm wide, and 4.5 cm high. What is its volume? Include units in your answer.
3. a. Listing What measurements must you make to find the density of a sample of matter?

b. Explaining How can you determine whether a solid substance is more dense or less dense than water?
c. Problem Solving Propose a way to determine the density of air.

Math Practice

4. Calculating Density A piece of metal has a volume of 38 cm^3 and a mass of 277 g. Calculate the density of the metal, and identify it based on the information below.

| Iron 7.9 g/cm^3 | Tin 7.3 g/cm^3 |
| Lead 11.3 g/cm^3 | Zinc 7.1 g/cm^3 |

Math Practice

Math Skill Calculating density

Answer
4. 7.3 g/cm^3; The metal is tin.

Lab zone Chapter Project

Keep Students on Track Have students begin testing their balances for accuracy by determining the mass of a known weight. Suggest that students use masses less than 20 grams. Students can also choose containers for measuring volume. Suggest they choose a container that is heavier than the amount of error in the balance. Possible containers include small plastic or paper cups, yogurt containers, soda cans, margarine tubs, or milk cartons.

Making Sense of Density

Problem

Does the density of a material vary with volume?

Skills Focus

drawing conclusions, measuring, controlling variables

Materials

- balance • water • paper towels
- metric ruler • graduated cylinder, 100-mL
- wooden stick, about 6 cm long
- ball of modeling clay, about 5 cm wide
- crayon with paper removed

Procedure

1. Use a balance to find the mass of the wooden stick. Record the mass in a data table like the one shown above right.

2. Add enough water to a graduated cylinder so that the stick can be completely submerged. Measure the initial volume of the water.

3. Place the stick in the graduated cylinder. Measure the new volume of the water.

4. The volume of the stick is the difference between the water levels in Steps 2 and 3. Calculate this volume and record it.

5. The density of the stick equals its mass divided by its volume. Calculate and record its density.

6. Thoroughly dry the stick with a paper towel. Then carefully break the stick into two pieces. Repeat Steps 1 through 5 with each of the two pieces.

7. Repeat Steps 1 through 6 using the clay rolled into a rope.

8. Repeat using the crayon.

Data Table

Object	Mass (g)	Volume Change (cm³)	Density (g/cm³)
Wooden stick			
Whole			
Piece 1			
Piece 2			
Modeling clay			
Whole			
Piece 1			
Piece 2			
Crayon			
Whole			
Piece 1			
Piece 2			

Analyze and Conclude

1. **Measuring** For each object you tested, compare the density of the whole object with the densities of the pieces of the object.

2. **Drawing Conclusions** Use your results to explain how density can be used to identify a substance.

3. **Controlling Variables** Why did you dry the objects in Step 6?

4. **Communicating** Write a paragraph explaining how you would change the procedure to obtain more data. Tell how having more data would affect your answers to Questions 1 and 2 above.

Design an Experiment

Design an experiment you could use to determine the density of olive oil. With your teacher's permission, carry out your plan.

Prepare for Inquiry

Key Concept

The density of a material is a characteristic property of that material.

Skills Objectives

After this lab, students will be able to

- measure mass using a balance
- measure volume using the water displacement method
- calculate density

⏱ **Prep Time** 10 minutes
Class Time 30 minutes

Advance Planning

Make sure the objects to be tested can be broken easily and will fit into graduated cylinders.

Safety

Caution students to handle graduated cylinders with care. Review the safety guidelines in Appendix A.

All in One Teaching Resources

- Lab Worksheet: *Making Sense of Density*

Guide Inquiry

Invitation

Ask: **What is the formula for calculating the volume of an object?** (*Volume = length × width × height.*) **How can you calculate the volume of an irregularly shaped object?** (*Measure the volume of water it displaces.*)

Introducing the Procedure

Have students develop a way to submerge objects that might float, such as wood or crayons, in order to measure their volumes without affecting the accuracy of the results.

Extend Inquiry

More to Explore Sample answer: Determine the mass of a graduated cylinder without the oil, then with the oil to determine its mass. Calculate the oil's density by dividing the mass by the volume.

Expected Outcome

Density values for all samples of each object should be equal.

Analyze and Conclude

1. The density of the whole object should equal the density of each piece.

2. Because every sample of a material has the same density, density is a characteristic of that material.

3. If the objects were wet, the mass and volume measurements would include water, introducing a source of error into the calculations.

4. Sample answer: Measure the mass and volume of each object several times. Then find the average mass and average volume in each case, and use these values to calculate density. Having more data would provide stronger evidence to support the answers to Questions 1 and 2.

Objectives

After this lesson, students will be able to

K.1.3.1 Describe what a physical change is.

K.1.3.2 Describe what a chemical change is.

K.1.3.3 Explain how changes in matter are related to changes in energy.

Target Reading Skill

Relating Cause and Effect Explain that cause is the reason for what happens. The effect is what happens because of the cause. Relating cause and effect helps students relate the reason for what happens to what happens as a result.

Answer

Sample effects:

A single substance changes to one or more other substances.

Two or more substances combine to form different substances.

All in One Teaching Resources

• Transparency K4

Preteach

Build Background Knowledge   L2

Experience with Changes

Invite students to share changes with which they are familiar. Prompt students by suggesting rusting bicycle chains, growing plants, burning candles, melting ice, and so on. Record student's responses on the board. Refer to them later in the section, classifying them as either physical or chemical changes.

Reading Preview

Key Concepts

• What is a physical change?

• What is a chemical change?

• How are changes in matter related to changes in energy?

Key Terms

• physical change
• chemical change
• law of conservation of mass
• energy   • temperature
• thermal energy
• endothermic change
• exothermic change

Target Reading Skill

Relating Cause and Effect A cause makes something happen. An effect is what happens. As you read, identify two effects caused by a chemical change. Write the information in a graphic organizer like the one below.

Cause

Chemical change

Effects

◄ Sand has been transformed into art.

Lab zone Discover **Activity**

Is a New Substance Formed?

1. Obtain a piece of chalk about the size of a pea. Observe it and record its properties.

2. On a piece of clean paper, crush the piece of chalk with the back of a metal spoon. Describe the changes that occur.

3. Place some of the crushed chalk into the bowl of the spoon. Add about 8 drops of vinegar. Describe what happens.

Think It Over

Drawing Conclusions Chalk is mostly a single substance, calcium carbonate. Do you think a new substance was formed when the chalk was crushed? Do you think a new substance was formed when vinegar was added? Provide evidence for your answers.

You look up from the sand sculpture you and your friends have been working on all afternoon. Storm clouds are gathering, and you know the sand castle may not last long. You pull on a sweatshirt to cover the start of a sunburn and begin to pack up. The gathering of storm clouds, the creation of sand art, and your sunburn are examples of changes in matter. Chemistry is mostly about changes in matter. In this section, you will read about some of those changes.

Lab zone Discover **Activity**

Skills Focus Drawing conclusions   L2

Materials piece of chalk, sheet of paper, metal spoon, vinegar, dropper

Time 10 minutes

Expected Outcome Crushing the chalk changes only its physical appearance. When vinegar is added to the crushed chalk, the chalk bubbles.

Think It Over Sample answer: Crushing the chalk changed only its physical appearance. When vinegar was added to the crushed chalk, the formation of gas bubbles indicated that a new substance had formed.

Physical Change

In what ways can matter change? A **physical change** is any change that alters the form or appearance of matter but does not make any substance in the matter into a different substance. For example, a sand artist may change a formless pile of sand into a work of art. However, the sculpture is still made of sand. **A substance that undergoes a physical change is still the same substance after the change.**

Changes of State As you may know, matter occurs in three familiar states—solid, liquid, and gas. Suppose you leave a small puddle of liquid water on the kitchen counter. When you come back two hours later, the puddle is gone. Has the liquid water disappeared? No, a physical change happened. The liquid water changed into water vapor (a gas) and mixed with the air. A change in state, such as from a solid to a liquid or from a liquid to a gas, is an example of a physical change.

Changes in Shape or Form Is there a physical change when you dissolve a teaspoon of sugar in water? To be sure, you would need to know whether or not the sugar has been changed to a different substance. For example, you know that a sugar solution tastes sweet, just like the undissolved sugar. If you pour the sugar solution into a pan and let the water dry out, the sugar will remain as a crust at the bottom of the pan. The crust may not look exactly like the sugar before you dissolved it, but it's still sugar. So, dissolving is also a physical change. Other examples of physical changes are bending, crushing, breaking, chopping, and anything else that changes only the shape or form of matter. The methods of separating mixtures—filtration and distillation—that you read about in Section 1 also involve physical changes.

 Reading Checkpoint Why is the melting of an ice cube called a physical change?

Iodine gas

Solid iodine

FIGURE 15
Change of State
At room temperature, the element iodine is a purple solid that easily becomes a gas.
Classifying *Why is the change in the iodine classified as a physical change?*

 Table sugar

Aluminum

FIGURE 16
Change in Form
Crushing aluminum soda cans doesn't change the aluminum into another metal (left). When table sugar dissolves in a glass of water, it is still sugar (right).

K ◆ 23

Instruct

Physical Change

Teach Key Concepts L2
Physical Changes

Focus Tell students that chemistry is about how matter changes.

Teach Explain that one type of change is a physical change. Ask: **What happens to a substance in a physical change?** *(It changes form or appearance.)* Invite students to identify physical changes. Evaluate each example.

Apply Ask: **Is dissolving sugar a physical change?** *(Yes. The sugar solution tastes sweet, like sugar. If the water dries up, the sugar remains.)* **learning modality: verbal**

Help Students Read L1
KWL Refer to the Content Refresher in this chapter, which provides guidelines for using the KWL strategy.

Before students read, have them make a KWL chart. They should write facts and examples they already know in the first column and questions in the second. As they read, they can complete the third column.

Independent Practice L2
All in One Teaching Resources
• Guided Reading and Study Worksheet: *Changes in Matter*

⊙ **Student Edition on Audio CD**

Differentiated Instruction

English Learners/Beginning L1
Comprehension: Prior Knowledge
Invite students to describe changes in matter that they may have experienced in their native culture. Prompt them by pointing out photographs in the text. Allow students to describe the changes with illustrations or native words. Then, help students classify those changes as physical or chemical. **learning modality: verbal**

English Learners/Intermediate L2
Comprehension: Prior Knowledge
Expand the Beginning strategy at left by having students match examples of physical and chemical changes given in this section to physical and chemical changes that they have experienced in their native culture. **learning modality: verbal**

Monitor Progress L2
Oral Presentation Ask students to give examples of physical changes.

Answers
Figure 15 It is still the same substance.

 Reading Checkpoint When an ice cube melts, it is still water.

Chemical Change

Teach Key Concepts L2
Chemical Changes

Focus Tell students that the other way in which matter can change is a chemical change.

Teach Ask: **How does a chemical change differ from a physical change?** (*A chemical change produces new substances with properties different from those of the original substances.*) Diagram on the board two types of chemical change: A → B + C and D + E → F. Point out that in the first type, one or more new substances can result. In the second, two or more substances can react, forming a new substance. Note that other types of chemical change are possible also, but that all involve the production of one or more new substances.

Apply Ask: **When natural gas, or methane, combusts, what are the substances that combine?** (*Methane and oxygen from the air*) **What new substances are produced?** (*Carbon dioxide and water vapor*)

Extend The *active art* will show students an activity about conserving matter. **learning modality: visual**

Teacher **Demo**

Demonstrating Tarnishing L1

Materials hard-boiled egg, polished silver or silver-plated spoon

Time 10 minutes

Focus Tell students that tarnishing is the combination of a bright metal with sulfur or another substance.

Teach At the start of the class period, show students the shiny spoon. Place the egg yolk on the spoon. Near the end, show students the spoon again. Ask: **How can you tell that a chemical reaction occurred?** (*The spoon has a dark coating on it.*)

Apply Explain that the silver reacted with the sulfur in the egg yolk to form silver sulfide, the black film on the spoon. Write this reaction as a word equation on the board. Ask: **What is the new substance that formed in the chemical change?** (*Silver sulfide*) **learning modality: visual**

Skills Activity

Inferring

Make a list of changes in matter that you observe during a single day. These changes may occur in your environment (such as changes in the weather), as a result of people's activities (such as cooking or driving a car), or in other situations. Try to classify each change on your list as a physical change or a chemical change. Then briefly explain your choice.

FIGURE 17
Four examples of chemical change are listed in the table.
Interpreting Photographs *What fuel is undergoing combustion in the photograph?*

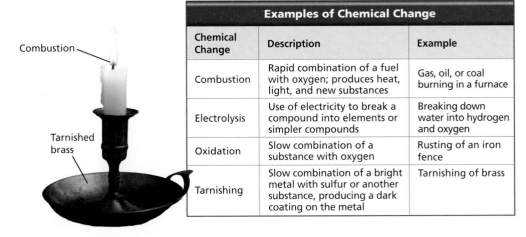

Combustion

Tarnished brass

24 ◆ K

Skills **Activity**

Skills Focus Inferring L2

Materials none

Time 10 minutes

Tips As students classify the changes, suggest that they ask themselves whether two or more substances have combined or whether a new substance has been produced.

Expected Outcome Students should identify changes that produce new substances as chemical changes and changes in form or physical state as physical changes.

Extend Challenge students to classify the chemical changes as combustion, electrolysis, oxidation, tarnishing, or other. **learning modality: logical/ mathematical**

Chemical Change

A second kind of change occurs when a substance is transformed into a different substance. A change in matter that produces one or more new substances is a **chemical change,** or a chemical reaction. In some chemical changes, a single substance simply changes to one or more other substances. For example, when hydrogen peroxide is poured on a cut on your skin, it breaks down into water and oxygen gas.

In other chemical changes, two or more substances combine to form different substances. For example, iron metal combines with oxygen from the air to form the substance iron oxide, which you call rust. **Unlike a physical change, a chemical change produces new substances with properties different from those of the original substances.**

Examples of Chemical Change One familiar chemical change is the burning of natural gas on a gas stove. Natural gas is mostly the compound methane, CH_4. When it burns, methane combines with oxygen in the air and forms new substances. These new substances include carbon dioxide gas, CO_2, and water vapor, H_2O, which mix with air and are carried away. Both of these new substances can be identified by their properties, which are different from those of the methane. The chemical change that occurs when fuels such as natural gas, wood, candle wax, and gasoline burn in air is called combustion. Other processes that result in chemical change include electrolysis, oxidation, and tarnishing. The table in Figure 17 describes each of these kinds of chemical changes.

Examples of Chemical Change		
Chemical Change	**Description**	**Example**
Combustion	Rapid combination of a fuel with oxygen; produces heat, light, and new substances	Gas, oil, or coal burning in a furnace
Electrolysis	Use of electricity to break a compound into elements or simpler compounds	Breaking down water into hydrogen and oxygen
Oxidation	Slow combination of a substance with oxygen	Rusting of an iron fence
Tarnishing	Slow combination of a bright metal with sulfur or another substance, producing a dark coating on the metal	Tarnishing of brass

Conservation of Mass A candle may seem to "go away" when it is burned, or water may seem to "disappear" when it changes to a gas. However, scientists long ago proved otherwise. In the 1770s, a French chemist, Antoine Lavoisier, carried out experiments in which he made accurate measurements of mass both before and after a chemical change. His data showed that no mass was lost or gained during the change. The fact that matter is not created or destroyed in any chemical or physical change is called the **law of conservation of mass.** Remember that mass measures the amount of matter. So, this law is sometimes called the law of conservation of matter.

Suppose you could collect all the carbon dioxide and water produced when methane burns, and you measured the mass of all of this matter. You would find that it equaled the mass of the original methane plus the mass of the oxygen that was used in the burning. No mass is lost, because during a chemical change, atoms are not lost or gained, only rearranged. A model for this reaction is shown in Figure 19.

 Reading Checkpoint Why is combustion classified as a chemical change?

FIGURE 18
Using Methane
Natural gas, or methane, is the fuel used in many kitchen ranges. When it burns, no mass is lost.

FIGURE 19
Conserving Matter
The idea of atoms explains the law of conservation of matter. For every molecule of methane that burns, two molecules of oxygen are used. The atoms are rearranged in the reaction, but they do not disappear.

Go Online
active art
For: Conserving Matter activity
Visit: PHSchool.com
Web Code: cgp-1013

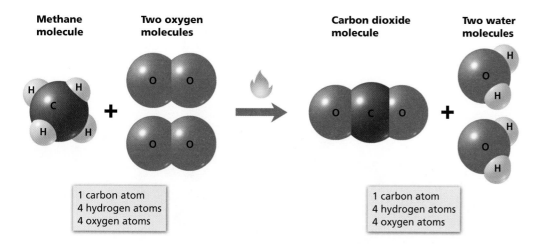

Methane molecule | Two oxygen molecules | Carbon dioxide molecule | Two water molecules

1 carbon atom
4 hydrogen atoms
4 oxygen atoms

1 carbon atom
4 hydrogen atoms
4 oxygen atoms

Chapter 1 K ◆ 25

Use Visuals: Figure 19   L2
Law of Conservation of Mass

Focus Have students study the chemical reaction and read the caption and labels in Figure 19.

Teach Ask: **How do you know this is a chemical change?** (*Two substances have combined to produce two different substances.*) **What kind of chemical change is this?** (*Combustion*) Have students count the molecules of carbon, hydrogen, and oxygen on both sides of the reaction. Ask: **Has any mass been lost?** (*No. The atoms are only rearranged.*)

Apply Ask: **What does the law of conservation of mass state?** (*Matter is not created or destroyed in any chemical or physical change.*) **learning modality: visual**

All in One Teaching Resources
• Transparency K5

Go Online
active art
For: Conserving Matter activity
Visit: PHSchool.com
Web Code: cgp-1013

Students can interact with the art that shows the conservation of matter online.

Monitor Progress   L2

Skills Check Have students explain how the law of conservation of mass applies to combustion.

Answers
Figure 17 Wax

Reading Checkpoint Combustion involves the rapid combination of a fuel with oxygen to produce new substances.

Matter and Thermal Energy

Teach Key Concepts L2
Matter and Energy

Focus Write on the board: Energy is the ability to do work or to cause change.

Teach Emphasize that every change in matter includes a change in energy. Ask: **Do all changes in matter absorb energy?** (*No. Some changes give off energy.*) Help students distinguish between temperature and thermal energy. Ask: **If you remove a cup of water from the ocean, does the water in the cup have the same temperature as the ocean?** (*Yes. Both have particles moving with the same average energy*) **Do both have the same thermal energy?** (*No. The ocean is much larger, so it has more particles and its total thermal energy is greater.*)

Apply Ask: **When ice melts, is thermal energy released or absorbed?** (*Absorbed*) **What is an example of a chemical change in which thermal energy is released?** (*Sample answer: Combustion*) **learning modality: verbal**

Math ▸ **Analyzing Data**

Math Skill Making and interpreting graphs

Focus Explain that a line graph can show how temperature changes over time.

Teach Draw students' attention to the graph. Ask: **What variables in the chemical reactions are plotted on the graph?** (*Temperature and time*) **How does temperature change on the *y*-axis?** (*Temperature increases going up the y-axis.*)

Answers
1. The experiment lasted for 10 minutes.
2. The temperature decreased in beaker B, but increased in beaker A.
3. Reaction A is exothermic because thermal energy was released, causing an increase in temperature.
4. Reaction A

All in One Teaching Resources
• Transparency K6

FIGURE 20
Flow of Thermal Energy
Thermal energy from a hot cup of cocoa can warm cold hands on a chilly day.
Developing Hypotheses *How will the flow of thermal energy affect the cocoa?*

FIGURE 21
An Endothermic Change
An iceberg melting in the ocean absorbs thermal energy from the surrounding water.

26 ◆ K

Matter and Thermal Energy

Do you feel as if you are full of energy today? **Energy** is the ability to do work or cause change. **Every chemical or physical change in matter includes a change in energy.** A change as simple as bending a paper clip takes energy. When ice changes to liquid water, it absorbs energy from the surrounding matter. When candle wax burns, it gives off energy.

Temperature and Thermal Energy Think of how it feels when you walk inside an air-conditioned building from the outdoors on a hot day. Whew! Did you exclaim about the change in temperature? **Temperature** is a measure of the average energy of random motion of particles of matter. The particles of gas in the warm outside air have greater average energy of motion than the particles of air in the cool building.

Thermal energy is the total energy of all of the particles in an object. Most often, you experience thermal energy when you describe matter—such as the air in a room—as feeling hot or cold. Temperature and thermal energy are not the same thing, but temperature is related to the amount of thermal energy an object has. Thermal energy always flows from warmer matter to cooler matter.

Thermal Energy and Changes in Matter When matter changes, the most common form of energy released or absorbed is thermal energy. For example, ice absorbs thermal energy from its surroundings when it melts. That's why you can pack food and drinks in an ice-filled picnic cooler to keep them cold. The melting of ice is an **endothermic change,** a change in which energy is taken in. Changes in matter can also occur when energy is given off. An **exothermic change** releases energy. Combustion is a chemical change that releases energy in the form of heat and light. You've taken advantage of an exothermic change if you've ever warmed your hands near a wood fire.

Differentiated Instruction

Special Needs L1
Modeling Temperature Place ten marbles in a metal pie pan, and cover the pan tightly with plastic wrap. Have students gently shake the pan to model the movement of particles in a cold object. Ask: **What do the marbles represent?** (*The particles of matter in a substance*) Then, tell students to demonstrate what happens as the substance heats. (*Students should shake the pan more vigorously to simulate the increased motion of the particles.*) **learning modality: kinesthetic**

Math ▸ Analyzing Data

Comparing Energy Changes

A student observes two different chemical reactions, one in beaker A and the other in beaker B. The student measures the temperature of each reaction every minute. The student then plots the time and temperature data and creates the following graph.

1. **Reading Graphs** What do the numbers on the x-axis tell you about the length of the experiment?

2. **Comparing and Contrasting** How did the change in temperature in beaker B differ from that in beaker A?

3. **Interpreting Data** Which reaction is exothermic? Explain your reasoning.

4. **Calculating** Which reaction results in a greater change in temperature over time?

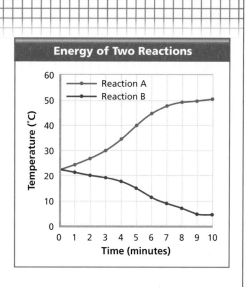

Energy of Two Reactions

Reaction A
Reaction B

Temperature (°C) vs. Time (minutes)

Section 3 Assessment

Target Reading Skill

Relating Cause and Effect Refer to your graphic organizer about chemical change to help you answer Question 2 below.

Reviewing Key Concepts

1. a. **Listing** Identify three different kinds of physical change that could happen to a plastic spoon.
   b. **Making Judgments** Which of the following processes is not a physical change: drying wet clothes, cutting snowflakes out of paper, lighting a match from a matchbook?

2. a. **Defining** What evidence would you look for to determine whether a chemical change has occurred?
   b. **Applying Concepts** Why is the electrolysis of water classified as a chemical change but the freezing of water is not?

   c. **Problem Solving** Explain why the mass of a rusted nail would be greater than the mass of the nail before it rusted. Assume that all the rust is still attached to the nail. (*Hint:* The nail rusts when exposed to the air.)

3. a. **Reviewing** What is thermal energy?
   b. **Explaining** How can you tell whether one glass of water has more thermal energy than another, identical glass of water?
   c. **Inferring** How might you cause an endothermic chemical change to begin and keep going?

Writing in Science

Persuasive Letter Write a letter to persuade a friend that a change in temperature does not necessarily mean that a chemical change has occurred.

Chapter 1 K ◆ 27

Monitor Progress _____ L2

Answer
Figure 20 The cocoa will become cooler as thermal energy flows from the warm cocoa to the cold hands.

Assess

Reviewing Key Concepts

1. a. Sample answer: Bend the spoon, break it in pieces, and melt it. b. Lighting a match is not a physical change.
2. a. If a new substance is formed, a chemical change has occurred. b. In electrolysis, water is broken down into hydrogen and oxygen, two different substances. When water freezes, it is the same substance, but in a different form. c. During rusting, oxygen in the air combines with iron in the nail. The rusted nail has atoms of oxygen that the nail did not have before it rusted.
3. a. Thermal energy is the total energy of all of the particles in an object. b. If the temperatures are different, the glass of water with the higher temperature has the greater thermal energy. c. You have to add thermal energy.

Reteach L1

Have students construct a concept map that describes physical and chemical changes and examples of each.

Performance Assessment L2

Drawing Have students choose an object or substance and diagram how that substance might change physically and chemically.

All in One Teaching Resources

- Section Summary: *Changes in Matter*
- Review and Reinforce: *Changes in Matter*
- Enrich: *Changes in Matter*

Writing in Science

Writing Mode Persuasion

Scoring Rubric

4 Exceeds criteria
3 Meets criteria
2 Letter is only slightly persuasive and/or includes facts that are not quite accurate
1 Letter is not persuasive and includes inaccuracies and/or omissions

K ● 27

Science and Society

Transporting Hazardous Chemicals

Key Concept
Hazardous substances could be accidentally released while being transported. If released, these hazardous substances could harm people and the environment.

Build Background Knowledge
Substances and Their Properties
Ask: **What is a pure substance?** *(A single kind of matter with a specific set of properties.)* Tell students that hazardous substances include those that are flammable or explosive when exposed to air. Ask: **How are these two properties examples of chemical properties?** *(Both describe the ability of a substance to change into different substances, usually by combining with another substance.)*

Introduce the Debate
As students consider the options for the regulation of transporting hazardous substances, ask: **Is it possible to completely avoid transporting hazardous substances?** *(Sample answer: No. In many cases, a less hazardous substance would not have the same chemical and physical properties as the more hazardous substance that is needed for a specific use.)* Point out that there are two basic positions to take in this debate: either more regulation or more reinforcement of current regulations. Ask: **Who should be responsible for funding these regulations?** *(Sample answer: Chemical companies, companies purchasing the chemicals, or local taxes)*

Science and Society

Transporting Hazardous Chemicals

Each year, millions of tons of hazardous substances criss-cross the country by truck and rail. These substances can be poisonous, flammable, and even explosive. The chemical industry tries to make the transport of hazardous substances safe, and problems are rare. But when spills do happen, these compounds can damage the environment and threaten human lives. How can hazardous substances be transported safely?

Why Do People Transport Hazardous Substances?

Useful products are made from the hazardous materials that trucks and trains carry. For example, CDs are made from plastics. To produce plastics, manufacturers use compounds such as benzene and styrene. Benzene fumes are poisonous and flammable. Styrene can explode when exposed to air. Public health experts say it is important to find safe substitutes for dangerous substances. But finding alternatives is difficult and expensive.

What Are the Risks?

Since 2000, the number of accidents in the United States involving hazardous chemical releases has dropped steadily from more than 350 to less than 20 in 2003. Still, public health experts say that some substances are too hazardous to transport on roads and railroads. An accidental release near a city could harm many people.

Some people say that vehicles carrying hazardous substances should be restricted to isolated roads. However, many factories that use the chemical compounds are located in cities. Chemicals often must be transported from where they are made to where they are used. For example, trucks and trains must transport gasoline to every neighborhood and region of the country.

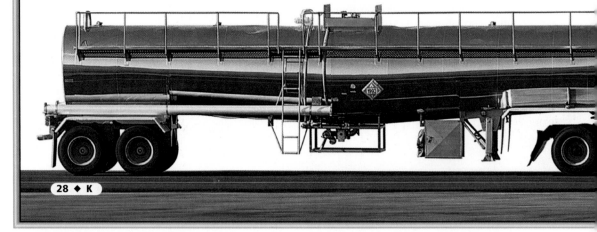

Facilitate the Debate
- Have students read the feature and answer the questions.
- Guide the class in a discussion of the regulation of transporting hazardous chemicals by asking such questions as: **How can hazardous chemicals be transported safely? What can be done to prevent accidents involving hazardous chemicals? Whose responsibility is it to pay for inspections?**
- Organize the class into two groups. Arbitrarily assign one group to argue that current laws for transporting hazardous chemicals are adequate. Assign the other group to argue that more regulation is required, either by hiring more inspectors and/or by adding more restrictions.

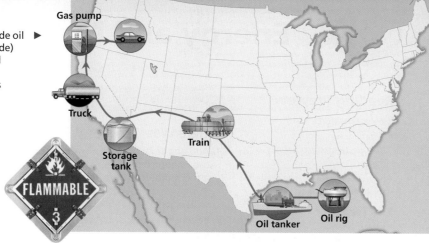

Gasoline (or the crude oil from which it is made) may be transported many ways before reaching a local gas station.

Gas pump
Truck
Storage tank
Train
Oil tanker
Oil rig

FLAMMABLE
3

How Should Transportation Be Regulated?

Manufacturers that use hazardous chemicals say that there already are adequate laws. The Hazardous Materials Transportation Act (1975, revised in 1994) requires carriers of hazardous substances to follow strict labeling and packaging rules. They must keep records of what they carry and where they travel. Local emergency officials in communities near transportation routes must also be trained to handle accidents involving these substances.

On the other hand, public health experts say there are not enough inspectors to check all trucks and trains and make sure rules are followed. But hiring more inspectors would cost additional tax money.

You Decide

1. Identify the Problem
In your own words, explain the problem of safely transporting hazardous substances.

2. Analyze the Options
Examine the pros and cons of greater regulation of the transport of hazardous substances. In each position, consider the effects on chemical industries and on the public.

3. Find a Solution
You are the emergency planning director in your city. Create regulations for transporting hazardous substances through your community.

Go Online
PHSchool.com

For: More on transporting hazardous chemicals
Visit: PHSchool.com
Web Code: cgh-1010

You Decide

1. Sample answer: Although many hazardous chemicals are transported safely, accidents do happen. When a hazardous chemical spills, it can damage the environment and harm people.

2. Sample answer: Greater regulation of transporting chemicals might be such a burden to chemical industries that they can no longer afford to be in business. However, more regulation might prevent accidental spills, keeping people and the environment safe.

3. Regulations that students might propose include designating special roads for the transport of hazardous chemicals, mandatory stops at inspection points, allowing transport only during hours of light traffic, requiring the trucks to travel at reduced speeds, or requiring vehicles with flashing lights to escort the trucks through the city.

Go Online
PHSchool.com

For: More on transporting hazardous chemicals
Visit: PHSchool.com
Web Code: cgh-1010

Students can research this issue online.

Extend

Encourage students to find out what laws exist in their community for transporting hazardous chemicals and how these laws are enforced. Alternatively, students can look in newspapers, news magazines, or Internet sources for recent incidents of accidental hazardous chemical spills. Have them find out the impact of these spills on the environment and the people in the community.

Background

Facts and Figures Current regulations for transporting hazardous chemicals specify how to load, unload, and pack the chemicals safely to prevent spills. Regulations also require drivers to be fully trained in handling their vehicles, as well as handling any emergency. Paperwork must accompany all loads of hazardous chemicals and must be readily accessible at all times. Vehicles carrying hazardous chemicals are not permitted to travel through tunnels. These vehicles are also subject to mandatory inspections for any potential causes of an accident or spill, such as faulty packaging or problems with the vehicle itself.

Energy and Matter

Objectives

After this lesson, students will be able to

K.1.4.1 Identify forms of energy that are related to changes in matter.

K.1.4.2 Describe how chemical energy is related to chemical change.

Target Reading Skill 🎯

Identifying Main Ideas Explain that identifying main ideas and details helps students sort the facts in the information into groups. Each group can have a main topic, subtopics, and details.

Answer

Sample answer:

Main Idea: There are many forms of energy.

Detail: Chemical energy is the energy stored in the chemical bonds between atoms.

Detail: Electromagnetic energy travels through space as waves.

Detail: Electrical energy is the energy of electrically charged particles moving from one place to another.

All in One Teaching Resources

• Transparency K7

Preteach

Build Background Knowledge L2

Finding Energy in a Ball

Hold a ball in the air and ask: **Does this ball have energy?** *(Sample answer: No. The ball is not moving.)* Then drop the ball and ask: **Does the ball have energy?** *(Sample answer: Yes. The ball is moving.)* Then ask: **Where did the ball get its energy?** Accept all answers. Explain that students will learn about forms of energy in this section.

Energy and Matter

Reading Preview

Key Concepts

• What are some forms of energy that are related to changes in matter?

• How is chemical energy related to chemical change?

Key Terms

• kinetic energy
• potential energy
• chemical energy
• electromagnetic energy
• electrical energy • electrode

Target Reading Skill

Identifying Main Ideas As you read Forms of Energy, write the main idea in a graphic organizer like the one below. Then write three supporting details that give examples of the main idea.

Main Idea

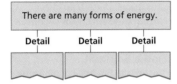

There are many forms of energy.

Detail	Detail	Detail

Where Was the Energy?

1. Add about 20 mL of tap water to an empty soda can. Measure the temperature of the water with a thermometer. (*Hint*: Tilt the can about 45 degrees to cover the bulb of the thermometer with water.)

2. Bend a paper clip into the shape shown in the photograph.

3. Stick a small ball of modeling clay into the center of an aluminum pie pan. Then stick the straight end of the paper clip into the ball.

4. Place one mini marshmallow on the flat surface formed by the top of the paper clip. Light the marshmallow with a match.

5. Use tongs to hold the can about 2 cm over the burning marshmallow until the flame goes out.

6. Measure the water temperature.

Think It Over

Drawing Conclusions How can you account for any change in the water's temperature? What evidence of a chemical change did you observe? What forms of energy were released when the marshmallow burned? Where did the energy come from?

Like matter, energy is never created or destroyed in chemical reactions. Energy can only be transformed—that is, changed from one form to another.

Forms of Energy

How do you know when something has energy? You would probably say that a basketball flying toward the hoop has energy because it is moving, and you'd be right. You can be sure that the player who threw the ball also has energy. Maybe you would mention light and heat from a burning candle. Again you would be right.

Energy is all around you, and it comes in many forms. **Forms of energy related to changes in matter may include kinetic, potential, chemical, electromagnetic, electrical, and thermal energy.**

Skills Focus Drawing conclusions L2

Materials cold water, empty soda can, thermometer, paper clip, modeling clay, aluminum pie pan, mini marshmallow, match, tongs, goggles

Time 15 minutes

Tips Warn students to use caution with matches and the thermometer. Depending on safety management in your school, you may elect to ignite the marshmallows for your students.

Expected Outcome Water temperature will increase and a black residue will form on the bottom of the can.

Think It Over The water absorbed thermal energy from the burning marshmallow. The burning marshmallow gave off energy and left a black residue on the bottom of the can. Light and thermal energy were released. The energy released had been stored in the marshmallow.

Near the top of the track, the slow-moving car has more potential energy than kinetic energy.

The car's kinetic energy increases as it gains speed on the downward track.

FIGURE 22
Energy Changes
The thrills of a roller coaster ride start with the transformation of potential energy into kinetic energy. *Applying Concepts* *Where did the potential energy of the car come from?*

Kinetic Energy and Potential Energy In Section 3, you learned that energy is the ability to do work or cause change. All matter has energy of at least one form. **Kinetic energy** is the energy of matter in motion. A rolling bowling ball has kinetic energy and can do work by knocking down bowling pins. If you drop the bowling ball on your toe, you'll experience the work done by the kinetic energy of the falling ball. Even though you can't see them, the smallest particles of matter have kinetic energy because they are in constant, random motion. Recall from Section 3 that the kinetic energy of particles contributes to the thermal energy of a substance.

Suppose you push your bike to the top of a hill. That action takes energy, doesn't it? But the energy isn't wasted. In a way, it is now stored in you and in the bike. This stored energy will change to kinetic energy as you enjoy an exciting coast back down the hill. As you went up the hill, you increased the potential energy of both you and the bike. **Potential energy** is the energy an object has because of its position. When a diver climbs up to a diving board, she increases her potential energy. When you stretch a rubber band, your action gives potential energy to the rubber band to snap back and do work.

Lab zone Try This **Activity**

Dropping the Ball
1. Work with a partner. Using a meter stick as a guide, hold a ball about 0.5 m off the floor. Let go of the ball and note how high it bounces.
2. Repeat Step 1 from heights of 1 m, 1.5 m, and 2 m.

Inferring When does the ball have the most potential energy? When does it have the most kinetic energy?

Lab zone Try This **Activity**

Skills Focus Inferring **L1**
Materials meter stick, tennis ball
Time 10 minutes
Tips Suggest that students perform several trials from each position and find the average height. Encourage students to use the same method of observation in every trial.

Expected Outcome The ball has the most potential energy at the greatest height. The ball has the most kinetic energy just before it hits the ground after it is dropped from the greatest height.

Extend Have students repeat the experiment using several different balls such as hard rubber balls, golf balls, and baseballs. **learning modality: kinesthetic**

Forms of Energy

Teach Key Concepts   L2
Forms of Energy

Focus Tell students that energy, like matter, is never created or destroyed in chemical changes.

Teach Explain that when matter changes, energy is often involved. This energy is not lost or gained, but it may change forms. Ask: **What kinds of energy are often associated with changes in matter?** (*Kinetic, potential, chemical, electromagnetic, electrical, and thermal*) Begin a table with these forms of energy listed as column headings. As you teach the section, have students complete the table with definitions and examples of each form.

Apply Ask: **What forms of energy are present when wood is burned?** (*Chemical energy is present in the unburned wood. Electromagnetic energy and thermal energy are given off when the wood is burning.*)
learning modality: verbal

Independent Practice   L2

All in One **Teaching Resources**
• Guided Reading and Study Worksheet: *Energy and Matter*

 Student Edition on Audio CD

Monitor Progress _____   L2

Writing Have students list three examples in which energy is stored or in motion. For each example, have them identify the energy as potential or kinetic.

Answer
Figure 22 The car's potential energy came from its height at the top of the track.

For: Links on matter and energy
Visit: www.SciLinks.org
Web Code: scn-1114

Download a worksheet that will guide students' review of Internet sources on matter and energy.

Transforming Energy

Teach Key Concepts   L2
Relating Chemical Change and Chemical Energy

Focus Remind students that chemical energy is the potential energy stored in the chemical bonds between atoms.

Teach Ask: **How do energy changes result from a chemical change?** (*When the chemical bonds between atoms break and new bonds form, chemical energy is changed into another form of energy.*) **What forms of energy could result from a chemical change?** (*Sample answer: Thermal, electromagnetic, or chemical energy*)

Apply Ask: **What energy transformations occur when you ride a bike?** (*Sample answer: Chemical energy from food is transformed to kinetic energy of moving muscles and thermal energy, which is given off as heat.*) **learning modality: verbal**

For: Links on matter and energy
Visit: www.SciLinks.org
Web Code: scn-1114

FIGURE 23
Electrolysis of Water
Electrical energy can be used to break down water, H_2O, into its elements. Bubbles of oxygen gas and hydrogen gas form at separate electrodes.
Drawing Conclusions Why is the volume of hydrogen formed twice that of oxygen?

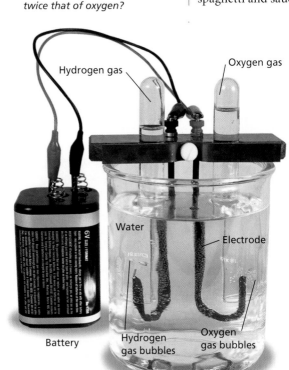

Hydrogen gas

Oxygen gas

Water

Electrode

Battery

Hydrogen gas bubbles

Oxygen gas bubbles

Chemical Energy The internal energy stored in the chemical bonds between atoms is a form of potential energy that is sometimes called **chemical energy**. When a chemical change occurs, these bonds are broken and new bonds are formed. If the change is exothermic, some of the chemical energy is transformed and released in a variety of other forms. As you read in Section 3, one of those forms is often thermal energy.

Electromagnetic Energy You probably know that energy reaches Earth in the form of sunlight. Energy from the sun can increase the temperature of the surface of a sidewalk or change your skin by burning it. Visible light is one example of **electromagnetic energy,** a form of energy that travels through space as waves. Radio waves, infrared "rays" from heat lamps, the waves that heat food in a microwave oven, ultraviolet rays, and X-rays are other types of electromagnetic energy.

Chemical changes can give off electromagnetic energy, such as the light from a wood fire. Also, both chemical and physical changes in matter may be *caused* by electromagnetic energy. For example, a microwave oven can change a frozen block of spaghetti and sauce into a hot meal—a physical change.

Electrical Energy Recall from Section 1 that an atom consists of a positively charged nucleus surrounded by a negatively charged cloud. This "cloud" symbolizes moving, negatively charged particles called electrons. **Electrical energy** is the energy of electrically charged particles moving from one place to another. Electrons move from one atom to another in many chemical changes.

Electrolysis—a chemical change you first read about in Section 3—involves electrical energy. In electrolysis, two metal strips called **electrodes** are placed in a solution, but the electrodes do not touch. Each electrode is attached to a wire. The wires are connected to a source of electrical energy, such as a battery. When the energy begins to flow, atoms of one kind lose electrons at one electrode in the solution. At the other electrode, atoms of a different kind gain electrons. New substances form as a result.

 Reading Checkpoint   **Where is chemical energy stored?**

Differentiated Instruction

Less Proficient Readers   L1
Drawing Diagrams Encourage students to draw diagrams of the energy transformations described in the reading. Instruct them to label the diagrams with the form of energy at each stage in the transformation. Also have them write a sentence to summarize the chemical change that causes the energy transformation. **learning modality: visual**

Transforming Energy

The burning of a fuel is a chemical change that transforms chemical energy and releases it as thermal energy and electromagnetic energy. When you push a bike (and yourself) up a hill, chemical energy from foods you ate is transformed into the kinetic energy of your moving muscles. Similarly, other forms of energy can be transformed, or changed, *into* chemical energy. **During a chemical change, chemical energy may be changed to other forms of energy. Other forms of energy may also be changed to chemical energy.**

One of the most important energy transformations on Earth that involves chemical energy is photosynthesis. During photosynthesis, plants transform electromagnetic energy from the sun into chemical energy as they make molecules of sugar. These plants, along with animals and other living things that eat plants, transform this chemical energy once again. It becomes the energy needed to carry out life activities. The carrots you have for dinner may supply the energy you need to go for a walk or read this book.

 Reading Checkpoint What type of energy transformation occurs during photosynthesis?

FIGURE 24
Photosynthesis
Photosynthesis is a series of chemical changes in which plants convert electromagnetic energy from the sun into chemical energy.

Section 4 Assessment

Target Reading Skill Identifying Main Ideas Use your graphic organizer to help you answer Question 1 below.

Reviewing Key Concepts

1. **a.** Listing What are six forms of energy related to changes in matter?
   b. Classifying Which form of energy is represented by a book lying on a desk? Which form of energy is represented by a book falling off a desk?
   c. Making Generalizations What happens to energy when matter undergoes a chemical or physical change?
2. **a.** Reviewing What happens to chemical energy during a chemical change?
   b. Relating Cause and Effect What are the two main forms of energy given off when paper burns, and where does the energy come from?
   c. Sequencing Describe the energy changes that link sunshine to your ability to turn a page in this book.

Lab zone At-Home **Activity**

Tracking Energy Changes
Volunteer to help cook a meal for your family. As you work, point out energy transformations, especially those that involve chemical energy. Explain to a family member what chemical energy is and what other forms of energy it can be changed into. Talk about energy sources for cooking and other tools and appliances used to prepare food. Try to identify foods that change chemically when they are cooked.

Chapter 1 K ◆ 33

Lab zone At-Home **Activity**

Tracking Energy Changes L1
Before students do this activity, review the forms of energy involved in chemical changes. Review chemical and physical changes in cooking; for example, stirring ingredients together compared to baking. Challenge students to relate chemical energy to chemical changes that occur during cooking.

Lab zone Chapter **Project**

Keep Students on Track By now, students will have refined their designs and completed their balances. Distribute test materials for students to calculate densities. Choose materials that vary significantly in density, such as honey, flour, yogurt, and sugar. Then give students time to plan their class presentations.

Monitor Progress L2

Answers
Figure 23 Water is made up of a ratio of two hydrogen atoms for every oxygen atom.

✓ **Reading Checkpoint** In the chemical bonds between atoms

✓ **Reading Checkpoint** Electromagnetic energy to chemical energy

Assess

Reviewing Key Concepts

1. **a.** Kinetic, potential, chemical, electromagnetic, electrical, and thermal energy **b.** When the book is lying on the desk, it has potential energy. When the book is falling, it has kinetic energy. **c.** Energy often changes form.
2. **a.** During a chemical change, chemical energy is changed to other forms of energy. **b.** Chemical energy stored in the paper is transformed and released as electromagnetic energy and thermal energy. **c.** Electromagnetic energy from the sun is converted to chemical energy by plants during photosynthesis. When you eat plants or plant products, this energy becomes available to your body. Your body converts this chemical energy to kinetic energy as you turn a page.

Reteach L1

Have students draw a diagram to illustrate each form of energy that is related to changes in matter.

Performance Assessment L2

Writing Have students use the major headings in this section to write brief summaries. Tell them that their summaries should also include examples.

All in One **Teaching Resources**

• Section Summary: *Energy and Matter*
• Review and Reinforce: *Energy and Matter*
• Enrich: *Energy and Matter*

K ● 33

Isolating Copper by Electrolysis

Prepare for Inquiry

Key Concept
Elements can be isolated from some compounds by passing an electric current through a solution containing the compound.

Skills Objective
After this lab, students will be able to
- model the laboratory setup in a diagram
- infer the changes occurring in a copper chloride solution during electrolysis
- observe the properties of the products and compare them to the starting solution
- interpret data about color change

⏱ **Prep Time** 15 minutes

⏱ **Class Time** 40 minutes

Advance Planning
- To make the 0.6 M copper chloride (cupric chloride) solution, add 9.5 g of copper (II) chloride dehydrate, $CuCl_2 \cdot 2H_2O$, to 100 mL of distilled water. For 12 pairs of students, you will need about 600 to 1,200 mL of the solution.
- The electrodes can be used repeatedly, but the tips must be cleaned with #0000 steel wool between uses to remove plated copper.
- To make wire connections, any small leads with alligator clips on both ends will work for this lab. A length of at least 8 cm is easier for students to handle.

Safety

Dispose of the copper chloride according to state or local regulations. Chlorine gas, a toxic substance, is produced in small quantities in this lab. Ensure good ventilation in the room during the lab. Review the safety guidelines in Appendix A.

All in One **Teaching Resources**
- Lab Worksheet: *Isolating Copper by Electrolysis*

Isolating Copper by Electrolysis

Problem
How can electrical energy be used to isolate copper metal?

Skills Focus
making models, inferring, observing, interpreting data

Materials
- glass jar, about 250 mL
- two metal paper clips • 6-volt battery
- index card
- wires with alligator clips or a battery holder with wires
- copper chloride solution (0.6 *M*), 100 mL

Procedure

1. Unbend a paper clip and make a hook shape as shown in the diagram. Push the long end through an index card until the hook just touches the card.

2. Repeat Step 1 with another paper clip so that the paper clips are about 3 cm apart. The paper clips serve as your electrodes.

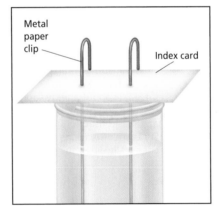

Metal paper clip

Index card

3. Pour enough copper chloride solution into a jar to cover at least half the length of the paper clips when the index card is set on top of the jar. **CAUTION:** *Copper chloride solution can be irritating to the skin and eyes. Do not touch it with your hands or get it into your mouth. The solution can stain skin and clothes.*

4. Place the index card on top of the jar. If the straightened ends of the paper clips are not at least half covered by the copper chloride solution, add more solution.

5. Attach a wire to one pole of a battery. Attach a second wire to the other pole. Attach each of the other ends of the wires to a separate paper clip, as shown in the diagram. Do not allow the paper clips to touch one another.

6. Predict what you think will happen if you allow the setup to run for 2 to 3 minutes. (*Hint:* What elements are present in the copper chloride solution?)

7. Let the setup run for 2 to 3 minutes or until you see a deposit forming on one of the electrodes. Also look for bubbles.

8. Disconnect the wires from both the battery and the paper clips. Bring your face close to the jar and gently wave your hand toward your nose. Note any odor.

9. Note whether the color of the solution has changed since you began the procedure.

Guide Inquiry

Invitation
Show students a bright penny. Ask: **How was the copper for this penny found?** (*Many will say the copper was found in the ground in its pure state.*) Point out that most elements are not found in their pure, elemental states. They must be processed to extract the pure element.

Introducing the Procedure
Display a sample apparatus for students to look at as they set up their own. Point out the positive and negative poles on the 9-volt battery. Remind students that they will be asked to identify which electrode collected the copper.

10. Note the color of the ends of the electrodes.

11. Discard the solution as directed by your teacher, and wash your hands.

Analyze and Conclude

1. **Making Models** Make a labeled diagram of your laboratory setup. Indicate which electrode is connected to the positive (+) side of the battery and which is connected to the negative (–) side.

2. **Inferring** Based on your observations, what substances do you think were produced at the electrodes? On which electrode was each substance produced? Recall that one of the substances was a solid you could see and the other was a gas you could smell.

3. **Observing** Compare the properties of the substances produced to those of the copper chloride in solution.

4. **Interpreting Data** If the color of the solution changed, how can you explain the change?

5. **Inferring** Based on your observations, does electrolysis produce a chemical change? Explain your reasoning.

6. **Communicating** Write a paragraph describing what you think happened to the copper chloride solution as the electric current flowed through it.

Design an Experiment

What do you think would happen if you switched the connections to the battery without disturbing the rest of the equipment? Design an experiment to answer this question. *Obtain your teacher's permission before carrying out your investigation.*

Troubleshooting the Experiment

- Caution students to avoid breaking the electrodes.
- Some students may have difficulty detecting chlorine gas in Step 8. There may not be enough produced to be noticeable, or students may be unfamiliar with the odor.

Expected Outcome

- The pale yellow-gold or pinkish color on the tip of the negative electrode shows that copper has been deposited there.
- The faint odor of chlorine tells students that another substance was also produced by this reaction. They may see small bubbles being produced at the positive electrode.

Analyze and Conclude

1. Students' diagrams should include all parts of the setup and be labeled correctly.

2. Solid copper forms on the negative electrode. Bubbles of chlorine gas form at the positive electrode.

3. Copper is a shiny, orange-colored metal. Chlorine is a gas with an irritating odor. Copper chloride solution is a clear green liquid.

4. The color of the solution changed, indicating that the copper chloride changed chemically to form new substances.

5. Yes, the dissolved copper chloride underwent chemical changes that formed new substances, solid copper and chlorine gas.

6. Sample answer: Electrolysis caused a chemical change by breaking the chemical bonds of copper chloride and separating the compound into copper and chlorine.

Extend Inquiry

Design an Experiment Students may predict that the copper and chlorine will form on the opposite electrodes when the polarity is reversed.

interactive Textbook

- Complete student edition
- Section and chapter self-assessment
- Assessment reports for teachers

Help Students Read L1

Building Vocabulary

Words in Context Help students learn the meaning of new words or phrases by examining context. Tell students to look for familiar words or phrases that surround a new term—these are clues to the new term's meaning. Have students reread the second paragraph under the heading *Properties of Matter* (in *Describing Matter*). Ask: **What word in the same sentence as *substance* helps you to remember its meaning?** *(Pure)*

Word/Part Analysis Have students look up the prefixes *endo-* and *exo-* in a dictionary. They should find that *endo-* means "inside" or "within" and *exo-* means "outside" or "external." Then, have students write definitions for *endothermic* and *exothermic* using the definitions they learned for the prefixes. Endothermic means "heat is inside" and exothermic means "heat is outside."

Connecting Concepts

Concept Maps Help students develop one way to show how the information in this chapter is related. Chemistry is the study of matter and how matter changes. When matter changes, energy often changes form. Have students brainstorm to identify the key concepts, key terms, details, and examples. Then write each item on a self-stick note and attach it at random to chart paper or to the board.

Tell students that this concept map will be organized in hierarchical order and to begin at the top with the key concepts. Ask students these questions to guide them to categorize the information on the self-stick notes: **What is matter? How is matter measured? How does matter change? What forms of energy are related to changes in matter?**

---

① Describing Matter

Key Concepts

- Every form of matter has two kinds of properties—physical properties and chemical properties.
- Elements are the simplest substances.
- When elements are chemically combined, they form compounds having properties that are different from those of the uncombined elements.
- Each substance in a mixture keeps its individual properties. Also, the parts of a mixture are not combined in a set ratio.

Key Terms

matter	compound
chemistry	chemical formula
substance	mixture
physical property	heterogeneous
chemical property	mixture
element	homogeneous
atom	mixture
chemical bond	solution
molecule	

② Measuring Matter

Key Concepts

- Unlike weight, mass does not change with location, even when the force of gravity on an object changes.
- Common units of volume include the liter (L), milliliter (mL), and cubic centimeter (cm^3).
- Volume = Length × Width × Height
- You can determine the density of a sample of matter by dividing its mass by its volume.

$$Density = \frac{Mass}{Volume}$$

Key Terms

weight
mass
International System of Units
volume
density

③ Changes in Matter

Key Concepts

- A substance that undergoes a physical change is still the same substance after the change.
- Unlike a physical change, a chemical change produces new substances with properties different from those of the original substances.
- Every chemical or physical change in matter includes a change in energy.

Key Terms

physical change
chemical change
law of conservation of mass
energy
temperature
thermal energy
endothermic change
exothermic change

④ Energy and Matter

Key Concepts

- Forms of energy related to changes in matter include kinetic, potential, chemical, electromagnetic, electrical, and thermal energy.
- During a chemical change, chemical energy may be changed to other forms of energy. Other forms of energy may also be changed to chemical energy.

Key Terms

kinetic energy	electromagnetic
potential energy	energy
chemical energy	electrical energy
	electrode

Prompt students by using connecting words or phrases, such as "includes," "results in," and "occurs when," to indicate the basis for the organization of the map. The phrases should form a sentence between or among a set of concepts.

Answer
Accept logical presentations by students.

All in One Teaching Resources

- Key Terms Review: *Introduction to Matter*
- Connecting Concepts: *Introduction to Matter*

Review and Assessment

Go Online
PHSchool.com
For: Self-Assessment
Visit: PHSchool.com
Web Code: cga-1010

Organizing Information

Concept Mapping Copy the concept map about matter onto a separate sheet of paper. Then complete the map by adding in the correct missing words or phrases. (For more on Concept Mapping, see the Skills Handbook.)

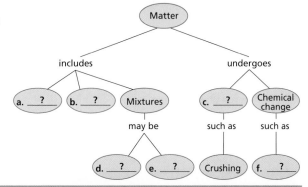

Reviewing Key Terms

Choose the letter of the best answer.

1. The ability to dissolve in water and to conduct electricity are examples of
   a. physical properties.
   b. chemical changes.
   c. chemical properties.
   d. chemical bonding.

2. Water is an example of
   a. an element.
   b. a homogeneous mixture.
   c. a compound.
   d. a heterogeneous mixture.

3. Density relates the mass of a material to the material's
   a. temperature.   b. volume.
   c. weight.   d. length.

4. New substances are always formed when matter undergoes a
   a. change in shape.
   b. physical change.
   c. change in temperature.
   d. chemical change.

5. Chemical energy is the potential energy of
   a. temperature.
   b. bonds between atoms.
   c. electricity.
   d. light.

If the statement is true, write *true*. If it is false, change the underlined word or words to make the statement true.

6. <u>Energy</u> is anything that has mass and takes up space.

7. A <u>mixture</u> is made of two or more elements that are chemically combined.

8. The <u>weight</u> of an object changes if the force of gravity changes.

9. Energy is taken in during an <u>exothermic</u> change.

10. Light is an example of <u>electromagnetic</u> energy.

Writing in Science

How-to Paragraph Suppose you are preparing for a long journey on the ocean or in space. Write a journal entry that describes your plan for having fresh, drinkable water throughout your entire trip.

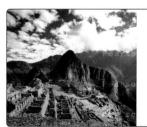

Discovery CHANNEL **SCHOOL**

Introduction to Matter
Video Preview
Video Field Trip
▶ Video Assessment

Chapter 1 K ◆ 37

Go Online
PHSchool.com
For: Self-Assessment
Visit: PHSchool.com
Web Code: cga-1010

Students can take a practice test online that is automatically scored.

All in One Teaching Resources

- Transparency K8
- Chapter Test
- Performance Assessment Teacher Notes
- Performance Assessment Student Worksheet
- Performance Assessment Scoring Rubric

ExamView® Computer Test Bank CD-ROM

Review and Assessment

Organizing Information
a. Elements (or Compounds)
b. Compounds (or Elements)
c. Physical change
d. Heterogeneous (or Homogeneous)
e. Homogeneous (or Heterogeneous)
f. Sample answer: Combustion

Reviewing Key Terms
1. a 2. c 3. b 4. d 5. b
6. Matter
7. compound
8. true
9. endothermic
10. true

Writing in Science

Writing Mode Exposition/How-to
Scoring Rubric
4 Exceeds criteria; includes highly detailed, step-by-step directions that describe how to build and use a device to get fresh water from the ocean
3 Meets criteria
2 Includes brief directions that contain a few errors or omissions
1 Includes sketchy directions with serious errors

Discovery CHANNEL **SCHOOL** Video Assessment

Introduction to Matter

Show the Video Assessment to review chapter content and as a prompt for the writing assignment. Discussion questions: **What is the difference between a compound and a mixture?** (*Compounds are chemically combined elements; mixtures are not chemically combined.*) **How are NASA engineers planning to provide astronauts with drinking water during space voyages?** (*By recycling the water they bring with them using water purification technology*)

Checking Concepts

11. Compounds: made up of two or more elements chemically combined, elements combined in a specific ratio, properties differ from those of combined elements; mixtures: made up or two or more elements and/or compounds not chemically combined, parts not combined in a specific ratio, mixed substances retain individual properties

12. Mass and volume

13. The material is less dense than water.

14. The burning wax releases energy in the form of light (electromagnetic energy) and heat (thermal energy). A change that gives off energy is an exothermic change.

15. Sample answer: Kinetic energy is the energy of matter in motion. Moving cars have kinetic energy.

Thinking Critically

16. Clear lemon soda is a solution because its parts retain their individual properties but are evenly mixed.

17. The 5-cm diagonal is not needed because volume is calculated by multiplying the length, width, and height of an object.

18. The volume of a kilogram of water increases when it freezes to ice.

19. Sample answer: The solution would taste salty so the salt would still be present. Boiling the liquid separates the water from the salt.

Math Practice

20. 2 : 5; the compound P_2O_5 has two atoms of phosphorus for every five atoms of oxygen.

21. 1.74 g/cm^3

Review and Assessment

Checking Concepts

11. What are three ways that compounds and mixtures differ?

12. What two quantities do you need to measure in order to determine the density of an object?

13. What can you infer about the density of a material if a sample of it floats in water?

14. How do you know that the burning of candle wax is an exothermic change?

15. What is kinetic energy? Give an example of a use of kinetic energy that you saw today.

Thinking Critically

16. Classifying Which of the following is a solution: pure water, clear lemon soda, cereal and milk in a bowl? Explain how you know.

17. Making Judgments Which measurement shown in the diagram is not needed to find the volume of the box? Explain.

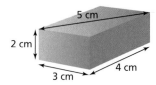

18. Inferring Ice has a lower density than liquid water. How does the volume of a kilogram of water change when it freezes to ice?

19. Problem Solving Suppose you dissolve some table salt in a glass of water. How could you prove to someone that the dissolving was a physical change, not a chemical change?

Math Practice

20. Ratios The elements phosphorus and oxygen form a compound with the formula P_2O_5. What is the ratio of phosphorus atoms to oxygen atoms in the compound?

21. Calculating Density A piece of magnesium metal has a mass of 56.5 g and a volume of 32.5 cm^3. What is the density of the magnesium?

Applying Skills

Use the information and the diagrams below to answer Questions 22–25. Some questions may have more than one answer.

Each diagram below represents a different kind of matter. Each ball represents an atom. Balls of the same color represent the same kind of atom.

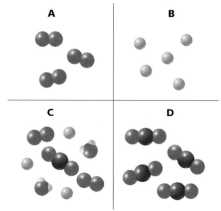

22. Interpreting Diagrams Which diagrams represent a single element? Explain.

23. Classifying Which diagrams represent pure substances? Explain.

24. Interpreting Data How do the molecules in diagram A differ from those in diagram D?

25. Interpreting Diagrams Which diagram represents a mixture? Explain.

 Chapter **Project**

Performance Assessment Present a brief summary of your experience with building your density-calculating system. Describe the most difficult part of construction. What steps were easiest? Defend the accuracy and reliability of your system, and describe its limitations.

 Chapter **Project** L3

Performance Assessment Provide class time for student presentations. In their presentations, students should summarize their design and construction process and describe the most difficult part and the easiest part of the construction. Make sure students also describe the accuracy and reliability of their systems and highlight the limitations.

Standardized Test Prep

Test-Taking Tip

Anticipating the Answer

You may be able to figure out the answer to a question before looking at the answer choices. After thinking of your own answer, compare it with the choices provided. Select the answer that most closely matches your own. This strategy can be especially useful for questions that test vocabulary. Try to answer the question below before looking at the answer choices.

Sample Question

Which two pieces of laboratory equipment would be most useful for measuring the mass and volume of a rectangular aluminum block?

  A metric ruler and stopwatch
  B balance and metric ruler
  C thermometer and graduated cylinder
  D balance and stopwatch

Answer

The correct answer is **B**. Mass is measured with a balance. The volume of a rectangular solid is found by multiplying length × width × height, which are measured with a metric ruler. Choices **A** and **D** each contain only one of the necessary pieces of equipment. A stopwatch measures time. In Choice **C**, the graduated cylinder measures volume, but a thermometer measures temperature, not mass.

Choose the letter of the best answer.

A scientist did an experiment, described by the words and symbols below, to demonstrate the law of conservation of mass. Use the information and your knowledge of science to answer Questions 1 to 2.

hydrogen + oxygen → water + energy

1. The scientist found that 2 grams of hydrogen reacted completely with 16 grams of oxygen. What was the total mass of water produced?

  A 8 grams   **B** 14 grams
  C 18 grams   **D** 32 grams

2. Which pair of terms best describes the type of change that occurred in the reaction?

  F chemical and exothermic
  G chemical and endothermic
  H physical and exothermic
  J physical and endothermic

3. What is the best title for the chart below?

?	
Helium	Colorless; less dense than air
Iron	Attracted to a magnet; melting point of 1,535°C
Oxygen	Odorless; gas at room temperature

  A The Periodic Table of the Elements
  B Gases Found in Air
  C Chemical Properties of Some Compounds
  D Physical Properties of Some Elements

4. Which diagram best represents a mixture of two kinds of gas molecules?

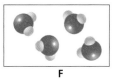

F

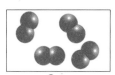

G

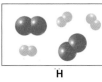

H

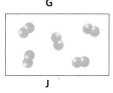

J

5. The density of a substance equals its mass divided by its volume. The density of sulfur is 2.0 g/cm^3. What is the mass of a sample of sulfur that has a volume of 6.0 cm^3?

  A 3.0 g   **B** 4.0 g
  C 8.0 g   **D** 12 g

Constructed Response

6. Describe three forms of energy related to changes in matter and provide an example of each.

Applying Skills

22. Diagrams A and B represent single elements because each is made up of a single type of atom.

23. Diagrams A, B, and D represent pure substances. Diagrams A and B represent elements. Diagram D represents a compound because its two kinds of atoms are chemically combined in a set ratio.

24. A—a single kind of atom; D—two kinds of atoms

25. Diagram C represents a mixture because it contains several different kinds of substances that are not chemically combined.

Standardized Test Prep

1. C   **2.** F   **3.** D   **4.** H   **5.** D
6. Sample answer: Chemical energy is the potential energy in the chemical bonds between atoms. During chemical reactions, chemical energy may be converted to other forms of energy. For example, when wood burns, energy is released in the form of heat and light. Microwaves, one form of electromagnetic energy, can be used to cook food. Adding thermal energy can melt ice.

Chapter at a Glance

 **Chapter Project** *A Story of Changes in Matter*

Technology

Local Standards

All in One Teaching Resources
- Chapter Project Teacher Notes, pp. 100–101
- Chapter Project Student Overview, pp. 102–103
- Chapter Project Student Worksheets, pp. 104–105
- Chapter Project Scoring Rubric, p. 106

Video Preview

Section 1

States of Matter

K.2.1.1 Describe the characteristics of a solid.

2 1/2 periods **K.2.1.2** Describe the characteristics of a liquid.

1–2 blocks **K.2.1.3** Describe the characteristics of a gas.

Section 2

Changes of State

K.2.2.1 Explain what happens to a substance during changes between solid and liquid.

3 periods

1 1/2 blocks **K.2.2.2** Explain what happens to a substance during changes between liquid and gas.

K.2.2.3 Explain what happens to a substance during changes between solid and gas.

Section 3

Gas Behavior

K.2.3.1 List the types of measurements used when working with gases.

3 1/2 periods

1–2 blocks **K.2.3.2** Explain how the volume, temperature, and pressure of a gas are related.

Video Field Trip

Section 4

Graphing Gas Behavior

K.2.4.1 Identify the type of relationship shown by the graph for Charles's law.

3 periods

1 1/2 blocks **K.2.4.2** Identify the type of relationship shown by the graph for Boyle's law.

Review and Assessment

All in One Teaching Resources
- Key Terms Review, p. 140
- Transparency K19
- Performance Assessment Teacher Notes, p. 147
- Performance Assessment Scoring Rubric, p. 148
- Performance Assessment Student Worksheet, p. 149
- Chapter Test, pp. 150–153

Video Assessment

Go Online
PHSchool.com

Test Preparation

Test Preparation Blackline Masters

Lab zone Chapter Activities Planner

For more activities
LAB ZONE
Easy Planner
CD-ROM

Student Edition	Inquiry	Time	Materials	Skills	Resources
Chapter Project, p. 41	Open-Ended	Ongoing (2–3 weeks)	**All in One Teaching Resources** See p. 100	Posing questions, forming operational definitions, communicating	**Lab zone Easy Planner** **All in One Teaching Resources** Support pp. 100–101
Section 1					
Discover Activity, p. 42	Guided	10 minutes	Fizzing antacid tablet, large balloon, 1-L plastic soda bottle, water	Forming operational definitions	**Lab zone Easy Planner**
Try This Activity, p. 46	Guided	10 minutes	2 clear jars with screw-top lids, honey, vegetable oil, paper towels	Drawing conclusions	**Lab zone Easy Planner**
At-Home Activity, p. 47	Guided	Home		Drawing conclusions, applying concepts	**Lab zone Easy Planner**
Section 2					
Discover Activity, p. 48	Guided	10 minutes	Hand mirror, dry cloth	Developing hypotheses	**Lab zone Easy Planner**
Try This Activity, p. 50	Directed	15 minutes	2 alcohol thermometers, 2 pieces of gauze, paper towel, aluminum foil, 2 medicine droppers, water, nail polish remover	Interpreting data	**Lab zone Easy Planner**
Skills Lab, p. 54	Guided	Prep: 15 minutes Class: 30 minutes	Stopwatch or timer, thermometer or temperature probe, 2 plastic cups, 2 plastic stirring rods, ice cubes, warm water, water at room temperature	Predicting, interpreting data, inferring	**Lab zone Easy Planner** **Lab Activity Video** **All in One Teaching Resources** Skills Lab: *Melting Ice,* pp. 121–122
Section 3					
Discover Activity, p. 55	Guided	10 minutes	3 pieces of chalk, sheet of wax paper or plastic wrap, plastic bubble wrap, tape	Inferring	**Lab zone Easy Planner**
Section 4					
Discover Activity, p. 62	Guided	15 minutes		Drawing conclusions	**Lab zone Easy Planner**
At-Home Activity, p. 65	Guided	Home		Classifying, applying concepts	**Lab zone Easy Planner**
Skills Lab, pp. 66–67	Guided	Prep: 10 minutes Class: 20 minutes	35-cm^3 plastic syringe (without needle), modeling clay, 4 books of uniform weight	Graphing, predicting, interpreting data, drawing conclusions, communicating	**Lab zone Easy Planner** **Lab Activity Video** **All in One Teaching Resources** Skills Lab: *It's a Gas,* pp. 137–139

Section 1 **States of Matter**

 2 1/2 periods, 1–2 blocks

ABILITY LEVELS
L1 Basic to Average
L2 For All Students
L3 Average to Advanced

Objectives

K.2.1.1 Describe the characteristics of a solid.
K.2.1.2 Describe the characteristics of a liquid.
K.2.1.3 Describe the characteristics of a gas.

Key Terms

• solid • crystalline solid • amorphous solid • liquid • fluid • surface tension
• viscosity • gas

Local Standards

Preteach

Build Background Knowledge

Students explain why it is easier to hold a rock than it is to hold water or helium.

 **Discover Activity** *What Are Solids, Liquids, and Gases?* L2

Targeted Print and Technology Resources

All in One Teaching Resources

L2 Reading Strategy

◉ **Presentation-Pro CD-ROM**

Instruct

Solids Lead a discussion about the characteristics of a solid.

Liquids Ask leading questions for a discussion on the characteristics of a liquid.

Gases Make comparisons between the movement of helium balloons and the characteristics of gas particles.

Targeted Print and Technology Resources

All in One Teaching Resources

L2 Guided Reading, pp. 109–111
L2 Transparency K9

◉ **Student Edition on Audio CD**

Assess

Section Assessment Questions

 Have students use their completed compare and contrast table to answer the questions.

Reteach

Students create a concept map that describes the characteristics of solids, liquids, and gases.

Targeted Print and Technology Resources

All in One Teaching Resources

• Section Summary, p. 108
L1 Review and Reinforce, p. 112
L3 Enrich, p. 113

Section 2 Changes of State

 3 periods, 1 1/2 blocks

ABILITY LEVELS
- **L1** Basic to Average
- **L2** For All Students
- **L3** Average to Advanced

Objectives

K.2.2.1 Explain what happens to a substance during changes between solid and liquid.

K.2.2.2 Explain what happens to a substance during changes between liquid and gas.

K.2.2.3 Explain what happens to a substance during changes between solid and gas.

Local Standards

Key Terms

- melting • melting point • freezing • vaporization • evaporation • boiling
- boiling point • condensation • sublimation

Preteach

Build Background Knowledge

Students describe their observations of water changing states.

 **Discover Activity** *What Happens When You Breathe on a Mirror?* **L1**

Targeted Print and Technology Resources

All in One Teaching Resources

L2 Reading Strategy Transparency K10: *Outlining*

⊙ **Presentation-Pro CD-ROM**

Instruct

Changes Between Solid and Liquid Use diagrams to illustrate how the addition and removal of energy affects the particles of a solid and a liquid.

Changes Between Liquid and Gas Use diagrams to compare condensation and vaporization.

Changes Between Solid and Gas Define *sublimation* and apply it to ice cubes in a freezer.

 **Skills Lab** *Melting Ice* **L2**

Targeted Print and Technology Resources

All in One Teaching Resources

L2 Guided Reading, pp. 116–118
L2 Transparencies K11, K12
L2 Skills Lab: *Melting Ice,* pp. 121–122

📼 **Lab Activity Video/DVD**
Skills Lab: *Melting Ice*

PHSchool.com Web Code: cgd-1022

⊙ **Student Edition on Audio CD**

Assess

Section Assessment Questions

↺ Have students use their completed outlines to answer the questions.

Reteach

Students diagram particles of matter as they change from one state to another.

Targeted Print and Technology Resources

All in One Teaching Resources

- Section Summary, p. 115
L1 Review and Reinforce, p. 119
L3 Enrich, p. 120

Section 3 Gas Behavior

 3 1/2 periods, 1–2 blocks

ABILITY LEVELS
L1 Basic to Average
L2 For All Students
L3 Average to Advanced

Objectives

K.2.3.1 List the types of measurements used when working with gases.

K.2.3.2 Explain how the volume, temperature, and pressure of a gas are related.

Key Terms

• pressure • Boyle's law • Charles's law

Local Standards

Preteach

Build Background Knowledge

Students observe a balloon to explore gas pressure.

 **Discover Activity** *How Can Air Keep Chalk From Breaking?* L1

Targeted Print and Technology Resources

All in One Teaching Resources

L2 Reading Strategy Transparency K13: *Asking Questions*

⊙ **Presentation-Pro CD-ROM**

Instruct

Measuring Gases Ask leading questions for a discussion on gas volume, temperature, and pressure.

Pressure and Volume Explain Boyle's law in a discussion on the relationship between gas pressure and volume.

Pressure and Temperature Use diagrams to relate gas pressure and temperature.

Volume and Temperature Describe Charles's law and how it relates gas volume and temperature.

Targeted Print and Technology Resources

All in One Teaching Resources

L2 Guided Reading, pp. 125–127
L2 Transparencies K14, K15, K16

PHSchool.com Web Code: cgp-1023

DISCOVERY SCHOOL
Video Field Trip

⊙ **Student Edition on Audio CD**

Assess

Section Assessment Questions

Have students use their completed graphic organizers to answer the questions.

Reteach

Use diagrams that students help complete to review the relationships among gas volume, temperature, and pressure.

Targeted Print and Technology Resources

All in One Teaching Resources

• Section Summary, p. 124
L1 Review and Reinforce, p. 128
L3 Enrich, p. 129

Section 4 Graphing Gas Behavior

 3 periods, 1 1/2 blocks

Objectives

K.2.4.1 Identify the type of relationship shown by the graph for Charles's law.
K.2.4.2 Identify the type of relationship shown by the graph for Boyle's law.

Local Standards

Key Terms

• graph • origin • directly proportional • vary inversely

Preteach

Build Background Knowledge

Students interpret graphs showing daily high or low temperatures for the last week.

 Discover Activity *Can You Graph Gas Behavior?* L2

Targeted Print and Technology Resources

 **Teaching Resources**
L2 Reading Strategy Transparency K17: *Previewing Visuals*

○ **Presentation-Pro CD-ROM**

Instruct

Temperature and Volume Use a graph to describe the relationship between gas temperature and volume as described by Charles's law.

Pressure and Volume Ask leading questions for a discussion on an experiment and resulting graph of Boyle's law.

 Skills Lab *It's a Gas* L3

Targeted Print and Technology Resources

 **Teaching Resources**
L2 Guided Reading, pp. 132–134
L2 Transparency K18
L2 Skills Lab: *It's a Gas,* pp. 137–139

▭ **Lab Activity Video/DVD**
Skills Lab: *It's a Gas*

www.SciLinks.org Web Code: scn-1124

○ **Student Edition on Audio CD**

Assess

Section Assessment Questions

↺ Have students use their questions and answers to answer the questions.

Reteach

Students label graphs of Charles's law and Boyle's law.

Targeted Print and Technology Resources

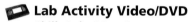 **Teaching Resources**
• Section Summary, p. 131
L1 Review and Reinforce, p. 135
L3 Enrich, p. 136

Go **Online**

NSTA–PD*L*INKS

For: Professional development support
Visit: www.SciLinks.org/PDLinks
Web Code: scf-1120

Professional Development

Professional Development

Section 1 **States of Matter**

The Kinetic Theory of Matter *Kinetic* refers to motion. Kinetic energy is the energy of an object caused by its motion. The kinetic theory of matter states that all matter is made up of small particles, namely atoms and molecules. These particles are always in motion. The kinetic energy of particles in matter tends to spread the particles apart. Their motion will speed up when heated, and will slow down when cooled.

Other forces work to hold the particles of matter together. Chemical bonds between atoms hold molecules together. These bonds form due to the attraction of atoms with opposite charges (ionic bonds) or when atoms share electrons (covalent bonds). Intermolecular attractions are attractions between molecules. Even though these attractions are weaker than chemical bonds, they usually determine the state of a substance. Three types of intermolecular attractions are van der Waals forces, dipole-dipole interactions, and hydrogen bonds. The diagram below illustrates how intermolecular interactions work. These attractions are based on the unequal distribution of positive and negative charges in a molecule, so that the negative portions of one molecule are attracted to positive portions of another. The lowercase Greek letter delta, δ, indicates that the charges are only partial charges, much less than the 1+ or 1– charges of protons or electrons.

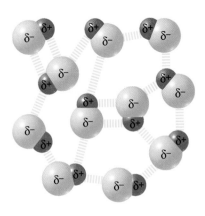

The physical state of a substance depends on the amount of kinetic energy of its particles and the strength of its chemical bonds and intermolecular attractions. In general, compounds formed with ionic bonds are solids at room temperature. (The bonds are stronger than the kinetic energy of the particles.) Compounds formed from covalent bonds can be solids, liquids, or gases, depending on the strength of their intermolecular attractions. Molecules with weak intermolecular attractions are gases at room temperature because the intermolecular attractions are not strong enough to counteract the kinetic energy of the particles. Molecules with strong intermolecular attractions are often liquids or solids.

Help Students Read

Use Prior Knowledge
Linking New Learning to Familiar Concepts
Strategy Help students construct meaning by linking new information to familiar concepts. Some references indicate that activating prior knowledge is the most important of all reading strategies. Choose a section from this chapter, such as *States of Matter*, to use in modeling this strategy.

Example
1. Have students turn to the pre-selected section, read the opening paragraph, and survey the headings and visuals. Ask students to recount experiences they have had with the topic and what they already know or believe they know about each subheading. Write student responses on the board. If noticeable misconceptions arise during this discussion, begin to address them immediately.
2. Have students generate and write several questions or predictions about the topic, based on their prior knowledge.
3. Instruct students to read the section with the purpose of answering their questions or evaluating their predictions. Consider dividing the section into several parts, so that students can pause after each part to check predictions and answer questions.
4. After reading, discuss with students the information learned. Discuss any new understandings that refute prior misconceptions.

Section 2 Changes of State

Physical Changes Changes in the state of matter, such as liquid changing to solid or gas changing to liquid, are physical changes. The substance itself does not change into a different substance; it is made up of the same atoms in the same proportions. However, the substance looks different because the arrangement of its atoms or molecules is different.

Address Misconceptions

Students may think that liquids freeze only at low temperatures. For a strategy to overcome this misconception, see **Address Misconceptions** in *Changes of State.*

The melting point and boiling point of a pure substance is always the same. In fact, melting point and boiling point are physical properties that can be used to identify a pure substance. Any deviation from the standard melting point and boiling point of a pure substance indicates the presence of impurities in that sample. (Boiling point is also dependent on air pressure.) Finding the melting point and boiling point of a pure substance is as easy as applying heat to a solid until it melts, and continuing to apply heat until it vaporizes.

When temperature data is plotted against time (as shown in the graph for *Analyzing Data* in Section 2), the result is sometimes referred to as a heat curve. The flat segments of the curve indicate the melting point and boiling point of the substance. These segments are flat because the phase change occurs without any change in temperature, or average motion of the particles. (Temperature is the average kinetic energy of the particles in a substance.) The heat energy is absorbed by the particles of the substance. Some of the energy increases the kinetic energy of particles until intermolecular attractions are broken and the particles rearrange. Any remaining energy is stored as potential energy. Once the phase change is complete, the temperature of the substance will increase because the average kinetic energy of the particles in the substance increases.

Section 3 Gas Behavior

Properties of Gas Particles Gases have different properties from either solids or liquids. Gases are easily compressed, or decreased in volume under pressure, because of the relatively large spaces between particles. Unlike liquids and solids, gases have little or no intermolecular attractions. As a result, gas molecules are completely free to move inside their containers. In fact, they move constantly and randomly, expanding to evenly fill the container.

Gas molecules can move extremely fast. Gas molecules that are more dense travel more slowly than less dense particles.

Gas molecules travel in straight paths, independently of each other. They change direction only after colliding with each other or with another object. During collisions, there is no net change in energy. These collisions explain why a smell moves slowly across a room, rather than instantly. As gas molecules of the smell diffuse, or move through the air, they collide with gas molecules already present in the air. So instead of a straight path to the nose, the gas molecules make a zigzagging path.

Section 4 Graphing Gas Behavior

Mathematical Relationships The graph of Charles's law shows that the relationship between volume and temperature in kelvins is directly proportional. *Directly proportional* means the same as *direct variation* and *varies directly.* When two variables such as volume and temperature are directly proportional, it means that both variables change in the same way. For example, when one variable gets larger, the other variable also gets larger. This relationship is written mathematically as

$$y = kx$$

where k is the constant of proportionality.

This equation is a variation of the standard equation of a line

$$y = mx + b$$

where m is the slope of the line and b is the point where the line crosses the y-axis. Since data that are directly proportional form a line that passes through the origin of a graph, b is equal to 0 and the proportionality constant (k) is equal to the slope of the line.

The slope of a line is equal to the change in y divided by the change in x, or

$$\frac{y_2 - y_1}{x_2 - x_1}.$$

Using the data from the experiment for Charles's law in Section 4, the slope of a line is equal to

$$\frac{293 - 283}{54 - 52} = \frac{10}{2} = 5$$

The equation for the line for Charles's law is then $y = 5x$ which means that for each increase (or decrease) in x, y increases (or decreases) by 5. This can also be stated as

$$\text{volume} = 5 \times \text{temperature}.$$

If Celsius temperatures were used to graph the data for Charles's law, the resulting line would intersect the y-axis at a point other than the origin. In this case, the relationship is no longer directly proportional. It is linear and would be written mathematically as $y = mx + b$.

interactive **Textbook**
- Complete student edition
- Video and audio
- Simulations and activities
- Section and chapter activities

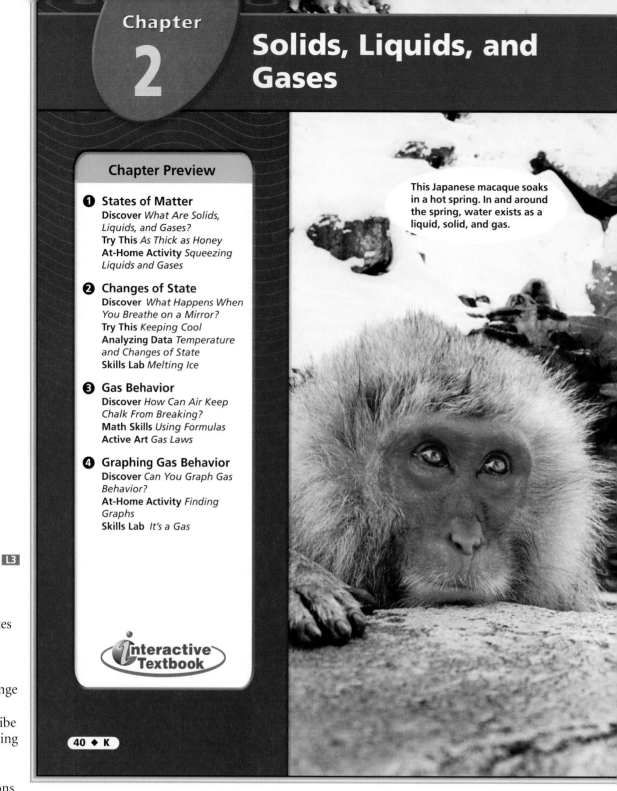

Chapter 2

Solids, Liquids, and Gases

This Japanese macaque soaks in a hot spring. In and around the spring, water exists as a liquid, solid, and gas.

interactive **Textbook**

Chapter **Project**   L3

Objectives

For this Chapter Project, students will prepare a skit or cartoon that demonstrates how particles of matter behave during a change of state. After completing this Chapter Project, students will be able to
- pose questions about how physical change affects the particles of matter
- form operational definitions that describe what happens to particles of matter during changes of state
- communicate their understanding of changes of state through skits or cartoons

Skills Focus

Posing questions, forming operational definitions, communicating

Project Time Line 2 to 3 weeks

All in One Teaching Resources
- Chapter Project Teacher Notes
- Chapter Project Worksheet 1
- Chapter Project Worksheet 2
- Chapter Project Scoring Rubric

Developing a Plan

On the first day of the project, students should decide whether to create a skit or cartoon. Following the completion of *Changes of State*, groups can begin developing a storyboard. Encourage groups to revise their storyboards as they learn more about the properties of gases in *Gas Behavior*. Then, groups can draw a cartoon or write a script based on their storyboards.

Possible Materials

Materials will vary depending on whether students perform skits or draw cartoons. Encourage students to be creative in selecting props for their skits. Students who choose to create cartoons will need large sheets of paper or poster board so that their cartoons are large enough to be seen by the entire class. They will also need various art supplies to draw their cartoons.

DISCOVERY
CHANNEL
SCHOOL

Solids, Liquids,
and Gases
▶ Video Preview
Video Field Trip
Video Assessment

Solids, Liquids, and Gases

Show the Video Preview to introduce the chapter and provide an overview of chapter content. Discussion question: **How does decompression sickness, or "the bends," affect divers?** (*It causes slower movement and confusion, leading to nerve damage or even death.*)

Lab zone™ Chapter Project

A Story of Changes in Matter

In this chapter, you will learn how particles of matter change from a solid to a liquid to a gas. As you read this chapter, you will build a model that shows these changes.

Your Goal To create a skit or cartoon that demonstrates how particles of matter behave as they change from a solid to a liquid to a gas and then from a gas to a liquid to a solid

To complete the project, you must

● describe what happens to the particles during each change of state

● outline your skit or cartoon in a storyboard format

● illustrate your cartoon or produce your skit

Plan It! With a group of classmates, brainstorm a list of the properties of solids, liquids, and gases. You'll be working on this project as you study this chapter. When you finish Section 2, describe the particles in solids, liquids, and gases, and begin preparing a story-board. Add information when you finish Section 3, and complete your cartoon or skit at the end of the chapter. Finally, present your completed skit or cartoon to the class.

Chapter 2   K ◆ 41

Launching the Project

Show students some examples of cartoons that present science concepts. Point out how these cartoons use exaggeration, slapstick humor, and puns to make scientific ideas easier to remember. Explain that a skit is similar to a cartoon in that both are visually orientated and involve humor. Organize students into groups based on whether they want to create a cartoon or a skit. Groups creating cartoons should have no more than two students. Groups creating a skit can have up to four or five students.

Get groups started by instructing them to list the properties of solids, liquids, and gases. Then, ask: **How could you use cartoons and skits to model the properties of solids, liquids, and gases?** (*Sample answer: In a skit, individual people could represent particles of matter in different states.*)

Performance Assessment

The Chapter Project Scoring Rubric will help you evaluate how well students complete the Chapter Project. You may want to share the rubric with your students so that they will know what is expected. Students will be assessed on

● how well they describe what happens to particles of matter during changes of state

● how well they organize the story outline in storyboard format

● how thoroughly their cartoons or skits illustrate chapter concepts

● their ability to work cooperatively

Students can keep their revised storyboards or completed scripts in their portfolios.

Portfolio

Section 1
States of Matter

Objectives

After this lesson, students will be able to

K.2.1.1 Describe the characteristics of a solid.

K.2.1.2 Describe the characteristics of a liquid.

K.2.1.3 Describe the characteristics of a gas.

Target Reading Skill 🔁

Building Vocabulary Explain that knowing definitions of key-concept words helps students understand what they read.

Answers

As students read this section, have them write the key terms and their definitions. When they have finished reading, tell students to write another definition for each term using their own words. Then, have them use each term in a sentence, either oral or written.

Preteach

Build Background Knowledge L2

Holding Matter

Ask: **Which is the easiest to hold in your hands—a small rock, 100 mL of water, or the helium from a balloon?** (*A rock, because it keeps it shape*) **Which is the most difficult?** (*Helium, because it cannot be seen or felt*)

Section 1
States of Matter

Reading Preview

Key Concepts
- What are the characteristics of a solid?
- What are the characteristics of a liquid?
- What are the characteristics of a gas?

Key Terms
- solid • crystalline solid
- amorphous solid • liquid
- fluid • surface tension
- viscosity • gas

🔁 Target Reading Skill

Building Vocabulary A definition states the meaning of a word or phrase by telling about its most important feature or function. After you read the section, reread the paragraphs that contain definitions of Key Terms. Use all the information you have learned to write a definition of each Key Term in your own words.

Lab zone · Discover **Activity**

What Are Solids, Liquids, and Gases?

1. Break an antacid tablet (fizzing type) into three or four pieces. Place them inside a large, uninflated balloon.
2. Fill a 1-liter plastic bottle about halfway with water. Stretch the mouth of the balloon over the top of the bottle, taking care to keep the tablet pieces inside the balloon.
3. Jiggle the balloon so that the pieces fall into the bottle. Observe what happens for about two minutes.
4. Remove the balloon and examine its contents.

Think It Over

Forming Operational Definitions Identify examples of the different states of matter—solids, liquids, and gases—that you observed in this activity. Define each of the three states in your own words.

It's a bitter cold January afternoon. You are practicing ice hockey moves on a frozen pond. Relaxing later, you close your eyes and recall the pond in July, when you and your friends jumped into the refreshing water on a scorching hot day. Was the water in July made of the same water you skated on this afternoon? Perhaps, but you're absolutely certain that solid water and liquid water do not look or feel the same. Just imagine trying to swim in an ice-covered pond in January or play hockey on liquid water in July!

FIGURE 1
A Wintry Solid
As a solid, water makes a great surface for ice hockey.
Observing *What useful property does the frozen water have here?*

Lab zone · Discover **Activity**

Skills Focus Forming operational definitions

Materials fizzing antacid tablet, large balloon, 1-L plastic soda bottle, water

Time 10 minutes

Tips Use only seltzer antacid tablets. Have some students use two tablets and predict what will happen.

L2

Expected Outcome The balloon inflates with carbon dioxide produced by the reaction of the antacid and water.

Think It Over Sample answer: Solid: tablet, balloon, bottle; liquid: water; gas: bubbles. Sample definitions: Gas can form bubbles in water or inflate a balloon; liquid takes the shape of its container; solid keeps its shape.

Your everyday world is full of substances that can be classified as solids, liquids, or gases. (You will read about a less familiar form of matter, called plasma, in Chapter 3.) Solids, liquids, and gases may be elements, compounds, or mixtures. Gold is an element. Water is a compound you've seen as both a solid and a liquid. Air is a mixture of gases. Although it's easy to list examples of these three states of matter, defining them is more difficult. To define solids, liquids, and gases, you need to examine their properties. The familiar states of matter are defined not by what they are made of but mainly by whether or not they hold their volume and shape.

Solids

What would happen if you were to pick up a solid object, such as a pen or a comb, and move it from place to place around the room? What would you observe? Would the object ever change in size or shape as you moved it? Would a pen become larger if you put it in a bowl? Would a comb become flatter if you placed it on a table-top? Of course not. A **solid** has a definite shape and a definite volume. If your pen has a cylindrical shape and a volume of 6 cubic centimeters, then it will keep that shape and volume in any position and in any container.

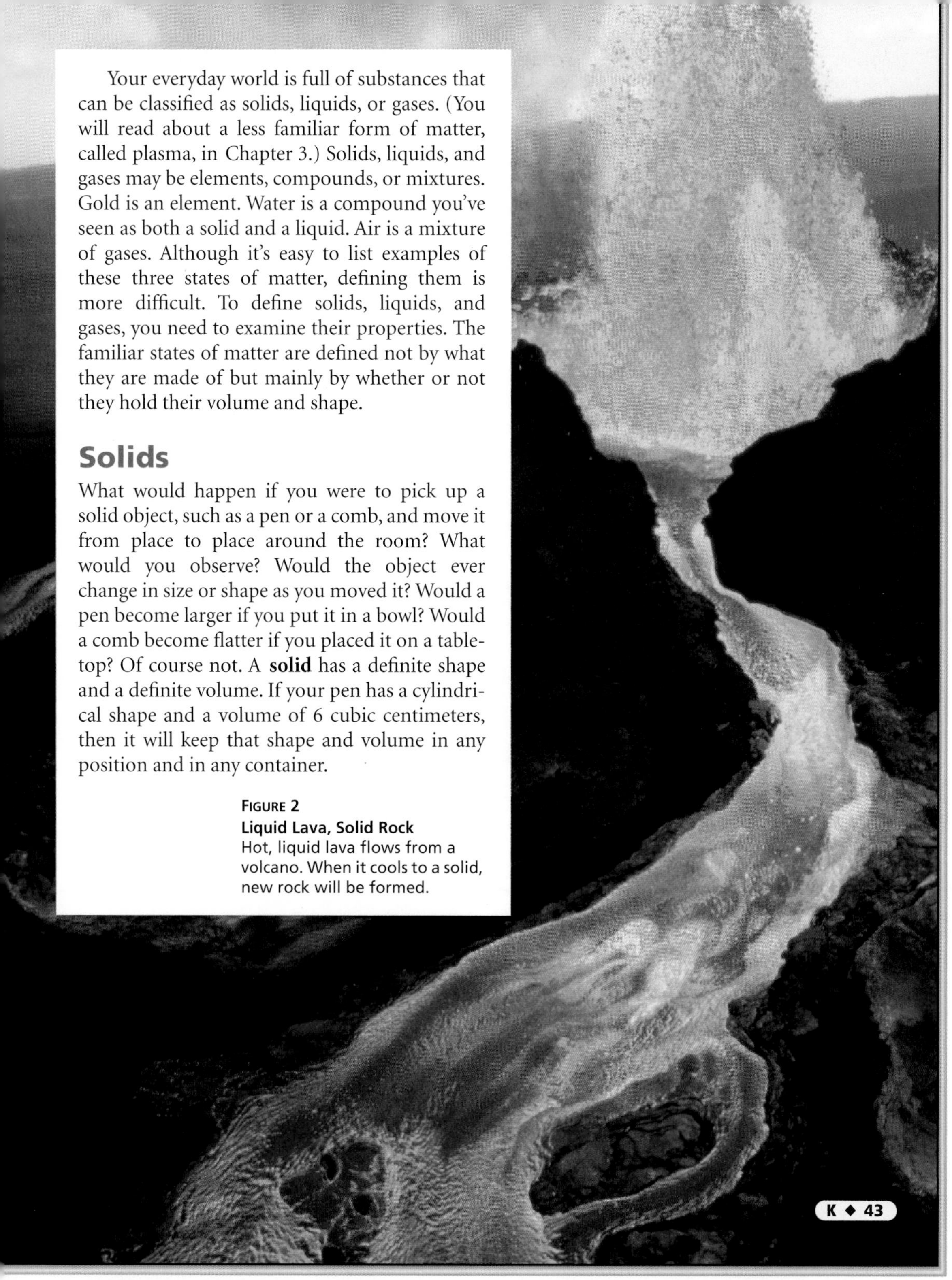

FIGURE 2
Liquid Lava, Solid Rock
Hot, liquid lava flows from a volcano. When it cools to a solid, new rock will be formed.

K ◆ 43

Differentiated Instruction

Less Proficient Readers   L1
Building Vocabulary Before students read the section, have them write a definition of *definite*. Then, read aloud the definitions of *solid*, *liquid*, and *gas* and have students revise their definitions. Challenge them to write synonyms for *definite*. Check these for accuracy, and encourage students to use the synonyms as they read. **learning modality: verbal**

Gifted and Talented   L3
Diagramming Plasma Particles Tell students that a fourth state of matter, called plasma, exists, although it is rarely found on Earth. It is found abundantly in space as the matter making up stars. Invite students to learn more about plasma particles. Challenge them to illustrate the characteristics of plasma particles in a diagram. **learning modality: visual**

Instruct

Solids

Teach Key Concepts   L2
Particles of Solids

Focus Tell students that solids have definite shapes and volumes.

Teach Ask: **How are the particles of a solid arranged?** (*They are packed very closely together and tightly fixed in one position.*) **What causes a solid to have a definite shape and volume?** (*The arrangement of particles*)

Apply Tell students that the volume of an object depends on its length, width, and height. Ask: **Why would an object with a definite shape also have a definite volume?** (*The dimensions of the object do not change, so its volume stays the same.*) **learning modality: verbal**

All in One Teaching Resources
• Transparency K9

Use Visuals: Figure 2   L1
Identifying States of Matter

Focus Invite students to study the photograph of the volcano.

Teach Ask: **What states of matter can you identify?** (*Sample answer: Solid—rocks; liquid—lava; gas—air*) **How do solids in the photograph differ from the liquids and gases?** (*Sample answer: Solid rock has a definite shape and a definite volume.*)

Apply Ask: **What will happen to the liquid lava when it cools?** (*It will form solid rock.*) **learning modality: visual**

Independent Practice   L2

All in One Teaching Resources
• Guided Reading and Study Worksheet: *States of Matter*

⊙ **Student Edition on Audio CD**

Monitor Progress   L2

Writing Have students write the definition of a solid in their own words.

Answer
Figure 1 Sample answer: Hard, slippery

Lab zone Build **Inquiry** L2

Modeling Particles in a Solid

Materials damp sand or brown sugar, small measuring cup, scoop

Time 10 minutes

Focus Ask: **How are the particles in a solid arranged?** *(They are packed closely together.)*

Teach Instruct students to tightly pack damp sand or brown sugar into a container. Then have them unmold it and observe the grains of sand or sugar.

Apply Ask: **Why do the grains of sand/sugar model the particles of a solid?** *(They are packed closely together and they do not move around one another.)* **learning modality: kinesthetic**

Lab zone Teacher **Demo** L1

Classifying Solids

Materials frozen bar of solid chocolate, goggles, hammer, lab apron, salt block

Time 10 minutes

Focus Ask: **In which type of solid do particles form a regular, repeating pattern?** *(Crystalline solids)* **How are the particles of an amorphous solid arranged?** *(The particles do not form a regular pattern.)*

Teach While wearing safety goggles and a lab apron, strike a block of salt with a hammer. Wipe the hammer, then strike a frozen chocolate bar. Invite students to compare the shapes of the broken fragments. *(Salt fragments will have square edges that mirror the repeating pattern of salt crystals. The chocolate fragments will have jagged edges because chocolate particles are not arranged in a regular pattern.)*

Apply Ask: **What kind of solid is salt?** *(Crystalline)* **Chocolate?** *(Amorphous)* **Which would you expect to melt at a specific temperature?** *(Salt)* **How will the chocolate bar melt?** *(It will not melt all at once. It will become softer and softer as the temperature rises.)* **learning modality: visual**

44 ● K

FIGURE 3
Behavior of Solid Particles
Particles of a solid vibrate back and forth but stay in place.

FIGURE 4
Types of Solids
Solids are either crystalline or amorphous.

Particles in a Solid The particles that make up a solid are packed very closely together. In addition, each particle is tightly fixed in one position. **This fixed, closely packed arrangement of particles causes a solid to have a definite shape and volume.**

Are the particles in a solid completely motionless? No, not really. The particles vibrate, meaning that they move back and forth slightly. This motion is similar to a group of people running in place. The particles that make up a solid stay in about the same position, but they vibrate in place.

Types of Solids In many solids, the particles form a regular, repeating pattern. These patterns create crystals. Solids that are made up of crystals are called **crystalline solids** (KRIS tuh lin). Salt, sugar, and snow are examples of crystalline solids. When a crystalline solid is heated, it melts at a specific temperature.

In **amorphous solids** (uh MAWR fus), the particles are not arranged in a regular pattern. Plastics, rubber, and glass are amorphous solids. Unlike a crystalline solid, an amorphous solid does not melt at a distinct temperature. Instead, it may become softer and softer or change into other substances.

 Reading Checkpoint How do crystalline and amorphous solids differ?

 Quartz is a crystalline solid. Its particles are arranged in a regular pattern.

 Butter is an amorphous solid. Its particles are not arranged in a regular pattern.

Differentiated Instruction

Special Needs L1

Modeling Students can model the particles in a crystalline solid by building cubes with interlocking sticks and balls. The balls represent the particles of a solid, and the sticks represent the forces that hold the particles in place. You might provide a diagram of a cubic crystal system to help students get started. To model an amorphous solid, students can form pea-sized balls of clay and gently stick them together in random, three-dimensional patterns. Explain that the balls of clay represent particles in an amorphous solid. **learning modality: kinesthetic**

Liquids

A **liquid** has a definite volume but no shape of its own. Without a container, a liquid spreads into a wide, shallow puddle. Like a solid, however, a liquid does have a constant volume. If you gently tried to squeeze a water-filled plastic bag, for example, the water might change shape, but its volume would not decrease or increase. Suppose that you have 100 milliliters of milk in a pitcher. If you pour it into a tall glass, you still have 100 milliliters. The milk has the same volume no matter what shape its container has.

Particles in a Liquid In general, the particles in a liquid are packed almost as closely as in a solid. However, the particles in a liquid move around one another freely. You can compare this movement to the way you might move a group of marbles around in your hand. In this comparison, the solid marbles serve as models for the particles of a liquid. The marbles slide around one another but stay in contact. **Because its particles are free to move, a liquid has no definite shape. However, it does have a definite volume.** These freely moving particles allow a liquid to flow from place to place. For this reason, a liquid is also called a **fluid,** meaning "a substance that flows."

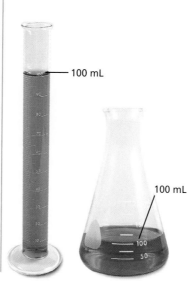

FIGURE 5
Equivalent Volumes
A liquid takes the shape of its container but its volume does not change.

— 100 mL

100 mL

FIGURE 6
Behavior of Liquid Particles
Particles in a liquid are packed close together but move freely, allowing liquids to flow.
Comparing and Contrasting How are liquids and solids alike? How do they differ?

Chapter 2   K ◆ 45

Liquids

Teach Key Concepts   L2
Particles in Liquids

Focus Ask: **Do liquids have a shape of their own?** *(No)* **What shape do liquids take?** *(The shape of their container)*

Teach Explain that unlike the particles of a solid, the particles of a liquid are free to move around one another. Ask: **Why doesn't a liquid have a definite shape?** *(Its particles are free to move.)* **Why do liquids have a definite volume?** *(The particles are packed together.)*

Apply Have students compare ice and water. Ask: **What characteristics of water classify it as a liquid at room temperature?** *(Water takes the shape of its container but has the same volume regardless of the shape of its container.)* **learning modality: verbal**

All in One Teaching Resources
• Transparency K9

Help Students Read   L1

Using Prior Knowledge Refer to the Content Refresher in this chapter, which provides guidelines for using this strategy.

Before students read about liquids, ask them to list what they already know about the characteristics of liquids. After students read, have them review their lists and determine how accurate their prior knowledge was. Instruct students to identify any misconceptions on the list and replace these with their new understanding of the concept.

Monitor Progress _____ L2

Skills Check Students can construct a Venn diagram to compare and contrast the characteristics of solids and liquids.

Students can save their Venn diagrams in their portfolios.

Portfolio

Answers
Figure 6 Both have definite volumes. Solids have definite shapes, while liquids do not.

Reading Checkpoint Crystalline solid: particles arranged in a regular, repeating pattern; distinct melting point. Amorphous solid: particles not in a regular pattern; no distinct melting point

Teacher Demo

Modeling Surface Tension L2

Materials circular magnets or paper circles
Time 10 minutes

Focus Explain that surface tension is caused by the position and attraction of liquid particles.

Teach Draw the outline of a container. Arrange the circle magnets or paper circles within the outline like liquid particles are arranged. Consider using Figure 6 as a model. Ask: **What do the circles represent?** *(Particles in a liquid)* Draw lines of attractive forces between all the particles. Ask: **How do the lines of force differ between surface particles and inner particles?** *(Surface particles have attractive forces on only one side.)* **What effect does a one-sided pull have on surface particles?** *(Surface particles pull together and toward the inner particles.)* Move the circles to reflect this.

Apply Ask: **Why does a drop of liquid form a sphere?** *(All outer particles pull together and inward.)* **learning modality: visual**

Gases

Teach Key Concepts L2

Particles of Gases

Focus Ask: **How do the particles in a fluid move?** *(They flow freely.)*

Teach Explain that like liquids, gases are fluids. Ask: **Why don't gases have a definite shape or volume?** *(Gas particles can spread apart or squeeze together, depending on the container.)*

Apply Release several helium balloons that had been confined in a small space. Encourage students to relate the movement of the balloons to gas particles. **learning modality: visual**

All in One Teaching Resources

• Transparency K9

FIGURE 7
Surface Tension
Water beads up on a leaf due to attractions between the water molecules. Surface tension in water is strong enough to support the weight of an insect.

Lab zone Try This Activity

As Thick as Honey

You can compare the viscosity of two liquids.

1. Place on a table a clear plastic jar almost filled with honey and another clear plastic jar almost filled with vegetable oil. Make sure that the tops of both jars are tightly closed.
2. Turn the jars upside down at the same time. Observe what happens.
3. Turn the two jars right-side up and again watch what happens.

Drawing Conclusions Which fluid has a greater viscosity? What evidence leads you to this conclusion?

Properties of Liquids One characteristic property of liquids is surface tension. **Surface tension** is the result of an inward pull among the molecules of a liquid that brings the molecules on the surface closer together. Perhaps you have noticed that water forms droplets and can bead up on many surfaces, such as the leaf shown in Figure 7. That's because water molecules attract one another strongly. These attractions cause molecules at the water's surface to be pulled slightly toward the water molecules beneath the surface.

Due to surface tension, the surface of water can act like a sort of skin. For example, a sewing needle floats when you place it gently on the surface of a glass of water, but it quickly sinks if you push it below the surface. Surface tension enables the water strider in Figure 7 to "walk" on the calm surface of a pond.

Another property of liquids is **viscosity** (vis KAHS uh tee)—a liquid's resistance to flowing. A liquid's viscosity depends on the size and shape of its particles and the attractions between the particles. Some liquids flow more easily than others. Liquids with high viscosity flow slowly. Honey is an example of a liquid with a particularly high viscosity. Liquids with low viscosity flow quickly. Water and vinegar have relatively low viscosities.

 Reading Checkpoint What property of liquids causes water to form droplets?

Lab zone Try This Activity

Skills Focus Drawing conclusions L2
Materials 2 clear jars with screw-top lids, honey, vegetable oil, paper towels
Time 10 minutes
Tips If possible, use clear plastic jars to avoid broken glass. Make sure the jars are tightly sealed. Use paper towels to wipe up spills.

Expected Outcome Honey has the greater viscosity. The air bubble in the jar of vegetable oil rose faster than the air bubble in the jar of honey.

Extend Suggest students compare the viscosities of a variety of liquids such as syrup, water, and shampoo. **learning modality: kinesthetic**

Gases

Like a liquid, a gas is a fluid. Unlike a liquid, however, a **gas** can change volume very easily. If you put a gas in a closed container, the gas particles will either spread apart or be squeezed together as they fill that container. Take a deep breath. Your chest expands, and your lungs fill with air. Air is a mixture of gases that acts as one gas. When you breathe in, air moves from your mouth to your windpipe to your lungs. In each place, the air has a different shape. When you breathe out, the changes happen in reverse.

What about the volume of the air? If you could see the particles that make up a gas, you would see them moving in all directions. The particles are no longer limited by the space in your body, so they move throughout the room. **As they move, gas particles spread apart, filling all the space available. Thus, a gas has neither definite shape nor definite volume.** You will read more about the behavior of gases in Section 3.

FIGURE 8
Modeling Gas Particles
The particles of a gas can be squeezed into a small volume.
Predicting *What will happen if the container lid is removed?*

 Reading Checkpoint How does breathing demonstrate that gases are fluids?

Section 1 Assessment

 Target Reading Skill

Building Vocabulary Use your definitions to help answer the questions below.

Reviewing Key Concepts

1. a. Listing What are the general characteristics of solids?
 b. Comparing and Contrasting How do crystalline solids differ from amorphous solids?
 c. Drawing Conclusions A glass blower can bend and shape a piece of glass that has been heated. Is glass a crystalline or an amorphous solid? Explain.
2. a. Describing How may liquids be described in terms of shape and volume?
 b. Explaining How do the positions and movements of particles in a liquid help to explain the shape and volume of the liquid?
 c. Relating Cause and Effect Explain why a sewing needle can float on the surface of water in a glass.

3. a. Reviewing What determines the shape and volume of a gas inside a container?
 b. Applying Concepts Use what you know about the particles in a gas to explain why a gas has no definite shape and no definite volume.

At-Home Activity

Squeezing Liquids and Gases Show your family how liquids and gases differ. Fill the bulb and cylinder of a turkey baster with water. Seal the end with your finger and hold it over the sink. Have a family member squeeze the bulb. Now empty the turkey baster. Again, seal the end with your finger and have a family member squeeze the bulb. Did the person notice any difference? Use what you know about liquids and gases to explain your observations.

At-Home Activity

Squeezing Liquids and Gases L2
Students should warn family members not to squeeze the bulb too hard when the baster is filled with water; the baster could leak where the bulb attaches to the tube. Family members will find it easier to squeeze the bulb filled with air. Water, a liquid, has a definite volume; air, a gas, does not.

Monitor Progress _____ L2

Answers
Figure 8 The gas particles will spread apart and move out of the container.

 Reading Checkpoint Surface tension

 Reading Checkpoint While you're breathing, gases in the air flow freely through the body and back out again.

Assess

Reviewing Key Concepts

1. a. Solids have definite shapes and definite volumes. **b.** Crystalline solid particles form a regular, repeating pattern and melt at a distinct temperature; amorphous solid particles are not arranged in a regular pattern and melt over a range of temperatures. **c.** Glass is an amorphous solid. Because glass does not have a definite melting point, it becomes softer and softer as it is heated. This is why heated glass may be soft enough to bend.
2. a. Liquids do not have definite shape, but do have definite volume. **b.** Because its particles can move freely around one another, a liquid takes the shape of its container. Because its particles are packed closely together, a liquid has a definite volume. **c.** Due to surface tension, a needle can float on the surface of water; the surface of the water acts like a a sort of skin.
3. a. The shape and volume of a gas are the same as those of its container. **b.** A gas has neither definite shape nor definite volume because its particles spread apart and move freely in all directions, restricted only by the walls of its container.

Reteach L1

Have students create a concept map for the states of matter. Students should include the names of each state, their shapes and volumes, and their particle arrangements.

Performance Assessment L2

Drawing Ask students to draw three simple diagrams that show how the particles of solids, liquids, and gases are arranged.

All in One Teaching Resources

- Section Summary: *States of Matter*
- Review and Reinforce: *States of Matter*
- Enrich: *States of Matter*

K ● 47

Objectives
After this lesson, students will be able to

K.2.2.1 Explain what happens to a substance during changes between solid and liquid.

K.2.2.2 Explain what happens to a substance during changes between liquid and gas.

K.2.2.3 Explain what happens to a substance during changes between solid and gas.

Target Reading Skill

Outlining Explain that using an outline format helps students organize information by main topic, subtopic, and details.

Answers
Sample outline:
Changes of State
  I. Changes Between Solid and Liquid
      A. Melting
      B. Freezing
  II. Changes Between Liquid and Gas
      A. Evaporation
      B. Boiling
      C. Boiling Point and Air Pressure
      D. Condensation
  III. Changes Between Solid and Gas

All in One Teaching Resources
• Transparency K10

Preteach

Build Background Knowledge   L2

Changing States of Water
Ask: **What happens to a puddle of water on a sunny day?** *(It dries up.)* **What happens to ice on a warm day?** *(It melts.)* **What happens to a pond in very cold temperatures?** *(It freezes.)* Encourage students to share any other experiences of water changing states. Challenge them to explain what was happening to the molecules of water.

Reading Preview

Key Concepts
• What happens to a substance during changes between solid and liquid?
• What happens to a substance during changes between liquid and gas?
• What happens to a substance during changes between solid and gas?

Key Terms
• melting • melting point
• freezing • vaporization
• evaporation • boiling
• boiling point • condensation
• sublimation

Target Reading Skill

Outlining As you read, make an outline about changes of state. Use the red headings for the main ideas and the blue headings for the supporting ideas.

Changes in State
I. Changes Between Solid and Liquid
A. Melting
B.
II. Changes Between Liquid and Gas

Lab zone Discover Activity

What Happens When You Breathe on a Mirror?

1. Obtain a hand mirror. Clean it with a dry cloth. Describe the mirror's surface.
2. Hold the mirror about 15 cm away from your face. Try to breathe against the mirror's surface.
3. Reduce the distance until breathing on the mirror produces a visible change. Record what you observe.

Think It Over
Developing Hypotheses What did you observe when you breathed on the mirror held close to your mouth? How can you explain that observation? Why did you get different results when the mirror was at greater distances from your face?

Picture an ice cream cone on a hot summer day. The ice cream quickly starts to drip onto your hand. You're not surprised. You know that ice cream melts if it's not kept cold. But why does the ice cream melt?

Particles of a substance at a warmer temperature have more thermal energy than particles of that same substance at a cooler temperature. Remember from Chapter 1 that thermal energy always flows as heat from a warmer substance to a cooler substance. So, when you take ice cream outside on a hot summer day, it absorbs thermal energy from the air and your hand. The added energy changes the ice cream from a solid to a liquid.

Increased thermal energy turns an ice cream cone into a gooey mess! ▶

Lab zone Discover Activity

Skills Focus Developing hypotheses   L1

Materials hand mirror, dry cloth

Time 10 minutes

Expected Outcome When held close to the face, water vapor in warm breath will condense on the mirror's cool surface, and the mirror will become clouded or fogged.

Think It Over Something clouded the surface of the mirror. Some students might explain that moisture from their warm breath condensed on the mirror's cool surface. At greater distances, the moisture in their breath dispersed in the air before reaching the mirror's surface.

Solid silver

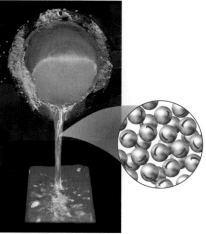

Liquid silver

FIGURE 9
Solid to Liquid
In solid silver, atoms are in a regular, cubic pattern. Atoms in liquid (molten) silver have no regular arrangement.
Applying Concepts *How can a jewelry maker take advantage of changes in the state of silver?*

Changes Between Solid and Liquid

How does the physical state of a substance relate to its thermal energy? Particles of a liquid have more thermal energy than particles of the same substance in solid form. As a gas, the particles of this same substance have even more thermal energy. A substance changes state when its thermal energy increases or decreases sufficiently. A change from solid to liquid involves an increase in thermal energy. As you can guess, a change from liquid to solid is just the opposite: It involves a decrease in thermal energy.

Melting The change in state from a solid to a liquid is called **melting.** In most pure substances, melting occurs at a specific temperature, called the **melting point.** Because melting point is a characteristic property of a substance, chemists often compare melting points when trying to identify an unknown material. The melting point of pure water, for example, is 0°C.

What happens to the particles of a substance as it melts? Think of an ice cube taken from the freezer. The energy to melt the ice comes mostly from the air in the room. At first, the added thermal energy makes the water molecules vibrate faster, raising their temperature. **At its melting point, the particles of a solid substance are vibrating so fast that they break free from their fixed positions.** At 0°C, the temperature of the ice stops increasing. Any added energy continues to change the arrangement of the water molecules from ice crystals into liquid water. The ice melts.

Instruct

Changes Between Solid and Liquid

Teach Key Concepts L2
Melting and Freezing

Focus Tell students that particles of a substance at a warmer temperature have more thermal energy than particles of the same substance at a cooler temperature.

Teach Explain that matter changes state when thermal energy is added or removed. Ask: **How do the particles in a solid substance change when energy is added?** (*They vibrate faster.*) Diagram how the addition of energy causes particles of a solid to move faster and faster until they break free from their fixed positions. Then diagram how liquid particles move more slowly as energy is removed until they form the regular patterns of a solid.

Apply Ask: **At what point do the particles of a solid break free from their fixed positions?** (*Melting point*) **Why do different substances have different melting points?** (*They have different arrangements of particles that respond differently to added thermal energy.*) **learning modality: visual**

Independent Practice L2

All in One Teaching Resources

- Guided Reading and Study Worksheet: *Changes of State*

⊙ **Student Edition on Audio CD**

Differentiated Instruction

English Learners/Beginning L1
Vocabulary: Science Glossary
Pronounce the key terms *melting, freezing,* and *boiling.* Encourage students to repeat them. Define the words using pictures or motions. Suggest that students write the definitions in a glossary. They might also draw diagrams or use their primary language to help them remember meaning. **learning modality: verbal**

English Learners/Intermediate L2
Vocabulary: Science Glossary Expand on the activity at left by adding the rest of the key terms in this section. Also suggest that students write a sentence for each term in their glossaries. Model how to write the sentence using words from the text or English words they already know. Invite students to read their sentences aloud. **learning modality: verbal**

Monitor Progress ——— L2

Oral Presentation Have students identify and describe examples of matter changing state between solid and liquid.

Answer
Figure 9 A jewelry maker can change the shape of liquid silver. The solid silver then holds the shape the jeweler has created.

Teacher **Demo**

Observing Melting Temperature L1

Materials large beaker, clock or stopwatch, hot plate, crushed ice or snow, stirring rod, thermometer

Time 15 minutes

Focus Ask: **What happens when thermal energy is added to a solid?** *(The solid particles move faster.)*

Teach Cover the bottom of the beaker with about 5 cm of crushed ice or snow. Insert the thermometer and carefully fill the beaker with more crushed ice or snow. Place the beaker on the hot plate and turn to medium-high heat. Stir the ice water carefully as it melts. Record temperature readings every 5 seconds until all the ice is melted. Continue heating and taking readings until the water reaches room temperature. Turn off the hot plate and remove the beaker to a heat-proof surface.

Apply Ask: **While the ice was melting, did the energy from the hot plate increase the temperature of the water?** *(No.)* **Then what happened to that energy?** *(The energy changed the arrangement of water molecules from ice crystals to liquid water.)* **learning modality: visual**

Address Misconceptions L2

Freezing Temperatures

Focus Many students may think that liquids freeze only at low temperatures.

Teach Ask: **Name solids that melt at temperatures that are higher than room temperature (about 20°C).** *(Sample answers: plastic, candle wax, chocolate, and butter)* **What happens when these materials cool from a liquid state?** *(They become solid.)*

Apply Point out that becoming a solid is the same as freezing, even when it occurs at room temperature. **learning modality: verbal**

 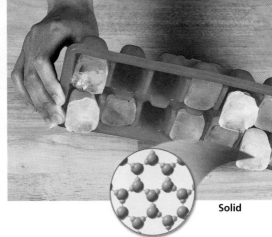

Liquid

Solid

FIGURE 10
Liquid to Solid
Just a few hours in a freezer will change liquid water into a solid.

Try This **Activity**

Keeping Cool

1. Wrap the bulbs of two alcohol thermometers with equal amounts of gauze.
2. Lay the thermometers on a paper towel on a table.
3. Use a medicine dropper to put 10 drops of water on the gauze surrounding the bulb of one thermometer.
4. Using rubbing alcohol rather than water, repeat step 3 with the second thermometer.
5. Read the temperatures on the two thermometers for several minutes.

Interpreting Data Which liquid evaporates faster? Explain your answer.

Freezing The change of state from liquid to solid is called **freezing.** It is just the reverse of melting. **At its freezing temperature, the particles of a liquid are moving so slowly that they begin to form regular patterns.**

When you put liquid water into a freezer, for example, the water loses energy to the cold air in the freezer. The water molecules move more and more slowly as they lose energy. Over time, the water becomes solid ice. When water begins to freeze, its temperature remains at 0°C until freezing is complete. The freezing point of water, 0°C, is the same as its melting point.

 Reading Checkpoint What happens to the particles of a liquid as they lose more and more energy?

Changes Between Liquid and Gas

Have you ever wondered how clouds form, or why rain falls from clouds? And why do puddles dry up after a rain shower? To answer these questions, you need to look at what happens when changes occur between the liquid and gas states.

The change from a liquid to a gas is called **vaporization** (vay puhr ih ZAY shun). **Vaporization takes place when the particles in a liquid gain enough energy to form a gas.** There are two main types of vaporization—evaporation and boiling.

Evaporation Vaporization that takes place only on the surface of a liquid is called **evaporation** (ee vap uh RAY shun). A shrinking puddle is an example. Water in the puddle gains energy from the ground, the air, or the sun. The added energy enables some of the water molecules on the surface of the puddle to escape into the air, or evaporate.

Try This **Activity**

Skills Focus Interpreting data L3

Materials 2 alcohol thermometers, 2 pieces of gauze, paper towel, 2 medicine droppers, water, rubbing alcohol

Time 15 minutes

Expected Outcome The rubbing alcohol evaporates faster because it cools the thermometer more than water.

Extend Have students compare the evaporation rates of water and salt water. **learning modality: visual**

Boiling Another kind of vaporization is called boiling. **Boiling** occurs when a liquid changes to a gas below its surface as well as at the surface. You see the results of this process when the boiling liquid bubbles. The temperature at which a liquid boils is called its **boiling point.** As with melting points, chemists use boiling points to help identify an unknown substance.

Boiling Point and Air Pressure The boiling point of a substance depends on the pressure of the air above it. The lower the pressure, the less energy needed for the particles of the liquid to escape into the air. In places close to sea level, the boiling point of water is 100°C. In the mountains, however, air pressure is lower and so is water's boiling point. In Denver, Colorado, where the elevation is 1,600 meters above sea level, water boils at 95°C.

FIGURE 11
Evaporation and Boiling
Liquids can vaporize in two ways.
Interpreting Diagrams *How do these processes differ?*

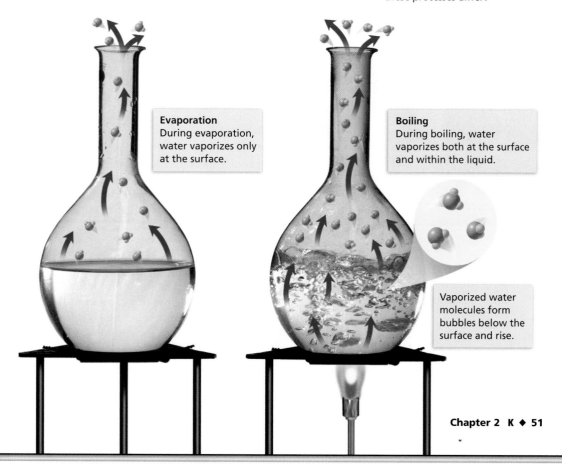

Evaporation
During evaporation, water vaporizes only at the surface.

Boiling
During boiling, water vaporizes both at the surface and within the liquid.

Vaporized water molecules form bubbles below the surface and rise.

Chapter 2 K ◆ 51

Differentiated Instruction

Gifted and Talented **L3**
Changing the Freezing Point of Water Explain that water in the Arctic and Antarctic Oceans is colder than the normal freezing point of water (0°C). Challenge students to determine the effect of salt on the freezing point of water by designing an experiment. One way to set up the experiment is to add salt to water in a plastic container, then place a thermometer in the container, and put the containers in the freezer. Or students may fill part of an ice cube tray with water and the other part with salt water. Encourage students to carry out their experiment after you have reviewed it. **learning modality: kinesthetic**

Changes Between Liquid and Gas

Teach Key Concepts **L2**
Vaporization and Condensation

Focus Ask: **How are the particles of a gas different from those of a liquid?** (*Gas particles can spread far apart.*)

Teach Explain that vaporization occurs when the particles of a liquid gain enough energy to become a gas. Ask: **What do you think happens when particles in a gas lose energy?** (*A liquid can form.*)

Apply Ask: **What are some examples of vaporization?** (*Evaporating puddle, boiling water*) **Condensation?** (*Breath on mirror, clouds, a "sweating" glass*) **learning modality: visual**

 **Teaching Resources**
• Transparency K11

 Teacher **Demo** **L1**

Contrasting Evaporation and Boiling

Materials beaker, dropper, hot plate, overhead projector, water, wax pencil

Time 20 minutes

Focus Ask: **What are the two main types of vaporization?** (*Evaporation and boiling*)

Teach With the projector on, place drops of water inside a small wax circle on the overhead until the circle is almost filled. Observe the water over time. Ask: **What is happening to the water?** (*It is evaporating.*) Heat 500 mL of water in a beaker until it boils. Ask: **What is happening to the water?** (*It is boiling.*)

Apply Ask: **How do boiling and evaporation differ?** (*Only surface particles vaporize when water evaporates.*) **learning modality: visual**

Monitor Progress _____ **L2**

Drawing Have students diagram evaporation and boiling.

Answers
Figure 11 Evaporation occurs only at the surface. Boiling occurs both at the surface and within the liquid.

 The particles move more and more slowly.

Math Skill Making and interpreting graphs

Focus Tell students that changes of state depend on temperature changes of a substance over time.

Teach Invite students to examine the graph. Point out the zigzag shape of the line. Ask: **Which variable is changing in places where the line is flat?** (Only time) **In places where the line moves up?** (Both time and temperature)

Answers

1. Temperature (°C) on the y-axis, time (minutes) on the x-axis

2. The temperature is rising from 0°C to 100°C.

3. Segment B: melting point of ice; segment D: boiling point of water

4. Change from solid to liquid; change from liquid to gas

5. Water molecules in segment E have more thermal energy because they are at a higher temperature.

All in One **Teaching Resources**

• Transparency K12

Changes Between Solid and Gas

Teach Key Concepts

Sublimation

Focus Review what happens when a solid melts and a liquid evaporates.

Teach Explain that during sublimation, solids form a gas without passing through the liquid state. Ask: **When does sublimation occur?** (When the surface particles of a solid gain enough energy to form a gas)

Apply Ask: **Why do ice cubes stored for a long time in the freezer get smaller?** (The ice sublimes.) **learning modality: verbal**

Temperature and Changes of State

A beaker of ice at −10°C was slowly heated to 110°C. The changes in the temperature of the water over time were recorded. The data were plotted on the graph shown here.

1. **Reading Graphs** What two variables are plotted on the graph?

2. **Reading Graphs** What is happening to the temperature of the water during segment C of the graph?

3. **Interpreting Data** What does the temperature value for segment B represent? For segment D?

4. **Drawing Conclusions** What change of state is occurring during segment B of the graph? During segment D?

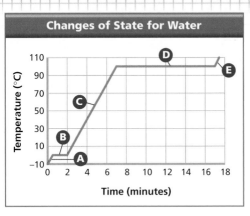

Changes of State for Water

5. **Inferring** In which segment, A or E, do the water molecules have more thermal energy? Explain your reasoning.

FIGURE 12
Condensation of Water
Water vapor from a hot shower contacts the cool surface of a bathroom mirror and condenses into a liquid.

Condensation The opposite of vaporization is called **condensation.** One way you can observe condensation is by breathing onto a mirror. When warm water vapor in your breath reaches the cooler surface of the mirror, the water vapor condenses into liquid droplets. **Condensation occurs when particles in a gas lose enough thermal energy to form a liquid.** For example, clouds typically form when water vapor in the atmosphere condenses into liquid droplets. When the droplets get heavy enough, they fall to the ground as rain.

You cannot see water vapor. Water vapor is a colorless gas that is impossible to see. The steam you see above a kettle of boiling water is not water vapor, and neither are clouds or fog. What you see in those cases are tiny droplets of liquid water suspended in air.

 Reading Checkpoint **How do clouds typically form?**

52 ◆ K

Changes Between Solid and Gas

If you live where the winters are cold, you may have noticed that snow seems to disappear even when the temperature stays well below freezing. This change is the result of sublimation. **Sublimation** occurs when the surface particles of a solid gain enough energy that they form a gas. **During sublimation, particles of a solid do not pass through the liquid state as they form a gas.**

One example of sublimation occurs with dry ice. Dry ice is the common name for solid carbon dioxide. At ordinary atmospheric pressures, carbon dioxide cannot exist as a liquid. So instead of melting, solid carbon dioxide changes directly into a gas. As it changes state, the carbon dioxide absorbs thermal energy. This property helps keep materials near dry ice cold and dry. For this reason, using dry ice is a way to keep temperature low when a refrigerator is not available. When dry ice becomes a gas, it cools water vapor in the nearby air. The water vapor then condenses into a liquid, forming fog around the dry ice.

FIGURE 13
Dry Ice
When solid carbon dioxide, called "dry ice," sublimates, it changes directly into a gas. *Predicting If you allowed the dry ice to stand at room temperature for several hours, what would be left in the glass dish? Explain.*

 Reading Checkpoint What physical state is skipped during the sublimation of a substance?

Section 2 Assessment

 Target Reading Skill Outlining Use the information in your outline about changes of state to help you answer the questions below.

Reviewing Key Concepts

1. **a.** Reviewing What happens to the particles of a solid as it becomes a liquid?
   b. Applying Concepts How does the thermal energy of solid water change as it melts?
   c. Making Judgments You are stranded in a blizzard. You need water to drink, and you're trying to stay warm. Should you melt snow and then drink it, or just eat snow? Explain.
2. **a.** Describing What is vaporization?
   b. Comparing and Contrasting Name the two types of vaporization. Tell how they are similar and how they differ.
   c. Relating Cause and Effect Why does the evaporation of sweat cool your body on a warm day?

3. **a.** Identifying What process occurs as pieces of dry ice gradually get smaller?
   b. Interpreting Photos What is the fog you see in the air around the dry ice in Figure 13? Why does the fog form?

Writing in Science

Using Analogies Write a short essay in which you create an analogy to describe particle motion. Compare the movements and positions of people dancing with the motions of water molecules in liquid water and in water vapor.

Lab zone Chapter **Project**

Keep Students on Track Have student groups write a description of how particles behave in each state of matter. Then have them decide how to model each state, using words and drawings. Groups should decide whether to create a cartoon or a skit, and then prepare a storyboard. Explain that a storyboard is made up of rough sketches with notes that outline the action of a story.

Writing in Science

Writing Mode Description
Scoring Rubric
4 Exceeds criteria; includes a highly imaginative analogy that accurately relates the particle motion of different states of matter to the movements of dancers
3 Meets criteria
2 Includes an analogy that is not quite accurate or completely developed
1 Essay is incomplete and/or contains serious errors

Monitor Progress [L2]

Answers
Figure 13 Nothing would be left because all the carbon dioxide would sublimate and mix with the air.

Reading Checkpoint Water vapor in the atmosphere condenses into liquid droplets.

Reading Checkpoint The liquid state

Assess

Reviewing Key Concepts

1. a. The particles break free from their fixed positions. **b.** The thermal energy increases. **c.** You should melt snow and then drink it. If you eat snow, your body must use some of its valuable energy to change the snow to a liquid.
2. a. The change from a liquid to a gas **b.** Evaporation and boiling; in both, a liquid becomes a gas. Evaporation occurs only on a liquid's surface, while boiling occurs both on the surface and below the surface. **c.** Your body supplies the thermal energy necessary to change the sweat from a liquid to a gas, causing the body to lose heat and become cooler.
3. a. Sublimation **b.** Water vapor; the water vapor in the air is cooled and condenses when dry ice sublimes.

Reteach [L1]

Have students diagram how particles of matter change as they change from one state to another. Ask: **What is required for matter to change from one state to another?** (*Addition or removal of thermal energy*)

Performance Assessment [L2]

Skills Check Have students create a concept map that describes the different changes of state. Students should also include whether thermal energy is being added or removed.

All in One Teaching Resources

- Section Summary: *Changes of State*
- Review and Reinforce: *Changes of State*
- Enrich: *Changes of State*

Lab zone Skills Lab

Melting Ice [L2]

Prepare for Inquiry

Skills Objectives
After this lab, students will be able to
- predict which ice cube will melt faster.
- interpret data about temperature changes.
- infer the source of thermal energy.

 Prep Time 15 minutes
Class Time 30 minutes

Advance Planning
- Make enough ice cubes for the class.
- Heat water or use warm tap water.
- If using probeware, refer to the *Probeware Lab Manual*.

Safety
  Review safety guidelines in Appendix A.

All in One Teaching Resources
- Lab Worksheet: *Melting Ice*

 **Go Online**
PHSchool.com
For: Data sharing
Visit: PHSchool.com
Web Code: cgd-1022

Students can go online to pool and analyze their data with students nationwide.

Guide Inquiry

Introduce the Procedure
- If using probeware, demonstrate its use.
- Emphasize the importance of recording time and temperature at the instant of total melting.

Troubleshooting the Experiment
- Remind students to keep the bulb of the thermometer completely immersed at all times.
- Have students wipe away any melted water from the ice cube before putting it in water.

Lab zone Skills Lab

Go Online
PHSchool.com
For: Data Sharing
Visit: PHSchool.com
Web Code: cgd-1022

Melting Ice

Problem
How does the temperature of the surroundings affect the rate at which ice melts?

Skills Focus
predicting, interpreting data, inferring

Materials
- stopwatch or timer
- thermometer or temperature probe
- 2 plastic cups, about 200 mL each
- 2 stirring rods, preferably plastic
- ice cubes, about 2 cm on each side
- warm water, about 40°C–45°C
- water at room temperature, about 20°C–25°C

Procedure
1. Read Steps 1–8. Based on your own experience, predict which ice cube will melt faster.
2. In your notebook, make a data table like the one below.
3. Fill a cup halfway with warm water (about 40°C to 45°C). Fill a second cup to the same depth with water at room temperature.
4. Record the exact temperature of the water in each cup. If you are using a temperature probe, see your teacher for instructions.
5. Obtain two ice cubes that are as close to the same size as possible.

Data Table			
Cup	Beginning Temperature (°C)	Time to Melt (s)	Final Temperature (°C)
1			
2			

54 ◆ K

6. Place one ice cube in each cup. Begin timing with a stopwatch. Gently stir each cup with a stirring rod until the ice has completely melted.
7. Observe both ice cubes carefully. At the moment one of the ice cubes is completely melted, record the time and the temperature of the water in the cup.
8. Wait for the second ice cube to melt. Record its melting time and the water temperature.

Analyze and Conclude
1. **Predicting** Was your prediction in Step 1 supported by the results of the experiment? Explain why or why not.
2. **Interpreting Data** In which cup did the water temperature change the most? Explain.
3. **Inferring** When the ice melted, its molecules gained enough energy to overcome the forces holding them together as solid ice. What is the source of that energy?
4. **Communicating** Write a paragraph describing how errors in measurement could have affected your conclusions in this experiment. Tell what you would do differently if you repeated the procedure. (*Hint*: How well were you able to time the exact moment that each ice cube completely melted?)

Design an Experiment
When a lake freezes in winter, only the top turns to ice. Design an experiment to model the melting of a frozen lake during the spring. *Obtain your teacher's permission before carrying out your investigation.* Be prepared to share your results with the class.

Expected Outcome
The ice cube in warmer water melts faster.

Analyze and Conclude
1. Sample answer: I predicted that the ice cube in warm water would melt faster, and that happened in the experiment.
2. In the cup with warm water; greater difference between initial temperature and melting point
3. The thermal energy of the water in each cup

4. Sample answer: Errors could include misreading the thermometer or not measuring the time correctly. Taking the final temperature too late will increase the time measurement.

Extend Inquiry

Design an Experiment Sample experiment: A partially frozen container of water with a layer of ice on top is exposed to a lamp (the "sun") while the other is kept in the shade. Check plans for safety.

Section
3 Gas Behavior

Reading Preview

Key Concepts
- What types of measurements are useful when working with gases?
- How are the volume, temperature, and pressure of a gas related?

Key Terms
- pressure • Boyle's law
- Charles's law

Target Reading Skill
Asking Questions Before you read, preview the red headings. In a graphic organizer like the one below, ask a *what* or *how* question for each heading. As you read, write the answers to your questions.

Gases

Question	Answer
What measurements are useful in studying gases?	Measurements useful in studying gases include . . .

▶ Before a flight, a hot-air balloon is filled with air.

Lab zone Discover Activity

How Can Air Keep Chalk From Breaking?

1. Stand on a chair and drop a piece of chalk onto a hard floor. Observe what happens to the chalk.
2. Wrap a second piece of chalk in wax paper or plastic food wrap. Drop the chalk from the same height used in Step 1. Observe the results.
3. Wrap a third piece of chalk in plastic bubble wrap. Drop the chalk from the same height used in Step 1. Observe the results.

Think It Over
Inferring Compare the results from Steps 1, 2, and 3. What properties of the air in the bubble wrap accounted for the results in Step 3?

How do you prepare a hot-air balloon for a morning ride? First, you inflate the balloon, using powerful air fans. Then you heat the air inside with propane gas burners. But the balloon and its cargo won't begin to rise until the warmer air inside is less dense than the air outside the balloon. How does this change occur? How can you keep the balloon floating safely through the atmosphere? How can you make it descend when you are ready to land? To answer these and other questions, you would need to understand the relationships between the temperature, pressure, and volume of a gas.

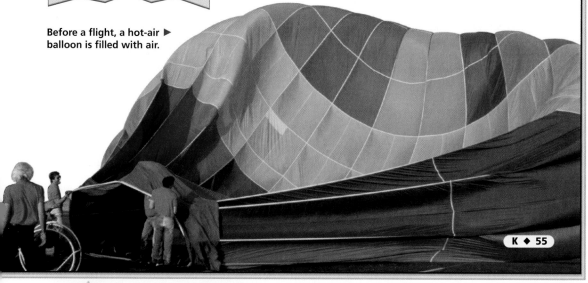

K ◆ 55

Lab zone Discover Activity

Skills Focus Inferring [L1]

Materials 3 pieces of chalk, sheet of wax paper or plastic wrap, plastic bubble wrap, tape

Time 10 minutes

Tips Each student should have a "spotter" to prevent him or her from falling off the chair.

Expected Outcome The chalk will break when dropped by itself and when wrapped in wax paper or plastic wrap. It will not break when wrapped in bubble wrap.

Think It Over The chalk did not break when wrapped in bubble wrap. Sample answer: The particles of air inside the bubble wrap squeezed together when it hit the floor and absorbed the force of impact.

Objectives
After this lesson, students will be able to
K.2.3.1 List the types of measurements used when working with gases.
K.2.3.2 Explain how the volume, temperature, and pressure of a gas are related.

Target Reading Skill

Asking Questions Explain that changing a head into a question helps students anticipate the ideas, facts, and events they are about to read.

Answers
Sample questions and answers:
What measurements are useful in studying gases? (*Volume, temperature, and pressure*)
How are the pressure and volume of gases related? (*When the pressure of a gas increases at constant temperature, its volume decreases.*)
How are the pressure and temperature of gases related? (*When the temperature of a gas increases at constant volume, its pressure increases.*) **How are the volume and temperature of gases related?** (*When the temperature of a gas increases at constant pressure, its volume increases.*)

All in One Teaching Resources
- Transparency K13

Preteach

Build Background Knowledge [L2]

Gas Pressure and a Balloon
Inflate a balloon. Hold it closed, then ask: **What happens if there is too much air in the balloon?** (*It will burst.*) Point out that the air, a mixture of gases, is pushing on the sides of the balloon. The balloon is also pushing on the gas particles, keeping them inside. Release the balloon. Ask: **How did the air get out of the balloon?** (*Sample answer: Gas particles pushing on the sides of the balloon escaped through the opening.*)

Instruct

Measuring Gases

Teach Key Concepts L2
Volume, Temperature, Pressure

Focus Ask: **What are the properties of gases?** *(No definite shape or volume)*

Teach Tell students that the volume, temperature, and pressure of a gas helps determine its properties. Ask: **What is volume?** *(The amount of space that matter fills)* Emphasize that temperature is the measure of the motion of the particles in matter. Ask: **How does gas exert pressure?** *(Gas particles collide with one another and the walls of their container.)*

Apply Ask: **What affects the shape and volume of a gas?** *(Sample answer: The temperature and pressure of the gas and the volume of the container it's in)* **learning modality: verbal**

Lab zone Build Inquiry L1

Modeling the Motion of Gas Particles

Materials small box or empty milk carton, small marbles or ball bearings

Time 5 minutes

Focus Ask: **What happens to the motion of gas particles when temperature increases?** *(They move faster.)*

Teach Fill the box with marbles, and invite students to shake the box at different speeds. Ask: **When you shake the box quickly, what are the marbles modeling?** *(Gas particles at high temperature)*

Apply Ask: **As "temperature" increased, how did the pressure exerted by the "gas particles" change?** *(The pressure increased—gas particles hit the sides of the box more often.)* **learning modality: kinesthetic**

Independent Practice L2

All in One Teaching Resources

- Guided Reading and Study Worksheet: *Gas Behavior*

⊙ **Student Edition on Audio CD**

56 ◆ K

Measuring Gases

How much helium is in the tank in Figure 14? If you don't know the mass of the helium, you may think that measuring the volume of the tank will give you an answer. But gases easily contract or expand. To fill the tank, helium was compressed—or pressed together tightly—to decrease its volume. When you use the helium to fill balloons, it fills a total volume of inflated balloons much greater than the volume of the tank. The actual volume of helium you get, however, depends on the temperature and air pressure that day. **When working with a gas, it is helpful to know its volume, temperature, and pressure.** So what exactly do these measurements mean?

Volume From Chapter 1, you know that volume is the amount of space that matter fills. Volume is measured in cubic centimeters (cm^3), milliliters (mL), liters (L), and other units. Because gas particles move and fill the space available, the volume of a gas is the same as the volume of its container.

Temperature Hot soup, warm hands, cool breezes—you are familiar with matter at different temperatures. But what does temperature tell you? Recall that the particles within any substance are constantly moving. Temperature is a measure of the average energy of random motion of the particles of a substance. The faster the particles are moving, the greater their energy and the higher the temperature. You might think of a thermometer as a speedometer for molecules.

Even at ordinary temperatures, the average speed of particles in a gas is very fast. At room temperature, or about 20°C, the particles in a typical gas travel about 500 meters per second—more than twice the cruising speed of a jet plane!

FIGURE 14
How Much Helium?
A helium tank the height of this girl can fill over 500 balloons!
Interpreting Photos *How is the helium in the tank different from the helium in the balloons?*

Differentiated Instruction

Less Proficient Readers L1
Building Vocabulary Before students read the section, introduce the words *contract, expand, compress,* and *inflate.* Help students group the words based on their meanings. Provide a synonym for a word if students do not know its meaning.

Then, give each student a balloon. Challenge students to demonstrate the meaning of each word with the balloon. Finally, ask students to identify an antonym of each word. **learning modality: kinesthetic**

Pressure Gas particles constantly collide with one another and with the walls of their container. As a result, the gas pushes on the walls of the container. The **pressure** of the gas is the force of its outward push divided by the area of the walls of the container. Pressure is measured in units of pascals (Pa) or kilopascals (kPa). (1 kPa = 1,000 Pa.)

$$\text{Pressure} = \frac{\text{Force}}{\text{Area}}$$

The firmness of a gas-filled object comes from the pressure of the gas. For example, the air inside a fully pumped basketball has a higher pressure than the air outside. This higher pressure is due to a greater concentration of gas particles inside the ball than in the surrounding air. (Concentration is the number of particles in a given unit of volume.)

When air leaks out of a basketball, the pressure decreases and the ball becomes softer. Why does a ball leak even when it has a tiny hole? The higher pressure inside the ball results in gas particles hitting the inner surface of the ball more often. Therefore, gas particles inside the ball reach the hole and escape more often than gas particles outside the ball reach the hole and enter. Thus, many more particles go out than in. The pressure inside drops until it is equal to the pressure outside.

 Reading Checkpoint What units are used to measure pressure?

 Math Skills

Using Formulas

Pressure can be calculated using the formula below. Force is measured in newtons (N). If area is measured in square meters (m^2), pressure is expressed in pascals (Pa).

$$\text{Pressure} = \frac{\text{Force}}{\text{Area}}$$

For example, a machine exerts a force of 252 N on a piston having an area of 0.430 m^2. What is the pressure on the piston in Pa?

$$\text{Pressure} = \frac{252 \text{ N}}{0.430 \text{ m}^2}$$

$$= 586 \text{ Pa}$$

Practice Problem A trash compactor exerts a force of 5,600 N over an area of 0.342 m^2. What pressure does the compactor exert in Pa?

FIGURE 15

A Change in Pressure

A punctured basketball deflates as the gas particles begin to escape.

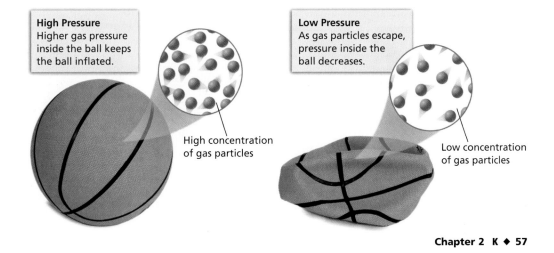

High Pressure Higher gas pressure inside the ball keeps the ball inflated.

High concentration of gas particles

Low Pressure As gas particles escape, pressure inside the ball decreases.

Low concentration of gas particles

 **Teacher Demo**   L2

Gas Pressure

Materials round balloon, push pin

Time 10 minutes

Focus Explain that the gas pressure is caused by gas particles pushing on the walls of a container.

Teach Inflate the balloon and knot the end. Ask: **Is the air pressure higher inside or outside the balloon?** *(Inside)* Explain that gas particles inside the balloon are hitting the inner surface of the balloon more often than gas particles outside the balloon are hitting the outside surface of the balloon. Carefully prick a hole in the balloon with a push pin.

Apply Ask: **Why did the balloon deflate?** *(The higher pressure inside the balloon forced more gas particles to leave rather than enter the balloon through the hole.)* **learning modality: visual**

 **Math Skills**

Math Skill Using formulas

Focus Tell students that the pressure of a gas is the force of its outward push divided by the area of the walls of its container.

Teach Explain that when using formulas, the values of the variables must have the appropriate units. Ask: **For pressure measured in Pascals, in what units must force be measured?** *(Newtons)* **In what units must area be measured?** *(Meters squared)*

Answer

$$P = \frac{5,600 \text{ N}}{0.342 \text{ m}^2} = 16,374 \text{ Pa}$$

Monitor Progress _____ L2

Writing Instruct students to write definitions for *volume, temperature,* and *pressure* using their own words.

Answers
Figure 14 The helium in the tank is at a higher pressure and occupies a smaller volume.

Reading Checkpoint Pascals (Pa) or kilopascals (kPa)

Pressure and Volume

Teach Key Concepts L2
Boyle's Law

Focus Ask: **Why doesn't a gas have a definite volume?** *(Gas particles can spread far apart so the gas takes the shape of its container.)*

Teach Explain that Boyle's law describes the relationship between the pressure and the volume of a gas. Ask: **What effect does increasing pressure have on gas particles?** *(It pushes them closer together.)* **As gas particles move closer together, how does the volume of the gas change?** *(It decreases.)*

Apply Ask: **Why do scientists only partially fill high-altitude balloons?** *(As air pressure on the outside of the balloon decreases at higher altitudes, the helium inside expands. If the balloon were overfilled, it would burst.)* **learning modality: verbal**

Help Students Read L1
Using Prior Knowledge Refer to the Content Refresher in this chapter, which provides guidelines for using this strategy.

Before students read, have them list what they know about the relationships of gas pressure, volume, and temperature based on their experience with balloons. After reading the rest of this section, have students revise their lists based on their new understanding.

Use Visuals: Figure 17
Boyle's Law

Focus Invite students to examine Figure 17 and compare the heights of the plungers.

Teach Ask: **As more weights are added, what happens to the pressure caused by the plunger?** *(It increases.)* **What happens to the space between gas particles?** *(It decreases.)* **What has happened to gas volume?** *(It has decreased.)*

Apply Have students predict what a fourth drawing would look like if two more weights were added to the plunger top. *(The pressure increases, and the gas particles move closer together.)* **learning modality: visual**

All in One Teaching Resources
• Transparency K14

FIGURE 16
Inflating a Tire
A bicycle pump makes use of the relationship between the volume and pressure of a gas.

Pressure and Volume

Suppose you are using a bicycle pump. By pressing down on the plunger, you force the gas inside the pump through the rubber tube and out the nozzle into the tire. What will happen if you close the nozzle and then push down on the plunger?

Boyle's Law The answer to this question comes from experiments done by the scientist Robert Boyle in an effort to improve air pumps. In the 1600s, Boyle measured the volumes of gases at different pressures. **Boyle found that when the pressure of a gas at constant temperature is increased, the volume of the gas decreases. When the pressure is decreased, the volume increases.** This relationship between the pressure and the volume of a gas is called **Boyle's law.**

Boyle's Law in Action Boyle's law plays a role in research using high-altitude balloons. Researchers fill the balloons with only a small fraction of the helium gas that the balloons can hold. As a balloon rises through the atmosphere, the air pressure around it decreases and the balloon expands. If the balloon were fully filled at takeoff, it would burst before it got very high.

Boyle's law also applies to situations in which the *volume* of a gas is changed. Then the *pressure* changes in the opposite way. A bicycle pump works this way. As you push on the plunger, the volume of air inside the pump cylinder gets smaller and the pressure increases, forcing air into the tire.

Reading Checkpoint What could cause a helium balloon to burst as it rises in the atmosphere?

Least pressure, greatest volume

Increasing pressure, decreasing volume

Greatest pressure, least volume

FIGURE 17
Boyle's Law
As weights are added, the gas particles occupy a smaller volume. The pressure increases.

Differentiated Instruction

Special Needs L1
Modeling Volume and Pressure Give students a handful of marbles to model the particles of a gas. Encourage students to experiment using the same number of marbles in smaller and smaller spaces. For example, students can place the marbles on a desktop, then use their hands to push them closer and closer together. Or, students can use rectangular blocks to define the space. As they push the blocks closer together, the space between the marbles decreases. Point out that every time they move the marbles closer together with their hands, they are increasing the pressure on the marbles. Be sure students also experiment with decreasing pressure to observe how the space between the marbles increases. **learning modality: kinesthetic**

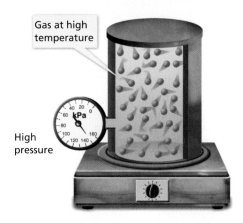

Gas at low temperature

Low pressure

Gas at high temperature

High pressure

Pressure and Temperature

If you dropped a few grains of sand onto your hand, you would hardly feel them. But what if you were caught in a sandstorm? Ouch! The sand grains fly around very fast, and they would sting if they hit you. The faster the grains travel, the harder they hit your skin.

Although gas particles are much smaller than sand grains, a sandstorm is a good model for gas behavior. Like grains of sand in a sandstorm, gas particles travel individually and at high speeds (but randomly). The faster the gas particles move, the more frequently they collide with the walls of their container and the greater the force of the collisions.

Increasing Temperature Raises Pressure Recall from Section 2 that the higher the temperature of a substance, the faster its particles are moving. Now you can state a relationship between temperature and pressure. **When the temperature of a gas at constant volume is increased, the pressure of the gas increases. When the temperature is decreased, the pressure of the gas decreases.** (*Constant volume* means that the gas is in a closed, rigid container.)

Pressure and Temperature in Action Have you ever looked at the tires of an 18-wheel truck? Because the tires need to support a lot of weight, they are large, heavy, and stiff. The inside volume of these tires doesn't vary much. On long trips, especially in the summer, a truck's tires can become very hot. As the temperature increases, so does the pressure of the air inside the tire. If the pressure becomes greater than the tire can hold, the tire will burst. For this reason, truck drivers need to monitor and adjust tire pressure on long trips.

FIGURE 18
Gas Pressure and Temperature
When a gas is heated, the particles move faster and collide more with each other and with the walls of their container. The pressure of the gas increases.

Go Online active art

For: Gas Laws activity
Visit: PHSchool.com
Web Code: cgp-1023

DISCOVERY CHANNEL SCHOOL

Solids, Liquids, and Gases

Video Preview
▶ Video Field Trip
Video Assessment

Chapter 2   K ◆ 59

Pressure and Temperature

Teach Key Concepts   L2
Relating Gas Pressure and Temperature

Focus Ask: **What causes gas pressure?** (*Gas particles colliding with the walls of their container.*)

Teach Point out that the number of gas particles in each container in Figure 18 is the same. Ask: **Which container is at a higher temperature?** (*The container on the right*) **Why does that container have higher gas pressure?** (*When gas is heated, the faster moving particles bump into each other and the sides of the container more often.*)

Apply Ask: **Why should people check the air pressure in their tires in winter?** (*Air pressure will decrease because of decreased temperature and the tires may be too soft.*)

Extend The *active art* will show students the relationships among gas pressure, volume, and temperature. **learning modality: visual**

Go Online active art

For: Gas Laws activity
Visit: PHSchool.com
Web Code: cgp-1023

Students can interact with the art of gas laws online.

All in One Teaching Resources
• Transparency K15

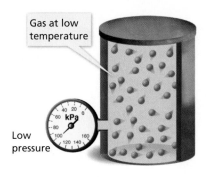

DISCOVERY CHANNEL SCHOOL
Video Field Trip

Solids, Liquids, and Gases

Show the Video Field Trip to let students experience the thrills and dangers of scuba diving. Discussion question: **What happens to the volume of nitrogen bubbles when pressure decreases?** (*Nitrogen bubbles expand as pressure decreases.*)

Monitor Progress ———— L2

Oral Presentation Invite students to relate Boyle's law in their own words.

Answers

Reading Checkpoint   Decreasing outside pressure causes the helium inside the balloon to expand.

K ● 59

Volume and Temperature

Charles's Law

Focus Ask: **How do gas particles respond to higher temperatures?** *(They move faster.)*

Teach Explain that the scientist Jacques Charles described the relationship between gas volume and temperature. Ask: **Which property of a gas is constant in Charles's law?** *(Pressure)* **How does the volume of a gas change as its temperature increases?** *(The volume increases because the particles are moving farther apart.)*

Apply Ask: **How does a hot-air balloon rise?** *(Heating increases the volume of air. Air particles escape from the bottom opening. Fewer air particles inside the balloon cause it to be less dense than the outside air, and the balloon rises.)* **learning modality: verbal**

Teaching Resources
- Transparency K16

Teacher Demo   L1

Hot and Cold Balloons

Materials 2 identical, small balloons, 2 large spoons, small tub of hot water, small tub of ice water

Time 5 minutes

Focus Remind students that as gas temperature increases, volume increases.

Teach Inflate the balloons to the same size, allowing room for expansion. Completely immerse one balloon in ice water and the other in hot water, using the spoons to keep them submerged. After 2 minutes, hold up the balloons for students to compare. Ask: **Which balloon is larger?** *(The balloon in hot water)*

Apply Ask: **Why does volume increase when the temperature of a gas increases?** *(The gas particles move faster and farther apart, and volume increases.)* **learning modality: visual**

FIGURE 19
Charles's Law

Changing the temperature of a gas at constant pressure changes its volume in a similar way.
Inferring *What happens to the gas particles in the balloon as the gas is warmed?*

▲ A gas-filled balloon is at room temperature.

▲ The balloon is lowered into liquid nitrogen at –196°C.

▲ The balloon shrinks as gas volume decreases.

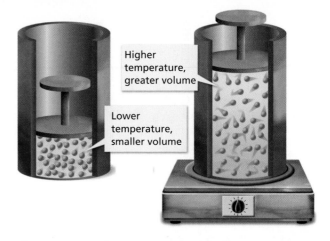

Higher temperature, greater volume

Lower temperature, smaller volume

Volume and Temperature

In the late 1700s, French scientist Jacques Charles helped start a new sport. He and others took to the skies in the first hydrogen balloons. Charles's interest in balloon rides led him to discover how gas temperature and volume are related.

Charles's Law Jacques Charles examined the relationship between the temperature and volume of a gas that is kept at a constant pressure. He measured the volume of a gas at various temperatures in a container that could change volume. (A changeable volume allows the pressure to remain constant.) **Charles found that when the temperature of a gas is increased at constant pressure, its volume increases. When the temperature of a gas is decreased at constant pressure, its volume decreases.** This principle is called **Charles's law.**

Charles's Law in Action In Figure 19, you can see the effects of Charles's law demonstrated with a simple party balloon. Time-lapse photos show a balloon as it is slowly lowered into liquid nitrogen at nearly −200°C, then removed. The changes to the balloon's volume result from changes in the temperature of the air inside the balloon. The pressure remains more or less constant because the air is in a flexible container.

▲ When removed from the nitrogen, the gas warms and the balloon expands.

▲ The balloon is at room temperature again.

Now think again about a hot-air balloon. Heating causes the air inside the balloon to expand. Some of the warm air leaves through the bottom opening of the balloon, keeping the pressure constant. But now, the air inside is less dense than the air outside the balloon, so the balloon begins to rise. If the pilot allows the air in the balloon to cool, the reverse happens. The air in the balloon contracts, and more air enters through the opening. The density of the air inside increases, and the balloon starts downward.

Boyle, Charles, and others often described the behavior of gases by focusing on only two factors that vary at a time. In everyday life, however, gases can show the effects of changes in pressure, temperature, and volume all at once. People who work with gases, such as tire manufacturers and balloonists, must consider these combined effects.

 What factor is kept unchanged when demonstrating Charles's law?

FIGURE 20
Hot-Air Balloon
Balloonists often use a propane burner to heat the air in a balloon.

Section 3 Assessment

Target Reading Skill Asking Questions Use the answers to the questions you wrote about the headings to help you answer the questions below.

Reviewing Key Concepts

1. a. Defining How is gas pressure defined?
   b. Describing Describe how the motions of gas particles are related to the pressure exerted by the gas.
   c. Relating Cause and Effect Why does pumping more air into a basketball increase the pressure inside the ball?

2. a. Reviewing How does Boyle's law describe the relationship between gas pressure and volume?
   b. Explaining Explain why increasing the temperature of a gas in a closed, rigid container causes the pressure in the container to increase.

c. Applying Concepts Suppose it is the night before a big parade, and you are in charge of inflating the parade balloons. You just learned that the temperature will rise 15°C between early morning and the time the parade starts. How will this information affect the way you inflate the balloons?

Math Practice

3. Using Formulas Suppose the atmosphere exerts a force of 124,500 N on a kitchen table with an area of 1.5m². What is the pressure in pascals of the atmosphere on the table?

Answers
Figure 19 The gas particles move faster and spread farther apart.

✓ Reading Checkpoint Pressure

Assess

Reviewing Key Concepts

1. a. Gas pressure is the force of its outward push divided by the area of the walls of its container. **b.** As the moving gas particles collide with the walls of their container, they push on the container walls. **c.** The greater number of gas particles inside the basketball results in more collisions, which increase the outward push of the gas.
2. a. At constant temperature, when gas pressure increases, gas volume decreases. **b.** When the temperature increases, gas particles move faster and collide more frequently with greater force. **c.** Because you know that the temperature will increase, the volume of the gas in the balloons will also increase. To prevent the expansion from bursting the balloons, you should not completely fill the balloons.

Reteach L1

Ask: **What measurements are useful when working with a gas?** (*Volume, temperature, and pressure*) Diagram how these three properties are related. Invite students to help complete the diagram.

Performance Assessment L2

Skills Check Have students create a table to show the relationships among gas volume, temperature, and pressure. Also have them identify the law that describes that relationship.

All in One Teaching Resources

• Section Summary: *Gas Behavior*
• Review and Reinforce: *Gas Behavior*
• Enrich: *Gas Behavior*

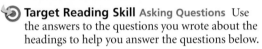

Math Skill Using formulas

Answers

3. Pressure (Pa) $= \dfrac{\text{Force (N)}}{\text{Area (m}^2)}$

$\dfrac{124{,}500 \text{ N}}{1.5 \text{ m}^2} = 83{,}000 \text{ Pa}$

K ● 61

Graphing Gas Behavior

Objectives
After the lesson, students will be able to
K.2.4.1 Identify the type of relationship shown by the graph for Charles's law.
K.2.4.2 Identify the relationship shown by the graph for Boyle's law.

Target Reading Skill 🔄

Previewing Visuals Explain that looking at the visuals before they read helps students activate prior knowledge and predict what they are about to read.

Answers
Sample answer:
What is the relationship between temperature and volume? (*The volume of a gas is directly proportional to its temperature under constant pressure.*) **What does the dotted line show?** (*The dotted line predicts how the graph would look if the gas could be cooled further.*)

All in One Teaching Resources
• Transparency K17

Preteach

Build Background Knowledge   L2

Reading Graphs
Show students a graph of daily high or low temperatures for the last week in your area. Challenge them to determine at a glance whether the temperature has risen or fallen (or stayed the same) over the last few days. Explain that graphs also show at a glance how scientific data change.

Graphing Gas Behavior

Reading Preview

Key Concepts
• What type of relationship does the graph for Charles's law show?
• What type of relationship does the graph for Boyle's law show?

Key Terms
• graph
• origin
• directly proportional
• vary inversely

🔄 Target Reading Skill
Previewing Visuals Before you read, preview Figure 23. In a graphic organizer like the one below, write questions that you have about the diagram. As you read, answer your questions.

Graphing Charles's Law

Q.	What is the relationship between gas volume and temperature?
A.	
Q.	

Lab zone Discover **Activity**

Temperature (°C)	Pressure (kPa)
0	8
5	11
10	14
15	17
20	20
25	23

Can You Graph Gas Behavior?
1. In an experiment, the temperature of a gas at a constant volume was varied. Gas pressure was measured after each 5°C change. Use the data in this table and follow Steps 2–4 to make a graph.
2. Show temperature on the horizontal axis with a scale from 0°C to 25°C. Show pressure on the vertical axis with a scale from 0 kPa to 25 kPa. (1 kPa = 1,000 Pa.)
3. For each pair of measurements, draw a point on the graph.
4. Draw a line to connect the points.

Think It Over
Drawing Conclusions What happens to the pressure of a gas when the temperature is increased at constant volume?

Graphs are a way to tell a story with data. A **graph** is a diagram that tells how two variables, or factors that change, are related. If you did the activity above, you made a graph that helped you understand how the pressure of a gas changes when its temperature is changed. In this section, you will learn how to make and interpret graphs that relate these and other properties of gases.

A graph consists of a grid set up by two lines, one horizontal and one vertical. Each line, or axis, is divided into equal units. The horizontal axis, or *x*-axis, shows the manipulated variable. The vertical axis, or *y*-axis, shows the responding variable. Each axis is labeled with the name of the variable, the unit of measurement, and a range of values.

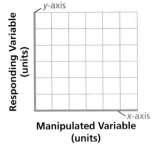

FIGURE 21
Making a Graph
The *x*-axis (horizontal) and the *y*-axis (vertical) form the "backbone" of a graph.

Lab zone Discover **Activity**

Skills Focus Drawing conclusions   L2

Time 15 minutes

Tips Ask: **What intervals will you use for the horizontal axis?** (*Sample answer: Intervals of 5°C*) **What intervals will you use for the vertical axis?** (*Sample answer: Intervals of 2.0 kPa*)

Expected Outcome The graphed data will define a line that slants upward to the right.

Think It Over The pressure increases as temperature increases.

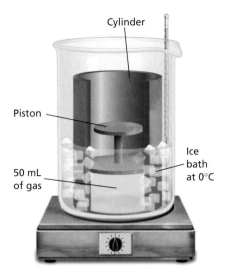

Cylinder

Piston

50 mL of gas

Ice bath at 0°C

Temperature (°C)	(K)	Volume (mL)
0	273	50
10	283	50
20	293	52
30	303	54
40	313	56
50	323	58
60	333	60
70	343	62
80	353	63
90	363	66
100	373	67
		69

FIGURE 22
Temperature and Gas Volume
As the temperature of the water bath increases, the gas inside the cylinder is warmed by the water. The data from the experiment are recorded in the notebook table. *Calculating How do you convert Celsius degrees to kelvins?*

Temperature and Volume

Recall that Charles's law relates the temperature and volume of a gas that is kept at a constant pressure. You can explore this relationship by doing an experiment in which you change the temperature of a gas and measure its volume. Then you can graph the data you have recorded and interpret the results.

Collecting Data As you can see from the cutaway view in Figure 22, the gas in the experiment is in a cylinder that has a movable piston. The piston moves up and down freely, which allows the gas to change volume and keep the same pressure. To control the temperature of the gas, the cylinder is placed in a water bath.

The experiment begins with an ice-water bath at 0°C and the gas volume at 50 mL. Then the water bath is slowly heated. Gradually, the temperature increases from 0°C to 100°C. Each time the temperature increases by 10°C, the volume of the gas in the cylinder is recorded.

You'll notice a second set of temperatures listed in the table in Figure 22. Scientists often work with gas temperatures in units called kelvins. To convert from Celsius degrees to kelvins (K), add 273. The kelvin temperatures will be used to graph the data.

 **Reading Checkpoint** What units do scientists use to measure gas temperatures?

Go Online
SciLINKS

For: Links on gases
Visit: www.SciLinks.org
Web Code: scn-1124

Temperature and Volume

Teach Key Concepts L2
Graphing Charles's Law

Focus Remind students that Charles's law relates the temperature and volume of a gas at constant pressure.

Teach Have students examine the graph of Charles's law in Figure 23. Ask: **What does the line look like?** (*Sample answer: A straight line that could pass through the origin*) **What type of relationship between temperature and volume does the graph of Charles's law show?** (*Sample answer: Volume is directly proportional to its temperature under constant pressure.*)

Apply Have students look at the line on the graph. Ask: **If the temperature goes down, how does the volume change?** (*Volume decreases proportionally.*) **learning modality: visual**

All in One Teaching Resources
• Transparency K18

Independent Practice L2
All in One Teaching Resources
• Guided Reading and Study Worksheet: *Graphing Gas Behavior*

◉ **Student Edition on Audio CD**

Go Online
SciLINKS

For: Links on gases
Visit: www.SciLinks.org
Web Code: scn-1124

Download a worksheet that will guide students' review of Internet sources on gases.

Monitor Progress L2

Skills Check Have students draw a grid for a graph in which the x-axis shows time in 5-minute intervals for 30 minutes and the y-axis shows temperature in 2°C intervals for 10 degrees starting at 0°C.

Answers
Figure 22 Add 273.

 Reading Checkpoint Scientists often work with gas temperatures in units called kelvins.

Differentiated Instruction

English Learners/Beginning L1
Comprehension: Link to Visual Use Figure 21 to make sure students can identify the origin and the axes. Review *variable, manipulated variable,* and *responding variable.* Have students point out where each variable is shown on the graph. Show how to label the graph with the variable name, the unit of measure, and the range of values. **learning modality: visual**

English Learners/Intermediate L2
Comprehension: Link to Visual Students can do the Beginning activity and then construct a graph, using the data from Figure 22. Model how to plot data points. Review *directly proportional* and *vary inversely.* Have students identify the relationship shown in their graph. **learning modality: logical/mathematical**

Interpreting Graphs

Materials none

Time 10 minutes

Focus Ask: **Which axis on a graph shows the manipulated variable?** (*Horizontal axis*) **Which axis shows the responding variable?** (*Vertical axis*)

Teach Challenge students to prove that the data table in Figure 22 was used to make the graph in Figure 23.

Apply Ask: **What is the manipulated variable in this experiment?** (*Temperature*) **The responding variable?** (*Volume*) **What gas measurement is held constant?** (*Pressure*) **learning modality: logical/ mathematical**

Pressure and Volume

Teach Key Concepts   L2

Graphing Boyle's Law

Focus Review Boyle's law. Ask: **How does the volume of a gas cause its pressure to change?** (*As volume increases, gas pressure decreases.*)

Teach Have students examine the experimental setup in Figure 24. Ask: **What units are on the pressure gauge?** (*kPa*) **Which property of gas is kept constant in this experiment?** (*Temperature*) **What do you think will happen to gas particles inside the cylinder and to the arrow on the pressure gauge if the piston were pushed down?** (*The gas particles will be closer together. The arrow on the gauge will point to a higher pressure.*)

Apply Have students look at the graph in Figure 25. Ask: **What is the shape of the line?** (*It curves downward from left to right.*) **What relationship does the graph show?** (*It shows that the pressure of a gas varies inversely with its volume.*) **learning modality: visual**

All in One Teaching Resources

• Transparency K18

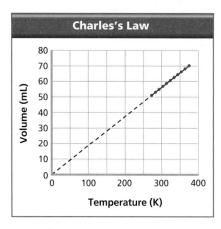

FIGURE 23
Graphing Charles's Law
A graph of the data from Figure 22 shows the relationship known as Charles's law. The dotted line predicts how the graph would look if the gas could be cooled further.

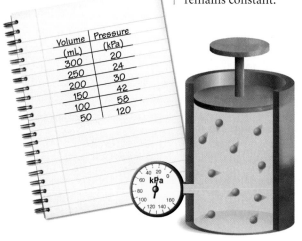

Graphing the Results Look at the graph in Figure 23. It appears as if the line would continue downward if data could be collected for lower temperatures. Such a line would pass through the point (0, 0), called the **origin.** When a graph of two variables is a straight line passing through the origin, the variables are said to be **directly proportional** to each other. **The graph of Charles's law shows that the volume of a gas is directly proportional to its kelvin temperature under constant pressure.**

In reality, the line on the graph cannot be extended as far as the origin. Remember that if a gas is cooled enough, it will condense into a liquid. After that, the volume would no longer change much. However, the line that results from the data represents a relationship that is directly proportional.

Pressure and Volume

A different experiment can show how gas pressure and volume are related when temperature is kept constant. Recall that this relationship is called Boyle's law.

Collecting Data The gas in this experiment is also contained in a cylinder with a movable piston. A gauge indicates the pressure of the gas inside the cylinder. The experiment begins with the volume of the gas at 300 mL. The pressure of the gas is 20 kPa. Next, the piston is pushed into the cylinder, making the gas volume smaller. The pressure of the gas is recorded after each 50-mL change in volume. Temperature remains constant.

FIGURE 24
Pushing on the top of the piston decreases the volume of the gas. The pressure of the gas increases. The data from the experiment are recorded in the notebook table.
Predicting *What would happen if you pulled up on the piston?*

64 ◆ K

Graphing the Results In this pressure-volume experiment, the manipulated variable is volume. Volume is shown on the scale of the horizontal axis from 0 mL to 300 mL. The responding variable is pressure. Pressure is shown on the scale of the vertical axis from 0 kPa to 120 kPa.

As you can see in Figure 25, the plotted points lie on a curve. Notice that the curve slopes downward from left to right. Also notice that the curve is steep at lower volumes and becomes less steep as volume increases. When a graph of two variables forms this kind of curve, the variables are said to **vary inversely** with one another. Such a relationship means that when one variable goes up, the other variable goes down in a regular way. **The graph for Boyle's law shows that the pressure of a gas varies inversely with its volume at constant temperature.**

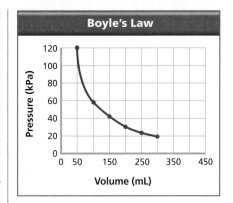

FIGURE 25
This graph of the data from Figure 24 shows the relationship between pressure and volume known as Boyle's law.

 Reading Checkpoint What is the manipulated variable in the pressure-volume experiment?

Section 4 Assessment

Target Reading Skill Previewing Visuals Refer to your questions and answers about Figure 23 to help you answer Question 1 below.

Reviewing Key Concepts

1. a. **Classifying** What term describes the relationship illustrated by the graph in Figure 23?
   b. **Relating Cause and Effect** How does the volume of a gas change when its temperature is increased at constant pressure?
   c. **Predicting** Suppose the temperature of the gas is increased to 400 kelvins (127°C). Use Figure 23 to predict the volume of the gas at this temperature.
2. a. **Classifying** What is the relationship between the pressure and the volume of a gas?
   b. **Estimating** Use the graph in Figure 25 to estimate the gas pressure when the gas volume is 125 mL.
   c. **Comparing and Contrasting** Compare and contrast the Charles's law and Boyle's law graphs. How can you tell the difference between a graph in which one variable is directly proportional to another and a graph in which two variables vary inversely?

Lab zone At-Home **Activity**

Finding Graphs Look for graphs in your newspaper or in magazines. Point out to members of your family which variable is the manipulated variable and which is the responding variable for each graph. Then compare any line graphs you have found to the graphs in this section. Which of your graphs show two variables that are directly proportional to each other? Do any show variables that vary inversely?

Monitor Progress ———— L2

Answers
Figure 24 Volume would increase and pressure would decrease.

Reading Checkpoint Volume

Assess

Reviewing Key Concepts

1. a. Directly proportional b. The volume increases. c. Approximately 74 mL
2. a. The pressure and the volume of a gas are inversely proportional. b. Approximately 49 kPa c. Directly proportional—the graph is a straight line that could pass through the origin; vary inversely—the graph is a curve that is steeper near the *y*-axis and less steep near the *x*-axis.

Reteach L1

Make copies of the graphs for Charles's law and Boyle's law. Have students label the graphs with the type of relationship shown by the graph. Also have them label the manipulated and responding variables.

Performance Assessment L2

Drawing Instruct students to briefly define *directly proportional* and *vary inversely*. Then have them draw a graph to illustrate each term.

All in One Teaching Resources

- Section Summary: *Graphing Gas Behavior*
- Review and Reinforce: *Graphing Gas Behavior*
- Enrich: *Graphing Gas Behavior*

Lab zone At-Home **Activity**

Finding Graphs L2 Before students begin, suggest that they define the following terms for their families: *manipulated variable, responding variable, directly proportional,* and *vary inversely.*

Lab zone Chapter **Project**

Keep Students on Track Have students revise their storyboards to include the information learned in this section. Make sure students review the entire storyboard; a change in one part may require a change in another. Then have students draw their cartoons or write their scripts and stage directions. Provide examples of popular cartoons for students to use as models. Give groups a place to rehearse their skits.

It's a Gas

Prepare for Inquiry

Key Concept
As the pressure applied to a gas increases, the volume that the gas occupies decreases.

Skills Objectives
After this lab, students will be able to
- graph data of gas volume and pressure.
- predict how the volume of a gas changes as pressure is increased and decreased.
- interpret data by comparing graphs that show how gas volume changes as pressure changes.
- draw conclusions about how the volume of a gas changes with changing pressure.
- communicate results in an explanatory paragraph.

 Prep Time 10 minutes

Class Time 20 minutes

Alternative Materials
If available, you can use syringes fitted with a Leur-type stopcock or have their own means of being sealed.

All in One Teaching Resources
- Lab Worksheet: *It's a Gas*

Guide Inquiry

Invitation
Display a small, hand-held pump, such as a bicycle pump, with the plunger in the "up" position. Ask: **What will happen when the plunger is pushed down?** (*Air is forced out.*) **What would happen if the plunger were pushed down but the nozzle of the pump were sealed to prevent air from getting out?** (*The air inside would be under more and more pressure.*) **CAUTION:** *Do not actually try this.*

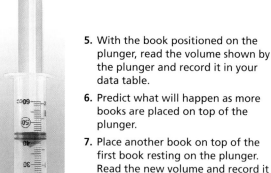

It's a Gas

Problem
How does the pressure you exert on a syringe affect the volume of the air inside it?

Skills Focus
graphing, predicting, interpreting data, drawing conclusions

Materials
- strong plastic syringe (with no needle), at least 35-cm^3 capacity
- modeling clay
- 4 books of uniform weight

Procedure

1. Make a data table in your notebook like the one below.
2. Lift the plunger of the syringe as high as it will move without going off scale. The volume inside the syringe will then be as large as possible.
3. Seal the small opening of the syringe with a piece of clay. The seal must be airtight.
4. Hold the syringe upright with the clay end on the table. With the help of a partner, place one book on top of the plunger. Steady the book carefully so it does not fall.
5. With the book positioned on the plunger, read the volume shown by the plunger and record it in your data table.
6. Predict what will happen as more books are placed on top of the plunger.
7. Place another book on top of the first book resting on the plunger. Read the new volume and record it in your data table.
8. One by one, place each of the remaining books on top of the plunger. After you add each book, record the volume of the syringe in your data table.
9. Predict what will happen as books are removed from the plunger one by one.
10. Remove the books one at a time. Record the volume of the syringe in your data table after you remove each book.

Data Table			
Adding Books		Removing Books	
Number of Books	Volume (cm^3)	Number of Books	Volume (cm^3)
0		4	
1		3	
2		2	
3		1	
4		0	

Introduce the Procedure
Have students read the procedure. Allow them to practice reading the volume of air inside the syringe. Ask: **Why must the clay seal for the syringe be airtight?** (*If air particles escape, the resulting volumes will not be accurate.*)

Troubleshooting the Experiment
- Have one student hold the syringe upright while another uses both hands to balance

the books. If students have trouble balancing the books on the syringe, glue the top of each syringe plunger to thick cardboard (about 10 cm square).
- Review how to estimate to the nearest 0.5 cm^3. This should give a smoother curve when students draw their graphs.
- If students' results are unusual, check whether they have sealed the syringes completely.

Analyze and Conclude

1. **Graphing** Make a line graph of the data obtained from Steps 5, 7, and 8. Show volume in cubic centimeters (cm^3) on the vertical axis and number of books on the horizontal axis. Title this Graph 1.

2. **Graphing** Make a second line graph of the data obtained from Step 10. Title this Graph 2.

3. **Predicting** Did the results you obtained support your predictions in Steps 6 and 9? Explain.

4. **Interpreting Data** Compare Graph 2 with Graph 1. How can you explain any differences in the two graphs?

5. **Drawing Conclusions** What does Graph 1 tell you about how the volume of a gas changes with increasing pressure?

6. **Communicating** Write a paragraph explaining how the volume of the gas changed as books were added one by one. Base your explanation on what was happening to the gas particles in the syringe.

Design an Experiment

How could you use ice and warm water to show how the temperature and volume of a gas are related? Design an experiment to test the effect on the volume of a gas when you change its temperature. *Obtain your teacher's permission before carrying out your investigation.*

Expected Outcome

As books are added, the volume of the gas in the syringe will decrease. As books are taken away, the volume of the gas will increase.

Analyze and Conclude

1. Students' graphs should have correct labels. Gas volume should decrease as books are added.

2. Students' graphs should have correct labels. Volume should increase as books are removed.

3. Predictions from Step 6 will likely be confirmed. Predictions from Step 9 may not be confirmed because the volume may not return to the original volume. As books are removed, gas volume may increase less than it decreased because of friction in the syringe.

4. Sample answer: The graphs are about the same shape. However, the data points differ because of friction in the syringe.

5. Increasing the pressure (by adding books) decreases the volume of air in the syringe.

6. Sample answer: Gas volume decreases by a smaller amount each time a book is added. Gas particles are being forced closer together as more weight is added. Eventually, volume will no longer decrease because the gas particles are as close as they can be.

Extend Inquiry

Design an Experiment Students may suggest placing the sealed syringe in a freezer or in ice water, then at room temperature, then in hot water. The amount of volume change for this temperature range, however, might not be very dramatic.

Interactive Textbook
- Complete student edition
- Section and chapter self-assessment
- Assessment reports for teachers

Help Students Read   **L1**

Building Vocabulary

Vocabulary Rating Chart Have students construct a chart with four columns labeled *Term, Can Define or Use It, Heard or Seen It,* and *Don't Know.* Tell them to copy the key terms from this chapter into the first column and rate their knowledge by putting a check in one of the other columns. Then have students reread the parts that pertain to key terms in question. Suggest that they write definitions for these terms in their own words.

Word/Part Analysis Tell students that *-ation* is a noun suffix. This suffix is used to change certain verbs to nouns, which name an action or a process. Demonstrate how *evaporate* becomes *evaporation.* The letter *e* at the end of the word is removed and the suffix *-ation* is added. Ask: **How does the meaning of *evaporate* differ from *evaporation*?** (*Evaporate* means "to change into vapor." *Evaporation* means "the process of changing into a vapor.") Challenge students to identify the verb forms for the following key terms: *vaporization, condensation,* and *sublimation.*

Connecting Concepts

Concept Maps Help students develop one way to show how the information in this chapter is related. Matter changes from one state to another as the motion of particles changes with temperature and pressure. Have students brainstorm to identify the key concepts, key terms, details, and examples. Then write each item on a self-stick note and attach it at random to chart paper or to the board.

Tell students that this concept map will be organized in hierarchical order and to begin at the top with the key concepts. Ask students these questions to guide them in

① States of Matter

Key Concepts
- A fixed, closely packed arrangement of particles causes a solid to have a definite shape and volume.
- Because its particles are free to move, a liquid has no definite shape. However, it does have a definite volume.
- As they move, gas particles spread apart, filling the space available. Thus, a gas has neither definite shape nor definite volume.

Key Terms
solid
crystalline solid
amorphous solid
liquid
fluid
surface tension
viscosity
gas

② Changes of State

Key Concepts
- At its melting point, the particles of a solid substance are vibrating so fast that they break free from their fixed positions.
- At its freezing temperature, the particles of a liquid are moving so slowly that they begin to form regular patterns.
- Vaporization takes place when the particles in a liquid gain enough energy to form a gas.
- Condensation occurs when particles in a gas lose enough thermal energy to form a liquid.
- During sublimation, particles of a solid do not pass through the liquid state as they form a gas.

Key Terms

melting	boiling
melting point	boiling point
freezing	condensation
vaporization	sublimation
evaporation	

③ Gas Behavior

Key Concepts
- When working with a gas, it is helpful to know its volume, temperature, and pressure.
- $\text{Pressure} = \dfrac{\text{Force}}{\text{Area}}$
- Boyle found that when the pressure of a gas at constant temperature is increased, the volume of the gas decreases. When the pressure is decreased, the volume increases.
- When the temperature of a gas at constant volume is increased, the pressure of the gas increases. When the temperature is decreased, the pressure of the gas decreases.
- Charles found that when the temperature of a gas is increased at constant pressure, its volume increases. When the temperature of a gas is decreased at constant pressure, its volume decreases.

Key Terms
pressure
Boyle's law
Charles's law

④ Graphing Gas Behavior

Key Concepts
- A graph of Charles's law shows that the volume of a gas is directly proportional to its kelvin temperature under constant pressure.
- A graph of Boyle's law shows that the pressure of a gas varies inversely with its volume at constant temperature.

Key Terms
graph
origin
directly proportional
vary inversely

categorizing the information on the self-stick notes: **What are the states of matter? How does matter change states? How do gases behave? What do graphs of gas behavior show?**

Prompt students by using connecting words or phrases, such as "include," "results in," and "occurs when," to indicate the basis for the organization of the map. The phrases should form a sentence between or among a set of concepts.

Answer
Accept logical presentations by students.

All in One Teaching Resources
- Key Terms Review: *Solids, Liquids, and Gases*
- Connecting Concepts: *Solids, Liquids, and Gases*

Go Online
PHSchool.com
For: Self-Assessment
Visit: PHSchool.com
Web Code: cga-1020

Organizing Information

Comparing and Contrasting Copy the graphic organizer about solids, liquids, and gases onto a separate piece of paper. Complete the table and add a title. (For more on Comparing and Contrasting, see the Skills Handbook.)

State of Matter	Shape	Volume	Example (at room temperature)
a. ___?___	Definite	b. ___?___	Diamond
Liquid	c. ___?___	Definite	d. ___?___
Gas	e. ___?___	Not definite	f. ___?___

Reviewing Key Terms

Choose the letter of the best answer.

1. A substance with a definite volume but no definite shape is a(n)
   a. crystalline solid.
   b. liquid.
   c. gas.
   d. amorphous solid.

2. Unlike solids and liquids, a gas will
   a. keep its volume in different containers.
   b. keep its shape in different containers.
   c. expand to fill the space available to it.
   d. have its volume decrease when the temperature rises.

3. The process in which a gas cools and becomes a liquid is called
   a. evaporation.
   b. sublimation.
   c. boiling.
   d. condensation.

4. According to Boyle's law, the volume of a gas increases when its
   a. pressure increases.
   b. pressure decreases.
   c. temperature falls.
   d. temperature rises.

5. The vertical axis of a graph shows the
   a. responding variable.
   b. manipulated variable.
   c. constant factors.
   d. same variable as the x-axis.

If the statement is true, write *true*. If it is false, change the underlined word or words to make the statement true.

6. Rubber and glass, which become softer as they are heated, are examples of <u>crystalline solids</u>.

7. When you see steam, fog, or clouds, you are seeing water in the <u>liquid</u> state.

8. A substance changes from a solid to a liquid at its <u>boiling point</u>.

9. The <u>volume</u> of a gas is the force of its outward push divided by the area of the walls of the container.

10. According to <u>Boyle's law</u>, the volume of a gas varies invesely with its pressure.

Writing in Science

Explanation Write an introduction to a safety manual for deep-sea divers who use compressed air (scuba) tanks. Explain what air pressure is and what happens to gas molecules when air is compressed.

Discovery CHANNEL SCHOOL
Solids, Liquids, and Gases
Video Preview
Video Field Trip
▶ Video Assessment

Chapter 2 K ◆ 69

Go Online
PHSchool.com
For: Self-Assessment
Visit: PHSchool.com
Web Code: cga-1020

Students can take a practice test online that is automatically scored.

**All in One Teaching Resources**
- Transparency K19
- Chapter Test
- Performance Assessment Teacher Notes
- Performance Assessment Student Worksheet
- Performance Assessment Scoring Rubric

💿 **ExamView® Computer Test Bank CD-ROM**

Compare/Contrast Table
a. Solid
b. Definite
c. Not definite
d. Sample: Water
e. Not definite
f. Sample: Oxygen

Reviewing Key Terms
1. b 2. c 3. d 4. b 5. a
6. amorphous
7. true
8. melting
9. pressure
10. true

Writing in Science

Writing Mode Explanation
Scoring Rubric
4 Exceeds criteria; includes a detailed, accurate explanation of what happens to gas molecules at high pressure and how to use this knowledge to develop safe practices for deep-sea divers
3 Meets criteria
2 Includes a brief explanation and/or contains a few errors or omissions
1 Includes a sketchy explanation with serious errors

Discovery CHANNEL SCHOOL
Video Assessment

Solids, Liquids, and Gases

Show the Video Assessment for review and as a prompt for the writing assignment. Ask: **Why does the regulator on the tank need to adjust the pressure of the air that divers breathe?** (*Divers require more air as water pressure increases. The regulator adjusts the amount of air the diver receives from the tank.*) **What happens to nitrogen gases in the body when the pressure around the body decreases too quickly?** (*Nitrogen molecules leave the tissues too fast, causing bubbles to form in the bloodstream.*)

Checking Concepts

11. Particles in a solid vibrate in place.

12. Both liquids and gases have freely moving particles that can flow from place to place.

13. All liquids flow. However, liquids with high viscosity flow more slowly than liquids with low viscosity.

14. Thermal energy increases from solid to liquid and from liquid to gas.

15. Sample answer: Ice melting is solid to liquid. Water freezing is liquid to solid. Water boiling is liquid to gas. Clouds forming is gas to liquid.

16. Water molecules gain enough energy to become a gas.

17. The gas particles inside the ball are at a higher pressure than the air outside the ball, so they hit the inner surface of the ball more often, reach the hole and escape.

18. The pressure of the gas increases.

Math Practice

19. Pressure $= \dfrac{660\text{N}}{0.20\text{ m}^2} = 3{,}300$ Pa

Thinking Critically

20. Heating the table-tennis ball causes the air inside it to expand and push the dent out of the ball.

21. Through sublimation, the solid turns into a gas as the room freshener's particles escape and mix with the air in the room.

22. The graph will be a curve that slopes downward from left to right, showing that pressure varies inversely with volume.

Review and Assessment

Checking Concepts

11. Describe the motion of particles in a solid.

12. Why are both liquids and gases called fluids?

13. Compare and contrast liquids with high and low viscosities.

14. How is the thermal energy of a substance related to its physical state?

15. Describe four examples of changes in state.

16. What happens to water molecules when water is heated from 90°C to 110°C?

17. What happens to the gas particles when the air in an inflated ball leaks out?

18. How does heating a gas in a rigid container change its pressure?

Math Practice

19. Using Formulas A skier exerts a force of 660 N on the snow. The surface area of the skis contacting the snow is about 0.20 m². What is the pressure in Pa of the skier on the snow?

Thinking Critically

20. Relating Cause and Effect Explain why placing a dented table-tennis ball in boiling water is one way to remove the dent in the ball. (Assume the ball has no holes.)

21. Applying Concepts When you open a solid room air freshener, the solid slowly loses mass and volume. How do you think this happens?

22. Interpreting Data Use the table below that shows the volume and pressure of a gas to predict how a graph of the data would look.

Volume (cm³)	Pressure (kPa)
15	222
21	159
31	108
50	67

Applying Skills

Use the table to answer Questions 23–25.

The data table tells how much mass of a compound dissolves in 100 mL of water as the temperature of the water is increased. Use the data to construct and interpret a graph.

Temperature (°C)	Mass of Compound Dissolved (g)
0	37
10	47
20	56
30	66
40	75

23. Graphing Label each axis of your graph with the appropriate variable, units, and range of values. Then plot the data in a line graph.

24. Interpreting Data What does the graph show about the effect of temperature on the amount of the compound that will dissolve in water?

25. Predicting Assume the amount of the compound dissolved continues to increase as the water is heated. Predict how many grams will dissolve at 50°C.

Lab zone — Chapter **Project**

Performance Assessment If you prepared a cartoon, read the captions to the class and discuss the illustrations. If you prepared a skit, perform the skit in front of the class. After you finish your presentation, invite the class to ask questions about your project. Be prepared to share the decisions you made in creating your presentation.

Lab zone — Chapter **Project**   L3

Performance Assessment Provide time for each group to present its skit or cartoon. Then, invite groups to describe the decisions they made while developing their models. During the presentations, have classmates take notes, comparing and contrasting the depictions of changes of state and record any questions. Afterward, encourage the class to identify ideas from specific cartoons or skits that helped them to better understand changes of state. Then lead a class discussion in which students identify similarities and differences in the depictions of changes of state among different skits and cartoons.

Standardized Test Prep

Test-Taking Tip

Interpreting Line Graphs

A line graph expresses a relationship between two variables. When answering a question related to a line graph, keep the following tips in mind. Read the question carefully. Also, read the title of the graph. It may help you identify what information is given in the graph. Examine the labels on each axis to determine what data are plotted on the graph and identify the scale of each axis. Once you have chosen your answer, check it against the graph.

Sample Question

The graph in Question 3 represents the changes in a 1.0-kg sample of a crystalline solid as it absorbs energy at a constant rate. What is the melting point of the substance?

A 0°C
B 40°C
C 80°C
D 200°C

Answer

The correct answer is **C**. Choice **A** is not shown on the graph. At 40°C **(B)**, the substance is a solid. At 200°C **(D)**, the substance is in the process of changing from a liquid to a gas.

Choose the letter of the best answer.

1. A wet towel is hanging on a clothesline in the sun. The towel dries by the process of

  A boiling.   **B** condensation.
  C evaporation.   **D** sublimation.

2. The pressure of a confined gas equals the force pushing on the surface divided by the area of the surface.

$$\text{Pressure} = \frac{\text{Force}}{\text{Area}}$$

What is the pressure if a force of 1,000 N acts on an area of 5.0 m²?

  F 200 Pa   **G** 500 Pa
  H 2,000 Pa   **J** 5,000 Pa

3. The graph below shows changes in 1 kg of a solid as energy is added.

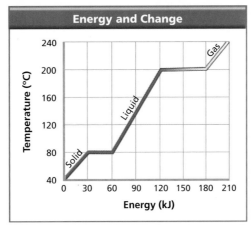

Energy and Change

Based on the graph, what is the total amount of energy absorbed by the substance as it changes from a solid at 40°C to a gas?

  A 30 kJ
  B 60 kJ
  C 120 kJ
  D 180 kJ

4. A gas at constant temperature is confined to a cylinder with a movable piston. The piston is slowly pushed into the cylinder, decreasing the volume of the gas. The pressure increases. What are the variables in this experiment?

  F temperature and time
  G time and volume
  H volume and pressure
  J pressure and temperature

Constructed Response

5. Spray cans filled with gas usually have a warning printed on their labels that say, "Store in a cool place." Explain the danger in storing the can near a source of heat. Describe the motion of the gas molecules in the can when they gain thermal energy.

Applying Skills

23. Graphs will have a straight line pointing up and to the right. Temperature is plotted on the *x*-axis, and the mass of the compound dissolved is plotted on the *y*-axis. The range of values on each axis should be reasonable. For example, on the *x*-axis, the temperature could range from zero to at least 40°C, in increments of 5 or 10. On the *y*-axis, the mass could range from zero to at least 75 or 80 g, in increments of 10 or 15.

24. The warmer the water, the more compound that dissolves in it.

25. About 85 g will dissolve.

Standardized Test Prep

1. C **2.** F **3.** D **4.** H

5. As the gas molecules in the can gain thermal energy, they move faster and hit the sides of the can more frequently and with greater force. The result is an increase in pressure inside the can. As the pressure increases, there is a greater danger that the can will explode.

Chapter at a Glance

PRENTICE HALL
Teacher EXPRESS™
Plan • Teach • Assess

 Chapter Project *Survey Properties of Metals*

All in One Teaching Resources
- Chapter Project Teacher Notes, pp. 164–165
- Chapter Project Student Overview, pp. 166–167
- Chapter Project Student Worksheets, pp. 168–169
- Chapter Project Scoring Rubric, p. 170

Technology

Discovery
CHANNEL
SCHOOL™
Video Preview

Local Standards

Section 1

2 periods
1 block

Introduction to Atoms

K.3.1.1 Describe the structure of an atom.
K.3.1.2 Describe elements in terms of their atoms.
K.3.1.3 Explain how models are useful for understanding atoms.

Go Online
PHSchool.com

Section 2

3 periods
1 1/2 blocks

Organizing the Elements

K.3.2.1 Explain how Mendeleev discovered the pattern that led to the periodic table.
K.3.2.2 Tell what data about elements is found in the periodic table.
K.3.2.3 Describe how the organization of the periodic table is used to predict the properties of elements.

Go Online
active art

Section 3

4–5 periods
2 1/2 blocks

Metals

K.3.3.1 List the physical properties of metals.
K.3.3.2 Explain how the reactivity of metals changes across the periodic table.
K.3.3.3 Explain how the elements that follow uranium are produced.

Go Online
SciLINKS NSTA

Section 4

4 periods
2 blocks

Nonmetals and Metalloids

K.3.4.1 Describe the properties of nonmetals.
K.3.4.2 Tell how metalloids are useful.

Go Online
SciLINKS NSTA

Section 5

1 1/2 periods
1 block

Elements From Stardust

K.3.5.1 Explain how elements are created in stars.
K.3.5.2 Identify the results of fusion in large stars.

Discovery
CHANNEL
SCHOOL™
Video Field Trip

Go Online
SciLINKS NSTA

Review and Assessment

All in One Teaching Resources
- Key Terms Review, p. 212
- Transparency K31
- Performance Assessment Teacher Notes, p. 219
- Performance Assessment Scoring Rubric, p. 220
- Performance Assessment Student Worksheet, p. 221
- Chapter Test, pp. 222–225

Discovery
CHANNEL
SCHOOL™
Video Assessment

Go Online
PHSchool.com

Test Preparation

Test Preparation Blackline Masters

Lab zone Chapter Activities Planner

For more activities

 LAB ZONE
Easy Planner
CD-ROM

Student Edition	Inquiry	Time	Materials	Skills	Resources
Chapter Project, p. 73	Open-Ended	Ongoing (2–3 weeks)	**All in One Teaching Resources** See p. 164	Observing, designing experiments, comparing and contrasting, communicating	**Lab zone Easy Planner** **All in One Teaching Resources** Support pp. 164–165
Section 1					
Discover Activity, p. 74	Guided	10 minutes	Tape, shoe box, an object such as a pencil, empty soda can, sock, marble, sponge	Inferring	**Lab zone Easy Planner**
At-Home Activity, p. 79	Guided	Home		Modeling	**Lab zone Easy Planner**
Section 2					
Discover Activity, p. 80	Guided	15 minutes	Four colors of paper, scissors, pen or pencil, stopwatch or clock with second hand	Inferring	**Lab zone Easy Planner**
Skills Activity, p. 82	Directed	20 minutes	Index cards	Classifying	**Lab zone Easy Planner**
Section 3					
Discover Activity, p. 88	Guided	10 minutes	Aluminum products such as a can, disposable pie plate, heavy-duty foil, foil-covered wrapping paper, and bare aluminum wire	Inferring	**Lab zone Easy Planner**
At-Home Activity, p. 95	Guided	Home		Classifying, applying concepts	**Lab zone Easy Planner**
Consumer Lab, pp. 96–97	Directed	Prep: 15 minutes Class: 30 minutes	1.5-V dry cell battery, 250-mL beaker, stopwatch, flashlight bulb and socket, 3 lengths of insulated wire, thin copper wire with no insulation, 2 graphite samples (lead from a mechanical pencil), hot plate, water	Observing, classifying, controlling variables, drawing conclusions	**Lab zone Easy Planner** **Lab Activity Video** **All in One Teaching Resources** Consumer Lab: *Copper or Carbon? That Is the Question,* pp. 193–194
Section 4					
Discover Activity, p. 98	Guided	5 minutes	Activated charcoal, paper, fork	Classifying	**Lab zone Easy Planner**
Try This Activity, p. 102	Directed	15 minutes	3% hydrogen peroxide solution, manganese dioxide, test tube, wooden splint, matches, safety goggles	Observing	**Lab zone Easy Planner**
At-Home Activity, p. 105	Guided	Home		Classifying, applying concepts	**Lab zone Easy Planner**
Skills Lab, pp. 106–107	Directed	Prep: 5 minutes Class: 30 minutes	Ruler, periodic table from text	Drawing conclusions, classifying, interpreting data, inferring	**Lab zone Easy Planner** **Lab Activity Video** **All in One Teaching Resources** Skills Lab: *Alien Periodic Table,* pp. 203–205
Section 5					
Discover Activity, p. 108	Guided	10 minutes		Developing hypotheses	**Lab zone Easy Planner**

Section 1 Introduction to Atoms

 2 periods, 1 block

ABILITY LEVELS
L1 Basic to Average
L2 For All Students
L3 Average to Advanced

Objectives

K.3.1.1 Describe the structure of an atom.

K.3.1.2 Describe elements in terms of their atoms.

K.3.1.3 Explain how models are useful for understanding atoms.

Key Terms

- nucleus • proton • neutron • electron • atomic number • isotope
- mass number • model

Local Standards

Preteach

Build Background Knowledge

Students learn that atoms make up matter in much the same way as tiny colored dots make up an image.

 Discover Activity *What's in the Box?* L2

Targeted Print and Technology Resources

All in One Teaching Resources

L2 Reading Strategy Transparency K20: Previewing Visuals

⊙ **Presentation-Pro CD-ROM**

Instruct

Structure of an Atom Draw a labeled sketch to use as a prompt for students to answer questions about atomic structure.

Atoms and Elements Use a diagram to show that each element has its own atomic number and atomic structure.

Modeling Atoms Ask leading questions for a discussion on modeling atoms.

Targeted Print and Technology Resources

All in One Teaching Resources

L2 Guided Reading, pp. 173–175
L2 Transparencies K21, K22

PHSchool.com Web Code: cgd-1031

⊙ **Student Edition on Audio CD**

Assess

Section Assessment Questions

Have students use their completed graphic organizers to answer the questions.

Reteach

Students relate matter, elements, atoms, and atomic particles in a concept map.

Targeted Print and Technology Resources

All in One Teaching Resources

- Section Summary, p. 172
L1 Review and Reinforce, p. 176
L3 Enrich, p. 177

Section 2 Organizing the Elements

🕐 *3 periods, 1 1/2 blocks*

Objectives

K.3.2.1 Explain how Mendeleev discovered the pattern that led to the periodic table.

K.3.2.2 Tell what data about elements is found in the periodic table.

K.3.2.3 Describe how the organization of the periodic table is used to predict the properties of elements.

Key Terms

• atomic mass • periodic table • chemical symbol • period • group

Local Standards

Preteach

Build Background Knowledge

Students examine the methods of organizing information organized in various charts.

 **Discover Activity** *Which Is Easier?* L1

Targeted Print and Technology Resources

All in One Teaching Resources

L2 Reading Strategy Transparency K23: Asking Questions

⊙ **Presentation-Pro CD-ROM**

Instruct

Patterns in the Elements Ask leading questions for a discussion about how Mendeleev developed the periodic table.

Finding Data on Elements Use the periodic table to lead a discussion about the kinds of information found in the table.

Organization of the Periodic Table Use the periodic table to help students understand how the organization of the table is useful for predicting the properties of elements.

Targeted Print and Technology Resources

All in One Teaching Resources

L2 Guided Reading, pp. 180–182

L2 Transparencies K24, K25

PHSchool.com Web Code: cgp-1032

⊙ **Student Edition on Audio CD**

Assess

Section Assessment Questions

 Have students use their completed graphic organizers to answer the questions.

Reteach

Have students use the periodic table to find patterns across the periods.

Targeted Print and Technology Resources

All in One Teaching Resources

• Section Summary, p. 179

L1 Review and Reinforce, p. 183

L3 Enrich, p. 184

Section 3 Metals

 4–5 periods, 2 1/2 blocks

ABILITY LEVELS
L1 Basic to Average
L2 For All Students
L3 Average to Advanced

Objectives

K.3.3.1 List the physical properties of metals.

K.3.3.2 Explain how the reactivity of metals changes across the periodic table.

K.3.3.3 Explain how the elements that follow uranium are produced.

Local Standards

Key Terms

• metal • malleable • ductile • reactivity • conductivity • corrosion • alkali metal
• alkaline earth metal • transition metal • alloy • particle accelerator

---

Preteach

Build Background Knowledge

Students list physical properties of metals that they observe.

 **Discover Activity** *Why Use Aluminum?* **L1**

Targeted Print and Technology Resources

All in One Teaching Resources

L2 Reading Strategy Transparency
K26: Using Prior Knowledge

Presentation-Pro CD-ROM

Instruct

Properties of Metals Ask leading questions for a discussion about the physical properties of metals.

Metals in the Periodic Table Develop a table in a discussion about the properties of the different metal groups.

Synthetic Elements Ask leading questions for a discussion about how synthetic elements are made.

 **Consumer Lab** *Copper or Carbon? That Is the Question* **L2**

Targeted Print and Technology Resources

All in One Teaching Resources

L2 Guided Reading, pp. 187–190
L2 Transparency K27
L2 Consumer Lab: *Copper or Carbon: That Is the Question*, pp. 193–194

Lab Activity Video/DVD
Consumer Lab: *Copper or Carbon? That Is the Question*

www.SciLinks.org Web Code: scn-1133

Student Edition on Audio CD

Assess

Section Assessment Questions

 Have students use their completed graphic organizers to answer the questions.

Reteach

Students label a periodic table with the locations and properties of the different metal groups.

Targeted Print and Technology Resources

All in One Teaching Resources

• Section Summary, p. 186
L1 Review and Reinforce, p. 191
L3 Enrich, p. 192

Section 4 Nonmetals and Metalloids

 4 periods, 2 blocks

ABILITY LEVELS
L1 Basic to Average
L2 For All Students
L3 Average to Advanced

Objectives

K.3.4.1 Describe the properties of nonmetals.
K.3.4.2 Tell how metalloids are useful.

Local Standards

Key Terms

• nonmetal • diatomic molecule • halogen • noble gas • metalloid • semiconductor

---

Preteach

Build Background Knowledge

Students describe experiences with chlorine.

 **Discover Activity** *What Are the Properties of Charcoal?* L1

Targeted Print and Technology Resources

 **Teaching Resources**

L2 Reading Strategy Transparency
K28: Using Prior Knowledge

⊙ **Presentation-Pro CD-ROM**

Instruct

Properties of Nonmetals Ask leading questions to contrast the properties of nonmetals and metals.

Families of Nonmetals Develop a table in a discussion about the properties of different nonmetal families.

The Metalloids Lead a discussion about the properties and uses of metalloids.

 Skills Lab *Alien Periodic Table* L2

Targeted Print and Technology Resources

 **Teaching Resources**

L2 Guided Reading, pp. 197–200
L2 Skills Lab: *Alien Periodic Table,* pp. 203–205

📼 **Lab Activity Video/DVD**
Skills Lab: *Alien Periodic Table*

www.SciLinks.org Web Code: scn-1134

⊙ **Student Edition on Audio CD**

Assess

Section Assessment Questions

Have students use their completed graphic organizers to answer the questions.

Reteach

Students make a table to compare the properties of metals and nonmetals.

Targeted Print and Technology Resources

 **Teaching Resources**

• Section Summary, p. 196
L1 Review and Reinforce, p. 201
L3 Enrich, p. 202

Section 5 Elements From Stardust

 *1 1/2 periods, 1 block*

ABILITY LEVELS
L1 Basic to Average
L2 For All Students
L3 Average to Advanced

Objectives

K.3.5.1 Explain how elements are created in stars.
K.3.5.2 Identify the results of fusion in large stars.

Key Terms

• plasma • nuclear fusion • nebula • supernova

Local Standards

Preteach

Build Background Knowledge

Students relate the formation of elements in stars to the synthesis of elements in particle accelerators.

 **Discover Activity** *Can Helium Be Made From Hydrogen?* **L3**

Targeted Print and Technology Resources

All in One Teaching Resources

L2 Reading Strategy Transparency K29: Sequencing

 Presentation-Pro CD-ROM

Instruct

How Elements Form in Stars Lead a discussion about nuclear fusion and the formation of new elements in stars.

Elements From Large Stars Use the definition of supernova to discuss the formation of heavier elements.

Targeted Print and Technology Resources

All in One Teaching Resources

L2 Guided Reading, pp. 208–209
L2 Transparency K30

www.SciLinks.org Web Code: scn-1135

 Student Edition on Audio CD

Assess

Section Assessment Questions

Have students use their completed flowcharts to answer the questions.

Reteach

Students diagram the formation of beryllium from the fusion of two helium atoms.

Targeted Print and Technology Resources

All in One Teaching Resources

• Section Summary, p. 207
L1 Review and Reinforce, p. 210
L3 Enrich, p. 211

Chapter 3 **Content Refresher**

Go Online

NSTA-PD**i**LINKS

For: Professional development support
Visit: www.SciLinks.org/PDLinks
Web Code: scf-1130

Professional Development

Section 1 **Introduction to Atoms**

Theories About Atoms One of the first people known to have thought that matter is made up of small particles was Democritus, a Greek philosopher who lived about 440 B.C. He suggested that matter could be divided in half over and over again until the point at which some particle could not be divided again. He called the smallest piece of matter *atomos,* which is Greek for "indivisible." Democritus did not test his ideas. Few other Greek philosophers of the time accepted Democritus' idea of atoms.

It was not until the early 1800s that the first theory about atoms was proposed. A British schoolteacher named John Dalton proposed the following ideas: atoms could not be broken into smaller pieces; all the atoms of an element are exactly alike; atoms of each element have a unique mass; atoms of different elements are different; and atoms of two or more elements could combine to form compounds. Although Dalton incorrectly envisioned the atom as tiny solid balls, many of his other ideas have continued to stand the test of time.

The first change to Dalton's theory came in 1897, when the English physicist J. J. Thomson discovered electrons. He proposed an atomic model, sometimes referred to as the "plum pudding" model, in which the electrons are scattered throughout the atom. Thomson was the first scientist to suggest that atoms are composed of smaller particles.

Address Misconceptions

Students may confuse the particles that make up elements and the particles that make up atoms. For a strategy for overcoming this misconception, see **Address Misconceptions** in *Introduction to Atoms.*

Thomson's atomic model became obsolete when the research team of another English physicist, Ernest Rutherford, discovered the nucleus in 1911. Rutherford proposed that the atom is mostly empty space and that all the positive charge and almost all the mass are concentrated in a central core of the atom. He called this central core of an atom the nucleus. Rutherford also suggested that an atom might look like a tiny solar system.

While using Rutherford's atomic model, physicists realized that the model did not completely explain their observations of atoms and that atoms did not behave as the model suggested. Two years after Rutherford discovered the nucleus, Niels Bohr, a Danish physicist who studied with Rutherford, theorized that electrons can orbit only at certain distances from the nucleus. His model shows electrons in fixed orbits, or energy levels, at certain distances from the nucleus. Electrons in energy levels farther from the nucleus have higher energy than those closer to the nucleus.

By this time, physicists had also developed mathematical models of the atom, which were used to predict the behavior of atoms. Calculations based on the Bohr model, however, did not agree with experimental data. Many intense debates between experimental physicists and theoretical physicists led to the development of the quantum mechanical model. In this model, the positions of the electrons are represented by an electron cloud around the nucleus. The electrons have certain probabilities of being located in certain places, or orbitals, within the cloud. Experimental evidence over time has made the quantum mechanical model the most accepted model today.

Section 2 Organizing the Elements

The Periodic Table Although the periodic table is organized by increasing atomic number (number of protons), it is the configuration, or arrangement, of electrons that really determines the physical and chemical properties of the elements. Within the electron cloud, electrons have a high probability of being found within specific regions called energy levels. The first energy level is closest to the nucleus. Electrons in this level have the lowest amount of energy. Each energy level can hold a maximum number of electrons, as shown below. This number is calculated by the formula $2n^2$, where n is the energy level. Note that there are seven periods in the periodic table, one for each energy level. The maximum number of electrons found in each of the first four energy levels is shown in the table.

Increasing energy $\longrightarrow$				
Energy Level n	1	2	3	4
Maximum number of electrons	2	8	18	32

With increasing atomic number in Periods 1 and 2, electrons are added to the outermost energy level of the atoms. But starting with Group 3, the outermost level remains at 2 electrons (or sometimes 1) while subsequent electrons are added to inner, unfilled levels. Electrons are again added to the outermost level in Groups 13 through Group 18. This pattern repeats in each period. Thus, the maximum number of *outermost* electrons an atom can have is eight (even if the energy level could otherwise hold more). Atoms with less than this number react with other atoms by gaining, losing, or sharing electrons. Since elements in a group have the same number of outermost electrons in their atoms, they react similarly. The noble gases are unreactive because their atoms already have eight outermost electrons and are stable.

Section 3 Metals

Source of Metallic Properties Most metals are found as solids at room temperature. Like all solids, metal atoms are arranged in very compact and orderly patterns to form crystals. These closely packed atoms are not neutral, however, which causes the physical properties observed in metals.

Metal ions can lose their outermost electrons—known as valence electrons—and form positively charged particles called cations. Metal crystals are actually made up of tightly packed cations surrounded by valence electrons. These valence electrons are mobile and can drift freely from one part of the metal to another. The attraction of the free-floating valence electrons to the metal cations is the force that holds metals together.

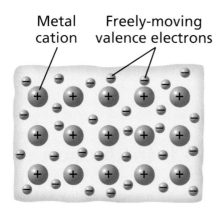

Metal cation   Freely-moving valence electrons

This force of attraction explains many of the physical properties of metals. Metals are good conductors of electricity (which is a flow of electrons) because electrons can flow freely. As electrons enter one end of a metal, an equal number leave the other end. The ductility and malleability of metals can also be explained in terms of mobility of valence electrons. A sea of drifting valence electrons insulates the metal cations from one another. When a metal is subjected to pressure, the metal cations easily slide past one another like ball bearings immersed in oil. This pressure causes the metal to change shape, but not to shatter.

Help Students Read

Anticipation Guide
Stimulating Interest in a Topic

Strategy Engage students in their reading by activating prior knowledge, arousing interest, and helping establish a purpose for reading. Do this by generating a series of statements related to key concepts in the section to which students respond and discuss before reading. Before students read about the periodic table, choose a passage from *Organizing the Elements,* and prepare a set of statements.

Example
1. Create an "anticipation guide" by writing five to ten short, but thought-provoking, declarative statements about the most important concepts in the section. The statements could be in a true-false or an agree-disagree format. If you are aware of any misconceptions, be sure to include statements that address those misconceptions.
2. Before assigning the section to read, display the statements for students to respond to individually or as a class. Discuss students' responses, asking students to support their answers using examples from past experience or prior reading.
3. Then, have students read the section. Encourage them to evaluate the statements from the anticipation guide as they read.
4. After reading, revisit the guide, encouraging students to compare and contrast their prereading responses with their current ones.

See *Organizing the Elements* for a script using the anticipation guide strategy with students.

Section 4 Nonmetals and Metalloids

Allotropes Many nonmetal elements exist naturally in different forms with different physical properties. Different forms of the same element in the same physical state are called allotropes. Some elements that form allotropes include oxygen, sulfur, phosphorus, and carbon.

Allotropes have different physical properties because each form has a different arrangement of atoms. For example, carbon has four allotropes: diamond, graphite, fullerenes, and nanotubes. Three of these allotropes are illustrated below.

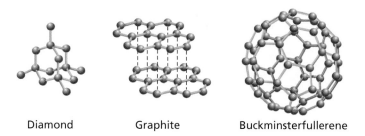

Diamond   Graphite   Buckminsterfullerene

In diamond, each carbon atom is strongly bonded to four other atoms to form a tetrahedron, a pyramid with four three-sided faces. It is very hard because of its rigid, compact structure. Diamond will break, however, if hit just right along the face of the crystal. Diamond forms when carbon crystallizes under tremendous pressure.

In graphite, the carbon atoms are arranged in widely spaced sheets of hexagon-shaped rings. Weak bonds (van der Waals forces) hold the sheets together, but allow the layers to slide over one another. This makes graphite a soft, greasy-feeling material. Graphite is also a fairly good conductor of heat and electricity because free electrons move along the layers of the crystal, similar to crystals of metals.

In fullerenes, distinct molecules form the unit of the crystal. The molecules are held together by weak van der Waals forces and are arranged in a pattern. One fullerene, known as buckminsterfullerene, looks like a soccer ball. This hollow sphere shape gives the molecule great strength and rigidity. Buckminsterfullerene is found in soot.

Nanotubes are hollow cylinders formed as if sheets of graphite were rolled into tubes. Some nanotubes have caps on their ends that are similar to segments of a fullerene. Nanotube technology is a growing field of research.

Section 5 Elements From Stardust

Using Nuclear Fusion to Make Energy When two atomic nuclei collide and fuse, not only is a larger nucleus formed, but a large amount of energy is released. In stars, this energy is released in the form of heat, light, and other forms of electromagnetic radiation. Nuclear fusion in the sun releases massive amounts of energy that "powers" life on Earth.

Scientists have long wanted to control nuclear fusion and use it as an energy source to produce electricity. Nuclear fusion has many advantages. The potential fuels are inexpensive and readily available. The products of fusion are usually not radioactive, as are the products of nuclear fission. (Nuclear fission is the reaction currently used in nuclear power plants. Large nuclei are hit with neutrons, causing them to split into smaller particles.)

The problems with fusion lie in achieving the high temperatures required to start the reaction, containing the reaction once it has started, and keeping the process sustainable. It is like trying to tuck the sun inside a processing plant. The high temperatures required to initiate fusion have been achieved by using a fission bomb. This process, however, is not useful as a controlled generator of power.

At the very high temperatures involved in fusion, matter exists as plasma. In the plasma state, matter exists as ions in a gaslike form. No known structural material can contain hot, corrosive plasma. Strong magnetic fields have been shown to contain plasmas, but they often leak.

Finally, there is the problem of keeping the reaction going once it has started. Plasma cools very quickly. No one has yet managed to generate a stable fusion reaction in which the reaction generates more energy than it requires to keep it going.

ⓘnteractive Textbook
- Complete student edition
- Video and audio
- Simulations and activities
- Section and chapter activities

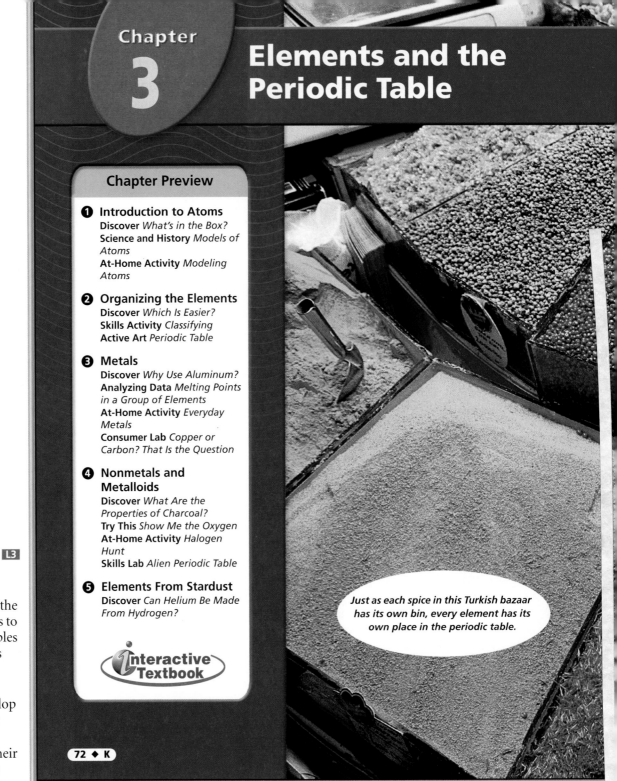

Chapter 3

Elements and the Periodic Table

Chapter Preview

ⓘnteractive Textbook

Just as each spice in this Turkish bazaar has its own bin, every element has its own place in the periodic table.

Lab zone Chapter **Project**   L3

Objectives
Students will apply what they learn about the periodic table and the properties of metals to compare their observations of metal samples to their predictions. After completing this Chapter Project, students will be able to
- observe properties of metals
- design experiments in which they develop hypotheses, control variables, interpret data, and draw conclusions
- compare and contrast their results to their predictions based on the periodic table
- communicate their findings to classmates

Skills Focus
Observing, designing experiments, comparing and contrasting, communicating

Project Time Line 2 to 3 weeks

All in One Teaching Resources
- Chapter Project Teacher Notes
- Chapter Project Worksheet 1
- Chapter Project Worksheet 2
- Chapter Project Scoring Rubric

Developing a Plan
On the first day, discuss what the students know about metals and distribute samples for students to observe. Allow a week for students to find information about their metals from the periodic table and to design experiments to test the physical and chemical properties of their metals. Make sure you review each experimental plan before students begin testing. Then students can perform their tests during the second week and prepare their presentations. Tell students to make repeated trials to get reliable results. On the final day, students can present their results.

Possible Materials
Obtain pure elemental metals such as copper rods or wires, aluminum rods or sheets, iron nails, silver wire, platinum wire, gold wire, and magnesium ribbon from hardware stores, chemical supply companies, or jewelry supply companies. Also, provide students with magnets, hot plates,

DISCOVERY CHANNEL **SCHOOL™**
Video Preview

Elements and the Periodic Table
▶ Video Preview
Video Field Trip
Video Assessment

Elements and the Periodic Table

Show the Video Preview to introduce the chapter and provide an overview of chapter content. Discussion question: **What is the process that fuses hydrogen to form helium?** *(Nuclear fusion)*

Lab zone™ Chapter **Project**

Survey Properties of Metals

Chemists have a system for organizing the elements. There are more than 100 elements, and as you will learn in this chapter, about 80 of them are classified as metals. In this project, you will examine more closely the physical and chemical properties of metals.

Your Goal To survey the properties of several samples of metallic elements

To complete the project, you must

● interpret what the periodic table tells you about your samples

● design and conduct experiments that will allow you to test at least three properties of your metals

● compare and contrast the properties of your sample metals

● follow the safety guidelines in Appendix A

Plan It! Study the periodic table in Section 2 to determine which elements are metals. Brainstorm with your classmates about the properties of metals. What properties allow you to recognize a metal? How do you think metals differ from nonmetals? Your teacher will assign samples of metals to your group. You will be observing their properties in this project.

Chapter 3 K ◆ 73

conductivity testers, thermometers, batteries, light bulbs, and weak acids for students to use for testing the metals.

Possible Shortcuts

To save time, have students work in small groups.

Launching the Project

Display a metal and a nonmetal and encourage students to compare and contrast their visible properties. Then, conduct a brief test of heat and electrical conductivity. Discuss experimental design and the value of distinguishing between the properties of metals as a group and the properties that distinguish individual metals from each other. Remind students that you must approve all experimental designs before they begin.

Performance Assessment

The Chapter Project Scoring Rubric will help you evaluate how well students complete the Chapter Project. You may want to share the scoring rubric with your students so that they will know what is expected. Students will be assessed on

● how well they use the periodic table to gain information about their metals

● their observations and how well they describe and compare the properties of each metal

● the thoroughness and organization of their experimental design for testing the metals

● the completeness and clarity of their presentations

Students can keep their experimental designs and presentation notes in their portfolios.

Portfolio

Introduction to Atoms

Objectives

After this lesson, students will be able to

K.3.1.1 Describe the structure of an atom.

K.3.1.2 Describe elements in terms of their atoms.

K.3.1.3 Explain how models are useful for understanding atoms.

Target Reading Skill

Previewing Visuals Explain that looking at the visuals before they read helps students activate prior knowledge and predict what they are about to read.

Answers

Sample questions and answers: **What particles are in the center of an atom?** (*Protons and neutrons*) **What particles move around the outside of the nucleus?** (*Electrons*)

All in One Teaching Resources

• Transparency K20

Preteach

Build Background Knowledge   L2

Parts Make Up the Whole

Distribute hand lenses and sections from the Sunday newspaper comics. Have students examine the comics with the hand lenses and describe what they see. Ask: **How do the Sunday comics compare to the painting in Figure 1?** (*Both are made up of tiny dots of color.*) Explain that like these images, matter is made of tiny parts called atoms.

Introduction to Atoms

Reading Preview

Key Concepts

• What is the structure of an atom?
• How are elements described in terms of their atoms?
• Why are models useful for understanding atoms?

Key Terms

• nucleus • proton
• neutron • electron
• atomic number • isotope
• mass number • model

Target Reading Skill

Previewing Visuals Before you read, preview Figure 2. Then write two questions you have about the diagram in a graphic organizer like the one below. As you read, answer your questions.

Structure of an Atom

Q. What particles are in the center of an atom?
A.
Q.

Lab zone | Discover Activity

What's in the Box?

1. Your teacher will give you a sealed box that contains an object. Without opening the box, move the box around to find out as much as you can about the object.

2. Make a list of your observations about the object. For example, does the object slide or roll? Is it heavy or light? Is it soft or hard? Is the object round or flat?

3. Think about familiar objects that could give you clues about what's inside the box.

Think It Over

Inferring Make a sketch showing what you think the object looks like. Tell how you inferred the properties of the object from indirect observations.

Glance at the painting below and you see people enjoying an afternoon in the park. Now look closely at the circled detail of the painting. There you'll discover that the artist used thousands of small spots of color to create these images of people and the park.

Are you surprised that such a rich painting can be created from lots of small spots? Matter is like that, too. The properties of matter that you can observe result from the properties of tiny objects that you cannot see. As you learned in Chapter 1, the tiny objects that make up all matter are atoms.

FIGURE 1

Sunday Afternoon on the Island of La Grande Jatte
This painting by artist Georges Seurat, which is made from tiny dots of paint, gives you a simple model for thinking about how matter is made of atoms.

Lab zone | Discover Activity

Skills Focus Inferring   L2

Materials tape, shoe box, an object such as a pencil, empty soda can, sock, marble, or sponge

Time 10 minutes

Tips Have students bring shoe boxes from home. Place a different object in each shoebox and securely tape it closed. Emphasize that students are making

indirect observations and may not draw precise conclusions.

Think It Over Students' sketches should be consistent with their observations, but may not be correct. Students should explain how their indirect observations led them to identify certain properties of the object. For example, a round object will roll and a soft object will make less sound when hitting the sides of the box.

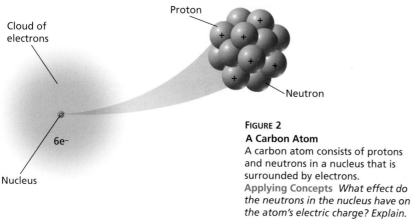

Cloud of electrons

Proton

6e⁻

Nucleus

Neutron

FIGURE 2
A Carbon Atom
A carbon atom consists of protons and neutrons in a nucleus that is surrounded by electrons.
Applying Concepts *What effect do the neutrons in the nucleus have on the atom's electric charge? Explain.*

Structure of an Atom

If you could look into a single atom, what might you see? Figuring out what atoms are made of hasn't been easy. Theories about their shape and structure have changed many times and continue to be improved even now. Until about 100 years ago, scientists thought atoms were the smallest particles of matter. Now, scientists know more. **Atoms are made of even smaller particles called protons, neutrons, and electrons.** Understanding the structure of atoms will help you understand the properties of matter.

Particles in Atoms An atom consists of a nucleus surrounded by one or more electrons. The **nucleus** (NOO klee us) (plural *nuclei*) is the very small center core of an atom. The nucleus is a group of smaller particles called protons and neutrons. **Protons** have a positive electric charge (indicated by a plus symbol, +). **Neutrons** have no charge. They are neutral. The third type of particle in an atom moves in the space outside the nucleus. **Electrons** move rapidly around the nucleus and have a negative electric charge. An electron is shown by the symbol e⁻.

Look at the model of a carbon atom in Figure 2. If you count the number of protons and electrons, you'll see there are six of each. In an atom, the number of protons equals the number of electrons. As a result, the positive charge from the protons equals the negative charge from the electrons. The charges balance, making the atom neutral.

 Reading Checkpoint What kind of charge does a proton have?

Go Online
PHSchool.com

For: More on atoms
Visit: PHSchool.com
Web Code: cgd-1031

Differentiated Instruction

English Learners/Beginning L1
Vocabulary: Link to Visual Point to each label in Figure 2 and pronounce each word, including *atom*. Invite students to repeat each word. Give students cards with one word from the diagram on each. Cover the words in the diagram and have students match the word cards to the diagram. Correct pronunciations as needed.
learning modality: visual

English Learners/Intermediate L2
Vocabulary: Link to Visual Have students do the activity described at left without word cards. Also, add the words *positive charge, negative charge,* and *no charge* and have students match the particle to its charge. **learning modality: visual**

Instruct

Structure of an Atom

Teach Key Concepts L2
Parts of an Atom

Focus Explain that all matter is made up of small particles called atoms.

Teach Diagram an atom on the board. Label the nucleus and electron cloud. Ask: **What particles of an atom are found in the nucleus?** *(Protons and neutrons)* **Where are electrons found?** *(In a cloud around the nucleus)* Add the symbols for the particles.

Apply Point out that protons have a positive electric charge, electrons are negative, and neutrons are neutral. Ask: **Why is the carbon atom in Figure 2 neutral?** *(The equal number of protons and electrons causes the positive and negative charges to cancel each other out.)* **learning modality: visual**

All in One Teaching Resources
• Transparency K21

Help Students Read L1
Vocabulary: Word Origin Explain that *atom* comes from the Greek word *atomos,* meaning "indivisible." Ask: **How is being indivisible related to the smallest unit of matter?** *(The atom is the smallest particle that matter can be broken into.)*

Go Online
PHSchool.com

For: More on atoms
Visit: PHSchool.com
Web Code: cgd-1031

Students can review atoms in an online activity.

Independent Practice L2

All in One Teaching Resources
• Guided Reading and Study Worksheet: *Introduction to Atoms*

 **Student Edition on Audio CD**

Monitor Progress _____ L2

Drawing Invite students to draw and label a diagram of an atom.

Students can save their diagrams in their portfolios. **Portfolio**

Answers
Figure 2 None; neutrons have no charge.

 Reading Checkpoint A proton has a positive charge.

Modeling Atomic Structure

Materials apron, beads in two colors, glue, disposable gloves, newspapers, large sheet of plain paper, tape, old toothbrush, water in disposable container, watercolor paint

Time 15 minutes

Focus Ask: **Can you see an atom?** *(No, atoms are too small.)* **Why is it useful to model an atom?** *(Sample answer: To learn about its structure and properties)*

Teach Students can choose different-colored beads for the protons and neutrons. Have students glue these in the center of the paper for the nucleus. Students may choose as many protons and neutrons as they wish. Students can model the electron cloud by dipping the toothbrush in paint and flicking the bristles over the top of the paper in a large circle around the nucleus. (Tape newspapers to the work surface.)

Apply Ask: **If your atom is neutral, how many electrons does it have?** *(The same number as the number of protons)* **Why are the electrons shown as a cloud?** *(The electrons move all the time and may be anywhere within the space shown by the cloud.)* **learning modality: kinesthetic**

Lab zone **Build Inquiry**   L2

Making Analogies About Atomic Particles

Time 15 minutes

Focus Tell students that an analogy makes an abstract idea easier to understand.

Teach Ask: **Which is easier to understand—the mass of an elephant compared to the mass of a cat or saying that a proton has 2,000 times more mass than an electron?** *(The elephant and the cat)* Explain that, like the proton, the elephant (about 8,000 kg) has 2,000 times more mass than the cat (about 4 kg). Challenge student groups to develop their own analogies.

Apply Ask: **Does your analogy also reflect the larger volume held by the electrons?** (In most student analogies, the larger mass will also have the larger volume.) Challenge students to develop an analogy to compare the volumes of the nucleus and electron cloud. **learning modality: logical/ mathematical**

A Cloud of Electrons Electrons move within a sphere-shaped region surrounding the nucleus. Scientists depict this region as a cloud of negative charge because electrons may be anywhere within it. Electrons with lower energy usually move in the space near the atom's nucleus. Electrons with higher energy move within the space farther from the nucleus.

Most of an atom's volume is the space in which electrons move. That space is huge compared to the space taken up by the nucleus. To picture the difference, imagine holding a pencil while standing at the pitcher's mound in a baseball stadium. If the nucleus were the size of the pencil's eraser, the electrons could be as far away as the top row of seats!

Science and **History**

Models of Atoms

For over two centuries, scientists have created models of atoms in an effort to understand why matter behaves as it does. As scientists have learned more, the model of the atom has changed.

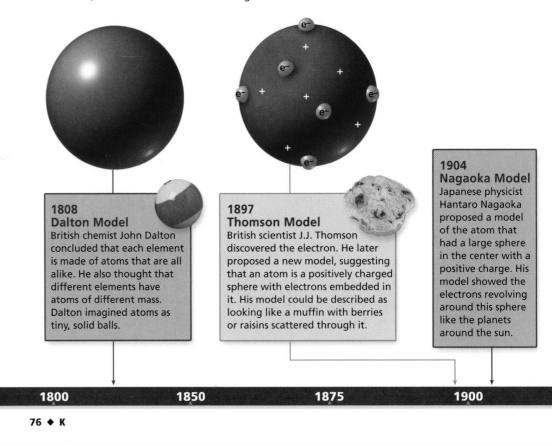

1808
Dalton Model
British chemist John Dalton concluded that each element is made of atoms that are all alike. He also thought that different elements have atoms of different mass. Dalton imagined atoms as tiny, solid balls.

1897
Thomson Model
British scientist J.J. Thomson discovered the electron. He later proposed a new model, suggesting that an atom is a positively charged sphere with electrons embedded in it. His model could be described as looking like a muffin with berries or raisins scattered through it.

1904
Nagaoka Model
Japanese physicist Hantaro Nagaoka proposed a model of the atom that had a large sphere in the center with a positive charge. His model showed the electrons revolving around this sphere like the planets around the sun.

| 1800 | 1850 | 1875 | 1900 |

76 ◆ K

Background

Facts and Figures Chemistry books often show electrons as they are in Bohr's atomic model, because the grouping of electrons in orbital shells helps explain the reactivity of atoms. It is the electrons in the outer shell of the atom that are gained, lost, or shared when an atom of one element reacts with the atom of another element. Using the Bohr model helps chemists describe the formation of chemical bonds.

The current atomic model is very similar to the one proposed in the 1920s. The refinements of the model have affected the structure of the nucleus. Subatomic particles, called quarks, make up protons and neutrons. The force that holds these subatomic particles together comes from other particles called gluons.

Comparing Particle Masses Although electrons occupy most of an atom's volume, they don't account for much of its mass. It takes almost 2,000 electrons to equal the mass of just one proton. On the other hand, a proton and a neutron are about equal in mass. Together, the protons and neutrons make up nearly all the mass of an atom.

Atoms are too small to be measured in everyday units of mass, such as grams or kilograms. Instead, scientists use units known as atomic mass units (amu). A proton or a neutron has a mass equal to about one amu. The mass of an electron is about 1/2,000 amu.

Writing in Science

Research and Write Find out more about one of the scientists who worked on models of the atom. Write an imaginary interview with this person in which you discuss his work with him.

Science and History

Focus Tell students that the first atomic model was proposed almost 200 years ago. A few years before this, in 1806, Lewis and Clark returned from exploring the Louisiana Territory. Also point out that the existence of neutrons was not discovered until the era of the Great Depression, a few years before World War II.

Teach Invite students to compare and contrast the atomic models diagrammed in the timeline. Ask: **What was one of the first theories about atomic structure that has stood the test of time?** (*Sample answer: The positive charge is located in the center of the atom.*) **How has the position of electrons changed over time?** (*Sample answer: The electrons moved from being embedded in the sphere to moving randomly about the nucleus to moving in specific layers to being impossible to locate at any given time.*)

Writing in Science

Writing Mode Research

Scoring Rubric

4 Exceeds criteria; includes a lively and imaginative interview with insightful questions and accurate and complete answers that reflect the life of the scientist

3 Meets criteria

2 Includes only brief but accurate information

1 Includes some incorrect and/or incomplete information

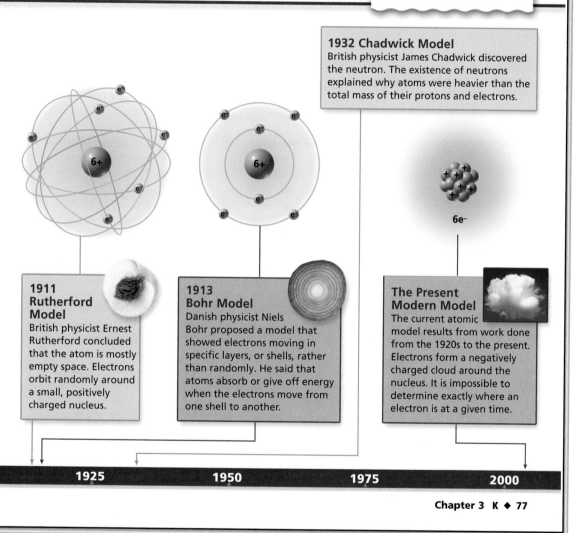

1932 Chadwick Model
British physicist James Chadwick discovered the neutron. The existence of neutrons explained why atoms were heavier than the total mass of their protons and electrons.

6+

6+

6e-

1911 Rutherford Model
British physicist Ernest Rutherford concluded that the atom is mostly empty space. Electrons orbit randomly around a small, positively charged nucleus.

1913 Bohr Model
Danish physicist Niels Bohr proposed a model that showed electrons moving in specific layers, or shells, rather than randomly. He said that atoms absorb or give off energy when the electrons move from one shell to another.

The Present Modern Model
The current atomic model results from work done from the 1920s to the present. Electrons form a negatively charged cloud around the nucleus. It is impossible to determine exactly where an electron is at a given time.

1925   1950   1975   2000

Differentiated Instruction

Special Needs   **L1**

Classifying Atomic Particles Give students two types of balls that differ in mass but are similar in size, such as marbles and foam balls. Invite students to choose a ball to represent a proton. Repeat for a neutron and an electron. (The heavier balls would be protons and neutrons; lighter ones, electrons.) **learning modality: kinesthetic**

Gifted and Talented   **L3**

Researching Quarks Tell students that protons and neutrons are made up of even smaller particles called quarks. Encourage students to use Internet sources to find out about these subatomic particles. Students can prepare a poster to share what they learned with the class. **learning modality: logical/mathematical**

Monitor Progress   **L2**

Skills Check Have students develop a table in which they compare and contrast the mass and volume of protons, neutrons, and electrons.

Atoms and Elements

Teach Key Concepts L2
Atoms Are Specific to Elements

Focus Remind students that an element is a pure substance.

Teach Explain that each element is made of atoms that are different from the atoms of other elements. Ask: **How do atoms of one element differ from those of another element?** *(In their number of protons)* Diagram the atomic nuclei of three different elements. Have students count the number of protons in each. Explain that the number of protons is the element's atomic number.

Apply Ask: **What does mass number equal?** *(The sum of protons and neutrons)* **learning modality: visual**

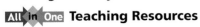 **Teaching Resources**
• Transparency K22

Address Misconceptions L2
Many Different Particles

Focus Students may confuse the particles that make up elements and the particles that make up atoms.

Teach Remind students that elements are a kind of matter. Ask: **What are the particles that make up elements and compounds?** *(Atoms)* Point out that an atom is the smallest particle of an element. Ask: **What particles make up an atom?** *(Protons, neutrons, and electrons)*

Apply Ask: **What would happen if protons were added to an atom?** *(The atom becomes a different element.)* **learning modality: verbal**

Modeling Atoms

Teach Key Concepts L2
Usefulness of Scientific Models

Focus Ask: **How can you guess what is inside a sealed box?** *(Sample answer: By making observations that don't depend on seeing what's inside the box)*

Teach Ask: **Why is it difficult for scientists to study atoms?** *(Atoms are too small to be seen, even by powerful microscopes.)* **Why is it helpful for scientists to use models to study atoms?** *(Scientists make predictions and test the models to see if the atoms behave as predicted.)*

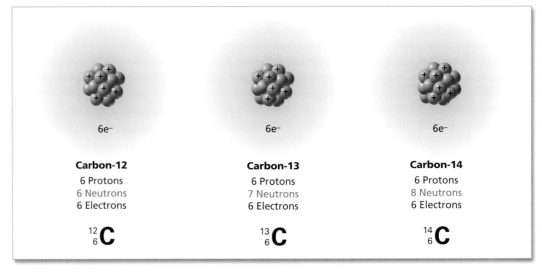

FIGURE 3
Isotopes
Atoms of all isotopes of carbon contain 6 protons, but they differ in their number of neutrons. Carbon-12 is the most common isotope. **Interpreting Diagrams** *Which isotope of carbon has the largest mass number?*

Atoms and Elements

Each element consists of atoms that differ from the atoms of all other elements. **An element can be identified by the number of protons in the nucleus of its atoms.**

Atomic Number Every atom of an element has the same number of protons. For example, the nucleus of every carbon atom contains 6 protons. Every oxygen atom has 8 protons, and every iron atom has 26 protons. Each element has a unique **atomic number**—the number of protons in its nucleus. Carbon's atomic number is 6, oxygen's is 8, and iron's is 26.

Isotopes Although all atoms of an element have the same number of protons, their number of neutrons can vary. Atoms with the same number of protons and a different number of neutrons are called **isotopes** (EYE suh tohps). Three isotopes of carbon are illustrated in Figure 3. Each carbon atom has 6 protons, but you can see that the number of neutrons is 6, 7, or 8.

An isotope is identified by its **mass number,** which is the sum of the protons and neutrons in the nucleus of an atom. The most common isotope of carbon has a mass number of 12 (6 protons + 6 neutrons) and may be written as "carbon-12." Two other isotopes are carbon-13 and carbon-14. As shown in Figure 3, a symbol with the mass number above and the atomic number below may also be used to represent an isotope. Although these carbon atoms have different mass numbers, all carbon atoms react the same way chemically.

Apply Ask: **Once scientists develop a model, can they change it?** *(Yes, as they get more observations from testing)* **learning modality: verbal**

Modeling Atoms

Atoms are hard to study because they are amazingly small. The smallest visible speck of dust may contain 10 million billion atoms! Even a sheet of paper is about 10,000 atoms thick. Powerful microscopes can give a glimpse of atoms, such as the one shown in Figure 4. But they do not show the structure of atoms or how they might work.

Because atoms are so small, scientists create models to describe them. In science, a **model** may be a diagram, a mental picture, a mathematical statement, or an object that helps explain ideas about the natural world. Scientists use models to study objects and events that are too small, too large, too slow, too fast, too dangerous, or too far away to see. These models are used to make and test predictions. For example, you may know that engineers use crash-test dummies to test the safety of new car designs. The dummies serve as models for live human beings. In chemistry, models of atoms are used to explain how matter behaves. The modern atomic model explains why most elements react with other elements, while a few elements hardly react at all.

FIGURE 4
Imaging Atoms
This image was made by a scanning tunneling microscope. It shows a zigzag chain of cesium atoms (red) on a background of gallium and arsenic atoms (blue). The colors were added to the image.

 Reading Checkpoint What are three types of situations for which models can be useful?

Section 1 Assessment

 **Target Reading Skill** Previewing Visuals Compare your questions and answers about Figure 2 with those of a partner.

Reviewing Key Concepts

1. **a. Reviewing** What are the three main particles in an atom?
   b. Comparing and Contrasting How do the particles of an atom differ in electric charge?
   c. Relating Cause and Effect Why do atoms have no electric charge even though most of their particles have charges?

2. **a. Defining** What is the atomic number of an element?
   b. Explaining How can atomic numbers be used to distinguish one element from another?
   c. Applying Concepts The atomic number of the isotope nitrogen-15 is 7. How many protons, neutrons, and electrons make up an atom of nitrogen-15?

3. **a. Reviewing** What is the main reason that scientists use models to study atoms?
   b. Making Generalizations What kind of information do scientists seek when using models to study atoms?

Lab zone At-Home **Activity**

Modeling Atoms Build a three-dimensional model of an atom to show to your family. The model could be made of beads, cotton, small candies, clay, plastic foam, and other simple materials. Describe how the mass of the nucleus compares to the mass of the electrons. Explain what makes atoms of different elements different from one another. Emphasize that everything in your home is made of atoms in different combinations.

Lab zone At-Home **Activity**

Modeling Atoms [L2] Consider displaying several three-dimensional atomic models made of household materials to give students some ideas. Students might explain that the mass of the nucleus makes up nearly the entire mass of the atom and that atoms of different elements have different numbers of protons.

Monitor Progress [L2]

Answers
Figure 3 Carbon-14

Reading Checkpoint Sample answer: When objects or events are too small, too large, too slow, too fast, too dangerous, or too far away to see.

Assess

Reviewing Key Concepts

1. **a.** Protons, neutrons, and electrons
b. Proton—positive charge; neutron—no charge; electron—negative charge **c.** Each atom has equal numbers of positively charged protons and negatively charged electrons.
2. **a.** The number of protons in each atom of that element **b.** Each element has a unique atomic number because all atoms of that element have the same number of protons. **c.** Each atom of nitrogen-15 contains 7 protons, 8 neutrons, and 7 electrons.
3. **a.** Atoms are too small to be seen. **b.** To describe the structure of atoms and explain how matter behaves

Reteach [L1]

Help students draw a concept map that shows elements as types of matter and the atom as the smallest particle of an element. Also show that atoms are composed of protons and neutrons in a nucleus with electrons in an electron cloud.

Performance Assessment [L2]

Writing Have students write a description of the model used to describe atoms. Also have them describe why scientists use this model.

All in One Teaching Resources

- Section Summary: *Introduction to Atoms*
- Review and Reinforce: *Introduction to Atoms*
- Enrich: *Introduction to Atoms*

Objectives
After this lesson, students will be able to
K.3.2.1 Explain how Mendeleev discovered the pattern that led to the periodic table.
K.3.2.2 Tell what data about elements is found in the periodic table.
K.3.2.3 Describe how the organization of the periodic table is used to predict the properties of elements.

Target Reading Skill 🔄
Asking Questions Explain that changing a head into a question helps students anticipate the ideas, facts, and events they are about to read.

Answers
Sample questions and answers: **What pattern of elements did Mendeleev discover?** *(Patterns appeared when the elements were arranged in order of increasing atomic mass.)* **What data about elements is found in the periodic table?** *(Atomic number, chemical symbols and names, and average atomic mass)* **How are elements organized in the periodic table?** *(Elements are organized in periods and groups based on their properties.)*

All in One Teaching Resources
• Transparency K23

Preteach

Build Background Knowledge ▫L2▫

Methods of Organizing Information
Display a variety of charts showing systems of organization. Useful examples include a weekly calendar showing a class schedule, a calendar showing the months in a year, and a multiplication table. Have students describe the elements in a row and a column of each chart. Invite them to share other ways to organize information.

Section

2

Organizing the Elements

Reading Preview

Key Concepts
• How did Mendeleev discover the pattern that led to the periodic table?
• What data about elements is found in the periodic table?
• How is the organization of the periodic table useful for predicting the properties of elements?

Key Terms
• atomic mass • periodic table
• chemical symbol • period
• group

🔄 Target Reading Skill
Asking Questions Before you read, preview the red headings. In a graphic organizer like the one below, ask a *what* or *how* question for each heading. As you read, write the answers to your questions.

Patterns in the Elements

Question	Answer
What pattern of elements did Mendeleev discover?	Patterns appeared when . . .

🔺 Lab zone — Discover **Activity**

Which Is Easier?
1. Make 4 sets of 10 paper squares, using a different color for each set. Number the squares in each set from 1 through 10.
2. Place all of the squares on a flat surface, numbered side up. Don't arrange them in order.
3. Ask your partner to name a square by color and number. Have your partner time how long it takes you to find this square.
4. Repeat Step 3 twice, choosing different squares each time. Calculate the average value of the three times.
5. Rearrange the squares into four rows, one for each color. Order the squares in each row from 1 to 10.
6. Repeat Step 3 three times. Calculate an average time.
7. Trade places with your partner and repeat Steps 2 through 6.

Think It Over
Inferring Which average time was shorter, the one produced in Step 4 or Step 6? Why do you think the times were different?

You wake up, jump out of bed, and start to get dressed for school. Then you ask yourself a question: Is there school today? To find out, you check the calendar. There's no school today because it's Saturday.

The calendar arranges the days of the month into horizontal periods called weeks and vertical groups called days of the week. This arrangement follows a repeating pattern that makes it easy to keep track of which day it is. The chemical elements can also be organized into something like a calendar. The name of the "chemists' calendar" is the periodic table.

◀ A calendar organizes the days of the week into a useful, repeating pattern.

🔺 Lab zone — Discover **Activity**

Skills Focus Inferring ▫L1▫

Materials four colors of paper, scissors, pen or pencil, stopwatch or clock with second hand

Time 15 minutes

Tips Have students mix up the squares before they begin the first trial. Review how to calculate an average.

Expected Outcome It will take less time for students to locate squares in an ordered pattern.

Think It Over Average times will be shorter for Step 6. Sample answer: It takes much longer to find a numbered square when the squares are not in any order.

Patterns in the Elements

By 1869, a total of 63 elements had been discovered. These elements had a wide variety of properties. A few were gases. Two were liquids. Most were solid metals. Some reacted explosively as they formed compounds. Others reacted more slowly. Scientists wondered if the properties of elements followed any sort of pattern. A Russian scientist, Dmitri Mendeleev (men duh LAY ef), discovered a set of patterns that applied to all the elements.

Mendeleev's Work Mendeleev knew that some elements have similar chemical and physical properties. For example, both fluorine and chlorine are gases that irritate the lungs and form similar compounds. Silver and copper, shown in Figure 5, are both shiny metals that tarnish if exposed to air. Mendeleev thought these similarities were important clues to a hidden pattern.

To try to find that pattern, Mendeleev wrote each element's melting point (M.P.), density, and color on individual cards. He also included the element's atomic mass and the number of chemical bonds it could form. The **atomic mass** of an element is the average mass of all the isotopes of that element. Mendeleev tried various arrangements of cards. **He noticed that a pattern of properties appeared when he arranged the elements in order of increasing atomic mass.**

Mendeleev's Periodic Table Mendeleev found that the properties of elements repeated. After fluorine (F), for instance, the next heaviest element he knew was sodium (Na). (Neon had not yet been discovered.) Sodium reacted with water the same way that lithium (Li) and potassium (K) did. So he placed the cards for these elements into a group. He did the same with other similar elements.

FIGURE 5
Metals That Tarnish
A copper weather vane and a silver spoon both tarnish from contact with air.

Cu
Tarnishes
M.P. 1,085°C
Mass 63 amu

Ag
Tarnishes
M.P. 962°C
Mass 108 amu

FIGURE 6
Metals That React With Water
Lithium and sodium both react with water. *Interpreting Photographs* *Which metal reacts more vigorously with water?*

Na
Reacts with water
M.P. 98°C
Mass 23 amu

Li
Reacts with water
M.P. 180°C
Mass 7 amu

Instruct

Patterns in the Elements

Teach Key Concepts   L2
Mendeleev Found Patterns

Focus Tell students that before Mendeleev's work, scientists wondered if the properties of elements followed any patterns.

Teach Ask: **What information did Mendeleev use to try to find a pattern in the elements?** (*Melting point, density, color, atomic mass, and number of chemical bonds*) **When did Mendeleev notice a pattern?** (*When he arranged the elements in order of increasing atomic mass*)

Apply Ask: **Why was Mendeleev able to predict the properties of elements that had not yet been discovered?** (*Because the properties of the elements repeated*) **learning modality: verbal**

Independent Practice   L2

All in One Teaching Resources

• Guided Reading and Study Worksheet: *Organizing the Elements*

⊙ **Student Edition on Audio CD**

Differentiated Instruction

Less Proficient Readers   L1
Building Vocabulary Before students read the section, encourage them to preview the definitions of the key terms. Have students compare the meanings of *atomic mass* (the average mass of all the isotopes of that element), *mass number* (sum of protons and neutrons), and *atomic number* (the number of protons in an atom). Review the meaning of *isotope* (atoms with the same number of protons

and different number of neutrons) and relate it to atomic mass. Instruct students to create a table to record these words, as well as the remaining key terms, with written definitions. Encourage students to refer to this table while reading this section to help them discern meaning. Instruct them to add other unfamiliar words from the reading. Then, help them write definitions for these words. **learning modality: verbal**

Monitor Progress   L2

Writing Have students list properties of elements that Mendeleev used when he looked for patterns in the elements.

Answer
Figure 6 Sodium

Build Inquiry

L2

Predicting From Patterns

Materials 3-year calendar

Time 5 minutes

Focus Ask: **How do patterns help you make predictions?** *(Sample answer: A pattern has information that repeats.)*

Teach Display a calendar with two consecutive years. Invite students to find the day of the week on which their birthday falls in the first year and in the second year. Then challenge them to predict what day of the week their birthday will be in the third year. *(The date will fall one day later each year, except during a leap year, when the dates after February 29 fall two days later.)*

Apply Encourage students to describe how their method of making a prediction is similar to Mendeleev's method. **learning modality: logical/mathematical**

Help Students Read

L1

Anticipation Guide Refer to the Content Refresher in this chapter, which provides guidelines for using this strategy.

Display the statements below before students read the rest of the section. Ask which of them are true:

1. In the modern periodic table, elements are arranged in order of atomic mass. *(False)*
2. Each square in the periodic table contains the element's atomic number, chemical symbol, name, and atomic mass. *(True)*
3. The properties of an element cannot be predicted by its position in the table. *(False)*
4. The periodic table is arranged in rows called groups and columns called periods. *(False)*

After students read the text, revisit these questions.

FIGURE 7
Mendeleev's Periodic Table
When Mendeleev published his first periodic table, he left question marks in some places. Based on the properties and atomic masses of surrounding elements, he predicted that new elements with specific properties would be discovered.

				Ti=50	Zr=90	?=180.
				V=51	Nb=94	Ta=182.
				Cr=52	Mo=96	W=186.
				Mn=55	Rh=104,4	Pt=197,4
				Fe=56	Ru=104,4	Ir=198.
			Ni=Co=59		Pl=106,6	Os=199.
H=1				Cu=63,4	Ag=108	Hg=200.
	Be=9,4	Mg=24		Zn=65,2	Cd=112	
	B=11	Al=27,4		?=68	Ur=116	Au=197?
	C=12	Si=28		?=70	Sn=118	
	N=14	P=31		As=75	Sb=122	Bi=210
	O=16	S=32		Se=79,4	Te=128?	
	F=19	Cl=35,5		Br=80	I=127	
Li=7	Na=23	K=39		Rb=85,4	Cs=133	Tl=204
		Ca=40		Sr=87,6	Ba=137	Pb=207.
		?=45	Ce=92			
		?Er=56	La=94			
		?Yt=60	Di=95			
		?In=75,6	Th=118?			

Predicting New Elements Mendeleev found that arranging the known elements strictly by increasing atomic mass did not always group similar elements together. So, he moved a few of his element cards into groups where the elements did have similar properties. After arranging all 63 elements, three blank spaces were left. Mendeleev predicted that the blank spaces would be filled by elements that had not yet been discovered. He even predicted the properties of those new elements.

In 1869, Mendeleev published the first periodic table. It looked something like the one shown in Figure 7. Within 16 years, chemists discovered the three missing elements—scandium, gallium, and germanium. Their properties are close to those that Mendeleev had predicted.

The Modern Periodic Table In the **periodic table** used today, the properties of the elements repeat in each period—or row—of the table. (The word *periodic* means "in a regular, repeated pattern.") The periodic table has changed a little since Mendeleev's time. New elements were added as they were discovered. Also, an important change occurred in the early 1900s. In 1913, Henry Moseley, a British scientist, discovered a way to measure the positive charge on an atom's nucleus—in other words, the atomic number. Not long after, the table was rearranged in order of atomic number, not atomic mass. As a result, a few of the elements shifted position, and some of the patterns of properties became more regular. An up-to-date version of the table appears on pages 84 and 85.

Skills Activity

Classifying

Choose any ten elements and assign them letters from *A* to *J*. On an index card for each element, write the letter for the element and list some of its properties. You may list properties that you learn about in this chapter or properties presented in another reference source.

Exchange cards with a classmate. Can you identify each element? Can you identify elements that have similar properties? Which properties are most helpful in identifying elements?

Skills Activity

Skills Focus Classifying

Materials index cards

Time 20 minutes

Tips Have students work in groups. Suggest that students avoid listing the atomic mass and atomic number of the element or other physical or chemical properties that are obvious clues to the identity of the element.

L1 **Extend** Ask the class which elements were easier to identify and which were more difficult. Discuss with students how many elements have similar properties. **learning modality: logical/mathematical**

Finding Data on Elements

The periodic table has one square for each element. **In this book, each square includes the element's atomic number, chemical symbol, name, and atomic mass.**

Atomic Number Look at the periodic table on the next two pages and find the square for iron. That square is reproduced below in Figure 8. The first entry in the square is the number 26, the atomic number of iron. From Section 1, you know that the atomic number tells you that every iron atom has 26 protons in its nucleus. Because it has 26 protons, an iron atom also has 26 electrons.

Chemical Symbols and Names Just below the atomic number are the letters Fe—the **chemical symbol** for iron. Most chemical symbols contain either one or two letters. Often, an element's symbol is an abbreviation of the element's name in English. For example, zinc's symbol is Zn, the symbol for calcium is Ca, and the symbol for silicon is Si. Other elements, especially those that were known in ancient times, have symbols that are abbreviations of their Latin names. For example, the Latin name of sodium is *natrium*, so its symbol is Na. The Latin name of potassium is *kalium*, so its symbol is K. The symbol Au for gold stands for *aurum*. Fe for iron stands for *ferrum*, and Pb for lead stands for *plumbum*.

Average Atomic Mass The last number in the square is the average atomic mass. For iron, this value is 55.847 amu. The atomic mass is an average because most elements consist of a mixture of isotopes. For example, iron is a mixture of four isotopes. About 92 percent of iron atoms are iron-56 (having 30 neutrons). The rest are a mixture of iron-54, iron-57, and iron-58. The average atomic mass of iron is determined from the combined percentages of all its isotopes.

 Reading Checkpoint Why is the atomic mass of an element an average?

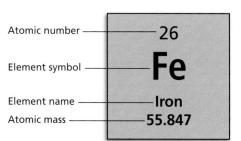

Atomic number —— 26
Element symbol —— **Fe**
Element name —— Iron
Atomic mass —— 55.847

FIGURE 8
Iron
Bok choy is a green, leafy vegetable used in Asian cooking. It is rich in iron.
Interpreting Diagrams *What does atomic number 26 in the square tell you about iron?*

Chapter 3 K ◆ 83

Finding Data on Elements

Teach Key Concepts [L2]
Data in the Periodic Table

Focus Point out that the periodic table has one square for each element.

Teach Display the periodic table in the classroom. Choose one element from the table and copy its square on the board. Ask: **What information about an element is given in this square?** (*Atomic number, chemical symbol, name, and atomic mass*) Label these in the element square.

Apply Ask: **From this information, what do you know about the structure of an atom for this element?** (*The number of protons and electrons and the average number of neutrons*) **learning modality: visual**

 **Teacher Demo**

Distinguishing Between Atomic Mass and Atomic Number [L1]

Materials 2 colors of modeling clay
Time 15 minutes

Focus Tell students that atomic mass is equal to the number of protons plus the number of neutrons in the nucleus of an atom.

Teach Use one color of clay to model three protons and the second color to model four neutrons. Assemble the "protons" and "neutrons" into a "nucleus" of lithium. Ask: **What is the atomic number of this atom?** (*Three*) **What is the atomic mass?** (*Seven amu*) **How many electrons does this atom have?** (*Three*)

Apply Ask: Why is the atomic mass of an element usually listed as an average number? (*Because most elements are found as a mixture of isotopes*) **learning modality: visual**

Monitor Progress [L2]

Oral Presentation Invite students to identify and describe the data included for each element in the periodic table.

Answers
Figure 8 An iron atom has 26 protons and 26 electrons.

 Reading Checkpoint Because most elements consist of a mixture of isotopes

Use Visuals: Figure 9

The Periodic Table

Focus Invite students to study the periodic table in Figure 9.

Teach Ask: **How many elements are in the table?** *(113)* **What characteristic of an element determines its place in the periodic table?** *(Its atomic number)* Have students trace the order of the elements. **Are any elements out of order in terms of atomic mass?** *(Sample answer: Ar and K; Co and Ni; and Te and I)* Remind students that Mendeleev ordered the elements by atomic mass.

Apply Ask: **Can you predict the existence of any elements?** *(Sample answer: Element 113)* Encourage students to give their opinions about the existence of elements larger than ununquadium. **learning modality: visual**

 **Teaching Resources**

• Transparency 24

Go Online
active art

For: Periodic Table activity
Visit: PHSchool.com
Web Code: cgp-1032

Students can interact with the art about the periodic table online.

FIGURE 9

Periodic Table of the Elements

The periodic table includes over 100 elements. Many of the properties of an element can be predicted by its position in the table.

Go Online
active art

For: Periodic Table activity
Visit: PHSchool.com
Web Code: cgp-1032

Key

C	Solid
Br	Liquid
H	Gas
Tc	Not found in nature

Symbol
One- or two-letter symbols identify most elements. Some periodic tables also list the names of the elements.

Group

Period

To make the table easier to read, the lanthanides and the actinides are printed below the rest of the elements. Follow the blue shading to see how they fit in the table.

Lanthanides

| 57 La Lanthanum 138.91 | 58 Ce Cerium 140.12 | 59 Pr Praseodymium 140.91 | 60 Nd Neodymium 144.24 | 61 Pm Promethium (145) | 62 Sm Samarium 150.4 |

Actinides

| 89 Ac Actinium (227) | 90 Th Thorium 232.04 | 91 Pa Protactinium 231.04 | 92 U Uranium 238.03 | 93 Np Neptunium (237) | 94 Pu Plutonium (244) |

Differentiated Instruction

Gifted and Talented **L3**

Mapping the Elements Each of the following elements is named after a place. Have students find the location of each place and label it on a world map. Magnesium—Magnesia, a district in Thessaly (Greece); copper—Cyprus; gallium—France, from the Latin word for France; germanium—Germany; ruthenium—Ruthenia, Ukraine; hafnium—Hafnia or Copenhagen, Denmark; berkelium—Berkeley, California; americium—America; californium—California **learning modality: logical/mathematical**

Key

- Metal
- Metalloid
- Nonmetal
- Properties not established

Atomic Mass
Atomic mass is the average mass of an element's atoms. Atomic masses in parentheses are those of the most stable isotope.

Atomic Number
The atomic number is the number of protons in an atom's nucleus.

Many periodic tables include a zigzag line that separates the metals from the nonmetals.

			13	**14**	**15**	**16**	**17**	**18**
								2 He Helium 4.0026
			5 B Boron 10.81	6 C Carbon 12.011	7 N Nitrogen 14.007	8 O Oxygen 15.999	9 F Fluorine 18.998	10 Ne Neon 20.179
10	**11**	**12**	13 Al Aluminum 26.982	14 Si Silicon 28.086	15 P Phosphorus 30.974	16 S Sulfur 32.06	17 Cl Chlorine 35.453	18 Ar Argon 39.948
28 Ni Nickel 58.71	29 Cu Copper 63.546	30 Zn Zinc 65.38	31 Ga Gallium 69.72	32 Ge Germanium 72.59	33 As Arsenic 74.922	34 Se Selenium 78.96	35 Br Bromine 79.904	36 Kr Krypton 83.80
46 Pd Palladium 106.4	47 Ag Silver 107.87	48 Cd Cadmium 112.41	49 In Indium 114.82	50 Sn Tin 118.69	51 Sb Antimony 121.75	52 Te Tellurium 127.60	53 I Iodine 126.90	54 Xe Xenon 131.30
78 Pt Platinum 195.09	79 Au Gold 196.97	80 Hg Mercury 200.59	81 Tl Thallium 204.37	82 Pb Lead 207.2	83 Bi Bismuth 208.98	84 Po Polonium (209)	85 At Astatine (210)	86 Rn Radon (222)
110 Ds Darmstadtium (269)	111 *Uuu Unununium (272)	112 *Uub Ununbium (277)		114 *Uuq Ununquadium				

*Name not officially assigned

63 Eu Europium 151.96	64 Gd Gadolinium 157.25	65 Tb Terbium 158.93	66 Dy Dysprosium 162.50	67 Ho Holmium 164.93	68 Er Erbium 167.26	69 Tm Thulium 168.93	70 Yb Ytterbium 173.04
95 Am Americium (243)	96 Cm Curium (247)	97 Bk Berkelium (247)	98 Cf Californium (251)	99 Es Einsteinium (252)	100 Fm Fermium (257)	101 Md Mendelevium (258)	102 No Nobelium (259)

Using the Periodic Table

Materials index cards

Time 15 minutes

Focus Explain that the only way to really understand what information is given in the periodic table is to use it.

Teach Challenge students to write five questions about the periodic table. Encourage them to write specific questions about elements or parts of the table that will require searching the table for the answer. Have students exchange cards and answer one another's questions.

Apply Ask: **What did you learn by using the table that you didn't know before?** *(Sample answer: All the elements in Group 18 are gases.)* **learning modality: visual**

Monitor Progress — L2

Skills Check Direct students to list five properties of mercury that they can find from the periodic table. *(Mercury is a liquid; it is a metal; its atomic mass is 200.59 amu; it has 80 protons; it has characteristics similar to zinc, cadmium, and element 112.)*

Organization of the Periodic Table

Teach Key Concepts L2

Predicting the Properties of Elements

Focus Tell students that the periodic table is useful because the properties of the elements change in a predictable way across a row or down a column.

Teach Invite students to look at the periodic table and ask: **What are the rows called?** *(Periods)* **How do the properties of the metals in a period change from left to right?** *(From highly reactive to very unreactive)* **What are the columns in the periodic table called?** *(Groups)* Explain that the elements in a group have similar characteristics.

Apply Challenge students to predict the properties of element 117, which has not been discovered. *(As a member of Group 17, it will react strongly with the elements from Group 1.)* **learning modality: logical/mathematical**

All in One Teaching Resources

- Transparency K25

Expanding the Periodic Table L1

Materials photocopy of the periodic table, scissors, tape

Time 10 minutes

Focus Point out the large gaps in the first three periods of the periodic table.

Teach Cut out the two rows of the lanthanide series and the actinide series from the periodic table. Then cut apart the main part of the table between Group 3 and Group 4. Tape the lanthanide and actinide series in place so that cerium follows lanthanum and hafnium follows lutetium. Do the same with actinium and thorium and lawrencium and rutherfordium.

Apply Point out that these elements follow Group 2. Ask: **Would you characterize these elements as highly reactive metals, relatively unreactive metals, metalloids, or nonmetals?** *(Sample answer: Relatively unreactive metals)*
learning modality: visual

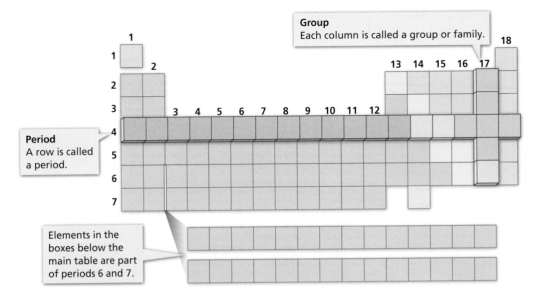

FIGURE 10
Periods and Groups
The 18 columns of the periodic table reflect a repeating pattern of properties that generally occur across a period. **Interpreting Tables** *How many periods are in the periodic table?*

Organization of the Periodic Table

Remember that the periodic table is arranged by atomic number. Look over the entire table, starting at the top left with hydrogen (H), which has atomic number 1. Follow the atomic numbers as they increase from left to right, and read across each row.

The properties of an element can be predicted from its location in the periodic table. As you look at elements across a row, the elements' properties change in a predictable way. This predictability is the reason that the periodic table is so useful to chemists.

Periods The table is arranged in horizontal rows called **periods.** A period contains a series of different elements, just as a week on a calendar has a series of seven days. As you move across a period from left to right, properties of the elements change according to a pattern.

As an example, look at the fourth period of the periodic table in Figure 10. The elements on the left of this period are highly reactive metals, such as potassium (K) and calcium (Ca). Elements in the center of the period are relatively unreactive metals, such as nickel (Ni) and copper (Cu). Elements to the right of these include metalloids such as arsenic (As) and the nonmetals selenium (Se) and bromine (Br). The last element in a period is always a very unreactive gas. In this period, that element is krypton (Kr).

Differentiated Instruction

English Learners/Beginning L1
Comprehension: Modified Cloze
Distribute a simplified paragraph about the periodic table, but leave some words blank. Model how to fill in the blank, using a sample sentence on the board. Give students correct answers as choices.
learning modality: verbal

English Learners/Intermediate L2
Comprehension: Modified Cloze
Distribute the same paragraph, but include additional terms as incorrect answer choices. After students complete the paragraph, help them write definitions for the answer choices that were not used.
learning modality: verbal

Groups The modern periodic table has 7 periods, which form 18 vertical columns. The elements in a column are called a **group.** Groups are also known as families. The groups are numbered, from Group 1 on the left of the table to Group 18 on the right. Group 17 is highlighted in Figure 10. Most groups are named for the first element in the column. Group 14, for example, is the carbon family. Group 15 is the nitrogen family.

Because the pattern of properties of elements repeats in each new period, the elements in each group have similar characteristics. The elements in Group 1 are all metals that react violently with water, while the metals in Group 2 all react with water slowly or not at all. Group 17 elements react violently with elements from Group 1. Group 18 elements rarely react at all.

 Reading Checkpoint How many groups are in the modern periodic table?

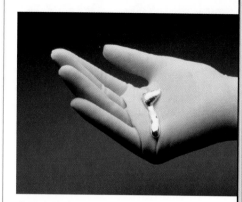

FIGURE 11
Group 13 Element
This sample of gallium metal is an element in Group 13.

Section 2 Assessment

 Target Reading Skill **Asking Questions** Use your graphic organizer about the section headings to help you answer the questions below.

Reviewing Key Concepts

1. a. Reviewing In what order did Mendeleev arrange the elements in the first periodic table?
b. Explaining What pattern did Mendeleev discover when he arranged the elements?
c. Comparing and Contrasting Describe two differences between Mendeleev's periodic table and the modern periodic table.
2. a. Identifying List three kinds of information about an element that can be found in a square of the periodic table.
b. Interpreting Tables What element has 47 protons in its nucleus?
c. Making Generalizations Why aren't the atomic masses of most elements whole numbers?

3. a. Describing What does an element's location in the periodic table tell you about that element?
b. Predicting Use the periodic table to name two elements that you would expect to have properties very much like those of calcium.

Writing in Science

Advertisement Write an advertisement that you could use to sell copies of Mendeleev's periodic table to chemists in 1869. Be sure to emphasize the benefits of the table to the chemical profession. Remember, the chemists have never seen such a table.

Chapter 3 K ◆ 87

Monitor Progress L2

Answer
Figure 10 Seven

Reading Checkpoint Eighteen

Assess

Reviewing Key Concepts

1. a. Mendeleev arranged the elements in order of increasing atomic mass. **b.** Mendeleev found that the properties of the elements repeated. **c.** In the modern periodic table, new elements have been added and the elements are ordered by atomic number.
2. a. Sample answers: Element's name, chemical symbol, atomic number, and atomic mass **b.** Silver **c.** The atomic mass is an average mass based on the combined percentages of all the isotopes of an element.
3. a. An element's location in the periodic table gives you information about its properties. **b.** Students' answers should include two of the following: beryllium, magnesium, strontium, barium, or radium.

Reteach L1

Use the periodic table to reinforce the pattern across the periods. Have students identify the locations of highly reactive metals, relatively unreactive metals, metalloids, nonmetals, and the very unreactive gases.

Performance Assessment L2

Writing Instruct students to write a statement that explains why the periodic table of elements is helpful to scientists.

All in One Teaching Resources

- Section Summary: *Organizing the Elements*
- Review and Reinforce: *Organizing the Elements*
- Enrich: *Organizing the Elements*

Lab zone **Chapter Project**

Keep Students on Track Encourage students to find the squares in the periodic table for each of their metals. They should prepare a table in which to record the chemical symbol, group number, atomic number, atomic mass, and characteristic properties for each metal. As students begin to generate their lists of properties, encourage them to think about what they know from their everyday experience with metals.

Writing in Science

Writing Mode Persuasion
Scoring Rubric
4 Exceeds criteria; includes a persuasive, creative advertisement with an accurate, detailed diagram and a clear, concise description
3 Meets criteria
2 Includes a diagram and explanation but contains some errors
1 Includes only a rough sketch and/or brief explanation or contains serious errors

Objectives

After this lesson, students will be able to

K.3.3.1 List the physical properties of metals.

K.3.3.2 Explain how the reactivity of metals changes across the periodic table.

K.3.3.3 Explain how the elements that follow uranium are produced.

Target Reading Skill

Using Prior Knowledge Explain that using prior knowledge helps students connect what they already know to what they are about to read.

Answers

Sample answers:

What You Know

1. Metals are shiny.

2. Some metals are magnetic.

What You Learned

1. Ductile metals can be pulled into a wire.

2. Alkali metals react by losing one electron.

All in One Teaching Resources

• Transparency K26

Preteach

Build Background Knowledge   L2

Observing Properties of Metals

Display various objects made of metal such as coins, wire, paper clips, toy cars, foil, jewelry, scissors, nails, and cookware. Invite students to observe the objects and, as a class, develop a list of physical properties of metals. Revise this list after completing the section.

Section 3 Metals

Reading Preview

Key Concepts

• What are the physical properties of metals?

• How does the reactivity of metals change across the periodic table?

• How are elements that follow uranium in the periodic table produced?

Key Terms

• metal • malleable • ductile
• conductivity • reactivity
• corrosion
• alkali metal
• alkaline earth metal
• transition metal • alloy
• particle accelerator

Target Reading Skill

Using Prior Knowledge Before you read, write what you know about metals in a graphic organizer like the one below. As you read, write what you learn.

What You Know
1. Metals are shiny.
2.

What You Learned
1.
2.

Lab zone Discover Activity

Why Use Aluminum?

1. Examine several objects made from aluminum, including a can, a disposable pie plate, heavy-duty aluminum foil, foil-covered wrapping paper, and aluminum wire.

2. Compare the shape, thickness, and general appearance of the objects.

3. Observe what happens if you try to bend and unbend each object.

4. For what purpose is each object used?

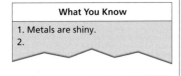

Think It Over

Inferring Use your observations to list as many properties of aluminum as you can. Based on your list of properties, infer why aluminum was used to make each object. Explain your answer.

Metals are all around you. The cars and buses you ride in are made of steel, which is mostly iron. Airplanes are covered in aluminum. A penny is made of zinc coated with copper. Copper wires carry electricity into lamps, stereos, and computers. It's hard to imagine modern life without metals.

Properties of Metals

What is a metal? Take a moment to describe a familiar metal, such as iron, copper, gold, or silver. What words did you use—*hard, shiny, smooth*? Chemists classify an element as a **metal** based on its properties. Look again at the periodic table in Section 2. All of the elements in blue-tinted squares to the left of the zigzag line are metals.

Physical Properties The physical properties of metals include shininess, malleability, ductility, and conductivity. A **malleable** (MAL ee uh bul) material is one that can be hammered or rolled into flat sheets and other shapes. A **ductile** material is one that can be pulled out, or drawn, into a long wire. For example, copper can be made into thin sheets and wire because it is malleable and ductile.

Lab zone Discover Activity

Skills Focus Inferring   L1

Materials aluminum can, disposable pie plate, heavy-duty foil, foil-covered wrapping paper, aluminum wire

Time 10 minutes

Tips Suggest students make charts of their observations and inferences.

Expected Outcome Students will observe that aluminum is lightweight,

flexible, and shiny; holds liquids; can conduct heat; and can be rolled into sheets and pulled into wires.

Think It Over Sample answer: Properties of aluminum are shininess, hardness, able to bend, and conductor of heat and electricity. Students should match the function of each object they examined with at least one property of aluminum.

Conductivity is the ability of an object to transfer heat or electricity to another object. Most metals are good conductors. In addition, a few metals are magnetic. For example, iron (Fe), cobalt (Co), and nickel (Ni) are attracted to magnets and can be made into magnets like the one in Figure 12. Most metals are also solids at room temperature. However, one metal—mercury (Hg)—is a liquid at room temperature.

Chemical Properties The ease and speed with which an element combines, or reacts, with other elements and compounds is called its **reactivity.** Metals usually react by losing electrons to other atoms. Some metals are very reactive. For example, you read in Section 2 that sodium (Na) reacts strongly when exposed to air or water. To prevent a reaction, sodium and metals like it must be stored under oil in sealed containers. By comparison, gold (Au) and platinum (Pt) are valued for their *lack* of reactivity and because they are rare.

The reactivities of other metals fall somewhere between those of sodium and gold. Iron, for example, reacts slowly with oxygen in the air, forming iron oxide, or rust. If iron is not protected by paint or plated with another metal, it will slowly turn to reddish-brown rust. The destruction of a metal through this process is called **corrosion.**

 Reading Checkpoint What are three physical properties of metals?

FIGURE 12
Properties of Metals
Metals have certain physical and chemical properties.
Classifying *Categorize each of the properties of metals that are shown as either physical or chemical.*

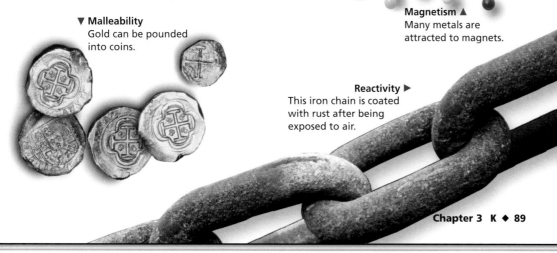

▼ **Malleability**
Gold can be pounded into coins.

Magnetism ▲
Many metals are attracted to magnets.

Reactivity ▶
This iron chain is coated with rust after being exposed to air.

Chapter 3 K ◆ 89

Differentiated Instruction

Special Needs L1
Classifying Metals Have students classify a wide variety of objects as metals or not metals. Consider providing instruments such as a magnet and a simple electrical conductivity tester. Discuss the criteria students used to classify the objects and relate them to the physical properties described in this section. **learning modality: kinesthetic**

Special Needs L1
Experiencing Properties Provide tactile experiences for students to learn the meanings of the words *malleable* and *ductile.* Students can pound modeling clay into shapes to experience malleability. They can pull modeling clay into a thin strand to experience ductility. **learning modality: kinesthetic**

Properties of Metals

Teach Key Concepts L2
Properties of Metals

Focus Show students the location of metals in the periodic table.

Teach Explain that elements are classified as metals based on their properties. Ask: **What are some physical properties of metals?** (*Shininess, malleability, ductility, conductivity, and magnetism.*)

Apply Tell students that not every metal has all of these physical properties. Ask: **Which metal is not a solid at room temperature?** (*Mercury*) **learning modality: verbal**

Help Students Read L1
Anticipation Guide Refer to the Content Refresher in this chapter, which provides guidelines for using this strategy.

Ask students which statements are true: **1.** A ductile material can be pounded into shapes. (*False*) **2.** Most metals react with atoms of other elements by losing electrons. (*True*) **3.** The reactivity of metals tends to increase from left to right across the periodic table. (*False*) **4.** Elements larger than uranium are not found in nature. (*True*)

After students read the section, revisit these questions.

Independent Practice L2

All in One Teaching Resources

• Guided Reading and Study Worksheet: *Metals*

◉ **Student Edition on Audio CD**

Monitor Progress _____ L2

Skills Check Have students make a concept map that classifies the properties of metals as physical or chemical.

Students can save their concept maps in their portfolios. **Portfolio**

Answers
Figure 12 Physical: magnetism and malleability; chemical: reactivity

✓ **Reading Checkpoint** Physical properties include shininess, malleability, ductility, conductivity, and attraction to magnets.

Metals in the Periodic Table

Teach Key Concepts L2
Characterizing Metal Groups

Focus Tell students that elements in the same group have similar properties and group properties change gradually across the periodic table.

Teach Begin a table on the board with the names of each metal group at the top. As you study each group, record the properties of that group, including the number of electrons lost when reacting with other elements. Also include examples of each. Ask: **How do these group properties change as you move across the table?** (*The reactivity of metals tends to decrease from left to right across the table.*)

Apply Ask: **Is reactivity a chemical or physical property?** (*Chemical property*) Explain that the number of electrons lost determines the reactivity of a metal.
learning modality: visual

Differentiating Alkali Metals L2

Materials Bunsen burner, hydrochloric acid (1*M* HCl), lithium chloride, matches, nichrome wire loop, potassium iodide, sodium chloride

Time 15 minutes

Focus Explain that scientists can identify certain metals with a flame test because they produce distinctive colors when heated in a flame.

Teach Dip the metal probe in one of the metal samples. Place the probe in the burner flame. Invite students to describe the color of the flame. Before testing another metal, clean the probe by dipping it in hydrochloric acid and heating it in the flame until the flame is not colored. Make sure students observe a different colored flame from each sample. (Sodium: yellow; potassium: purple; lithium: red)

Apply Explain that the yellow produced by sodium can be seen in sodium vapor lights, such as those used in parking lots and stadiums. These colors are also used to color fireworks and flares. **learning modality: visual**

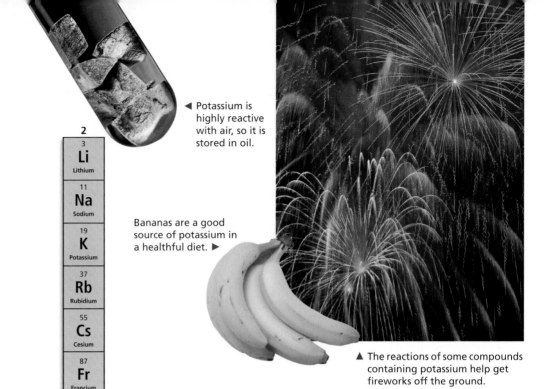

◄ Potassium is highly reactive with air, so it is stored in oil.

Bananas are a good source of potassium in a healthful diet. ►

▲ The reactions of some compounds containing potassium help get fireworks off the ground.

FIGURE 13
Alkali Metals
Potassium is an alkali metal.
Making Generalizations *What characteristics do other Group 1 elements share with potassium?*

Metals in the Periodic Table

The metals in a group, or family, have similar properties, and these family properties change gradually as you move across the table. **The reactivity of metals tends to decrease as you move from left to right across the periodic table.**

Alkali Metals The metals in Group 1, from lithium to francium, are called the **alkali metals.** Alkali metals react with other elements by losing one electron. These metals are so reactive that they are never found as uncombined elements in nature. Instead, they are found only in compounds. In the laboratory, scientists have been able to isolate alkali metals from their compounds. As pure, uncombined elements, some of the alkali metals are shiny and so soft that you can cut them with a plastic knife.

The two most important alkali metals are sodium and potassium. Examples of potassium are shown in Figure 13. Sodium compounds are found in large amounts in seawater and salt beds. Your diet includes foods that contain compounds of sodium and potassium, elements important for life. Another alkali metal, lithium, is used in batteries and some medicines.

Alkaline Earth Metals Group 2 of the periodic table contains the **alkaline earth metals.** Each is fairly hard, gray-white, and a good conductor of electricity. Alkaline earth metals react by losing two electrons. These elements are not as reactive as the metals in Group 1, but they are more reactive than most other metals. Like the Group 1 metals, the Group 2 metals are never found uncombined in nature.

The two most common alkaline earth metals are magnesium and calcium. Mixing magnesium and a small amount of aluminum makes a strong but lightweight material used in ladders, airplane parts, automobile wheels, and other products. Calcium compounds are an essential part of teeth and bones. Calcium also helps muscles work properly. You get calcium compounds from milk and other dairy products, as well as from green, leafy vegetables.

2
4 **Be** Beryllium
12 **Mg** Magnesium
20 **Ca** Calcium
38 **Sr** Strontium
56 **Ba** Barium
88 **Ra** Radium

▲ Without calcium, muscles and bones cannot grow and function.

FIGURE 14
Alkaline Earth Metals
Calcium is one of the Group 2 elements.

Math — Analyzing Data

Melting Points in a Group of Elements

The properties of elements within a single group in the periodic table often vary in a certain pattern. The following graph shows the melting points of Group 1 elements (alkali metals) from lithium to francium.

1. **Reading Graphs** As you look at Group 1 from lithium to francium, describe how the melting points of the alkali metals change.

2. **Predicting** If element number 119 were synthesized, it would fall below francium in Group 1 of the periodic table. Predict the approximate melting point of new element 119.

3. **Interpreting Data** Room temperature is usually about 22°C. Human body temperature is 37°C. Which of the alkali metals are liquids at room temperature? Which might melt if you could hold them in your hand?

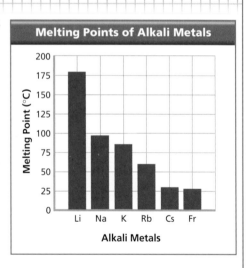

Melting Points of Alkali Metals

(Bar graph: Melting Point (°C) on y-axis from 0 to 200; x-axis shows Alkali Metals: Li, Na, K, Rb, Cs, Fr)

Identifying Elements Essential for Life

Focus Tell students that some of the nutrients they need for good health are metals.

Teach Give students Nutrition Facts labels from various food products. (Fortified cereals often have the most complete labels.) Instruct students to read the labels and make a list of elements on them. (*Students may find sodium, potassium, calcium, iron, phosphorus, magnesium, zinc, and copper.*) Then have students identify the family in which the elements belong. (*Alkali metals: sodium and potassium; alkaline earth metals: magnesium and calcium; transition metals: iron, zinc, and copper; phosphorous is a nonmetal*)

Apply Point out that the other nutrients and vitamins listed in the Nutrition Facts are made up of combinations of elements, or compounds. Ask: **What is the importance of elements to the body?** (*Without certain elements, the body cannot grow or work properly.*) **learning modality: logical/ mathematical**

Math — Analyzing Data

Math Skill Making and interpreting graphs

Focus Tell students that melting point is a physical property.

Answers
1. Melting points decrease from lithium to francium.
2. New element 119 should have a melting point of approximately 25°C.
3. None of the alkali metals are liquids at room temperature. Cesium and francium might melt if you could hold them in your hand.

All in One Teaching Resources
• Transparency K27

Differentiated Instruction

Less Proficient Readers L1
Comparing and Contrasting Give students a blank compare/contrast table to complete as they read about the metals in the periodic table. Use the names of the groups of metals as column headings. For row headings, use physical and chemical properties such as number of electrons lost when reacting with other elements, reactivity, shininess, conductivity, and magnetic attraction. Also have a space in which students can record examples of elements from each group. After students have read the section and completed the table, ask them to write a summary sentence to describe the characteristics of each metal group. Students should write sentences that use information gathered in their tables. **learning modality: verbal**

Monitor Progress L2

Writing Instruct students to write a sentence to explain how alkali metals and alkaline earth metals react with other elements.

Answer
Figure 13 They react by losing one electron, are found in nature only in compounds, and are shiny and soft.

Challenge students to explain the meaning of the word *transition* in their own words. Point out that the word *transition* comes from the Latin word *transire,* which means "to go across." Encourage students to speculate about how the name *transition metals* is appropriate. *(A bridge "goes across" something, and the transition metals act as a bridge between the very reactive metals on the left side of the table and the less reactive metals and elements on the right side.)*

Build Inquiry L2

Classifying Metals

Materials index cards

Time 15 minutes

Focus Remind students that metals in the same group, or family, have similar properties.

Teach Have student groups write a property or a use of a metal group on an index card. Each group should write at least ten different cards. Groups can exchange cards and classify the cards into the metal groups based on the property or use.

Extend Challenge students to arrange their groups of cards in order from most reactive to least. **learning modality: logical/mathematical**

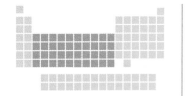

Transition Metals The elements in Groups 3 through 12 are called the **transition metals.** The transition metals include most of the familiar metals, such as iron, copper, nickel, silver, and gold. Most of the transition metals are hard and shiny. All of the transition metals are good conductors of electricity. Many of these metals form colorful compounds.

The transition metals are less reactive than the metals in Groups 1 and 2. This lack of reactivity is the reason ancient gold coins and jewelry are as beautiful and detailed today as they were thousands of years ago. Even when iron reacts with air and water, forming rust, it sometimes takes many years to react completely. Some transition metals are important to your health. For example, you would not survive without iron. It forms the core of a large molecule called hemoglobin, which carries oxygen in your bloodstream.

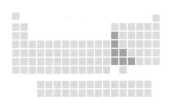

Metals in Mixed Groups Only some of the elements in Groups 13 through 15 of the periodic table are metals. These metals are not nearly as reactive as those on the left side of the table. The most familiar of these metals are aluminum, tin, and lead. Aluminum is the lightweight metal used in beverage cans and airplane bodies. A thin coating of tin protects steel from corrosion in some cans of food. Lead was once used in paints and water pipes. But lead is poisonous, so it is no longer used for these purposes. Now, its most common uses are in automobile batteries and weights for balancing tires.

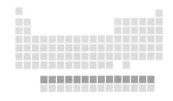

Lanthanides Two rows of elements are placed below the main part of the periodic table. This makes the table more compact. The elements in the top row are called the lanthanides (LAN thuh nydz). Lanthanides are soft, malleable, shiny metals with high conductivity. They are mixed with more common metals to make alloys. An **alloy** is a mixture of a metal with at least one other element, usually another metal. (You will read more about alloys in Chapter 4.) Different lanthanides are usually found together in nature. They are difficult to separate from one another because they all share very similar properties.

Differentiated Instruction

Gifted and Talented L3

Recycling Metals Challenge students to consider whether metals are renewable or nonrenewable resources. *(They are nonrenewable; metal resources cannot be replaced once they are used.)* Have students find out if metal resources can be sustainable (made, used, and disposed of in a way that allows them to be reused over and over again). Encourage students to investigate metal recycling in your area. Have them find out why companies are paying more and more for scrap metal. Suggest that they start a recycling program at your school or town if one does not exist. **learning modality: logical/mathematical**

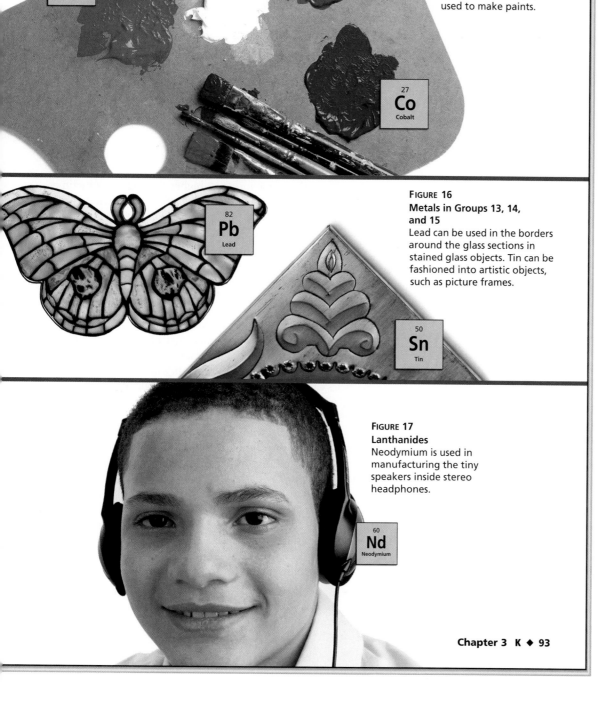

FIGURE 15
Transition Metals
Compounds made with transition metals can be very colorful. Several transition metals are used to make paints.

48
Cd
Cadmium

30
Zn
Zinc

24
Cr
Chromium

27
Co
Cobalt

FIGURE 16
Metals in Groups 13, 14, and 15
Lead can be used in the borders around the glass sections in stained glass objects. Tin can be fashioned into artistic objects, such as picture frames.

82
Pb
Lead

50
Sn
Tin

FIGURE 17
Lanthanides
Neodymium is used in manufacturing the tiny speakers inside stereo headphones.

60
Nd
Neodymium

Chapter 3 K ◆ 93

Finding Metals

Materials none

Time 15 minutes

Focus Point out that metals are found and used everywhere.

Teach Have students go on a metal "scavenger hunt." Give them the opportunity to examine themselves, the classroom, and the school building and grounds for examples of metals. Students should compile a list of metals they observe and how the metals are being used. When they return to their desks, have groups share their observations. Make a class list of metals observed. Then challenge students to identify the metals.

Apply Ask: **How is the use of the metal related to its reactivity?** (*Sample answer: Metals used outdoors or as jewelry are less reactive.*) **learning modality: kinesthetic**

Monitor Progress _____ L2

Oral Presentation Have students choose a family of metals and use the periodic table to name all the metals in that group.

Synthetic Elements

Teach Key Concepts L2

Some Elements Do Not Occur Naturally

Focus Tell students that not all elements are found naturally on Earth.

Teach Ask: **How do scientists make elements that are heavier than uranium?** (*By forcing nuclear particles to crash into one another*) **How does a particle accelerator work?** (*It moves atomic nuclei faster and faster until they have enough energy to crash into the nuclei of other elements and combine to form a single, larger nucleus.*)

Apply Illustrate this idea on the board by diagramming the nucleus of a helium atom and the nucleus of a plutonium atom colliding to form curium. Ask: **How many protons does helium have?** (*Two*) **Plutonium?** (*94*) **Curium?** (*96*) **learning modality: visual**

Modeling a Particle Accelerator

Materials small round magnets, steel balls bearings

Time 15 minutes

Focus Remind students how a particle accelerator works.

Teach Instruct students to place as many metal balls on the magnet as they can. Ask: **How many metal balls can you place on the magnet before they begin to fall off?** (Answers depend on the size of the magnet and the size of the balls.) Explain that the metal balls model the protons in the nucleus of an atom. Ask: **If the magnet represents energy, how could you get a larger nucleus?** (*By adding another magnet*)

Apply Ask: **Why do you think these elements are not found naturally on Earth?** (*Sample answer: The atoms are so large that they are not stable.*) **learning modality: kinesthetic**

Go Online
SCLINKS NSTA

For: Links on metals
Visit: www.SciLinks.org
Web Code: scn-1133

Download a worksheet that will guide students' review of Internet resources on metals.

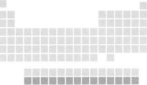

FIGURE 18
Mars Exploration Rover
Curium, one of the actinide elements, is used as a source of high-energy particles that heat and provide power for certain scientific equipment aboard the Mars Exploration Rover.
Posing Questions *Based on this information, write a question about curium.*

Go Online
SCLINKS NSTA

For: Links on metals
Visit: www.SciLinks.org
Web Code: scn-1133

94 ◆ K

Actinides The elements below the lanthanides are called actinides (AK tuh nydz). Of the actinides, only thorium (Th) and uranium (U) occur naturally on Earth. Uranium is used to produce energy in nuclear power plants. All of the elements after uranium in the periodic table were created artificially in laboratories. The nuclei of these elements are very unstable, meaning that they break apart very quickly into smaller nuclei. In fact, many of these elements are so unstable that they last for only a fraction of a second after they are made.

 Reading Checkpoint **Where are the actinides located in the periodic table?**

Synthetic Elements

Elements with atomic numbers higher than 92 are sometimes described as synthetic elements because they are not found naturally on Earth. **Instead, elements that follow uranium are made—or synthesized—when nuclear particles are forced to crash into one another.** For example, plutonium is made by bombarding nuclei of uranium-238 with neutrons in a nuclear reactor. Americium-241 (Am-241) is made by bombarding plutonium nuclei with neutrons.

To make even heavier elements (with atomic numbers above 95), scientists use powerful machines called particle accelerators. **Particle accelerators** move atomic nuclei faster and faster until they have reached very high speeds. If these fast-moving nuclei crash into the nuclei of other elements with enough energy, the particles can sometimes combine into a single nucleus. Curium (Cm) was the first synthetic element to be made by colliding nuclei. In 1940, scientists in Chicago synthesized curium by colliding helium nuclei with plutonium nuclei.

In general, the difficulty of synthesizing new elements increases with atomic number. So, new elements have been synthesized only as more powerful particle accelerators have been built. For example, German scientists synthesized element 112 in 1996 by accelerating zinc nuclei and crashing them into lead. Element 112, like other elements with three-letter symbols, has been given a temporary name and symbol. In the future, scientists around the world will agree on permanent names and symbols for these elements.

Reading Checkpoint **Which elements are described as synthetic elements and why?**

Americium-241 is produced in nuclear reactors. It is widely used in smoke detectors.

FIGURE 19
Synthetic Elements
Synthetic elements are not found naturally on Earth.

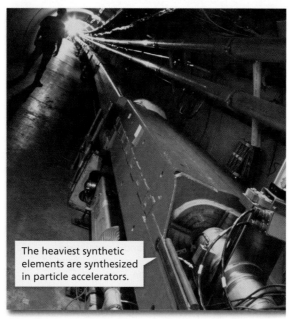

The heaviest synthetic elements are synthesized in particle accelerators.

Section 3 Assessment

Target Reading Skill Using Prior Knowledge Review your graphic organizer about metals and revise it based on what you learned in the section.

Reviewing Key Concepts

1. **a. Defining** What properties of metals do the terms *conductivity* and *ductility* describe?
   b. Classifying Give an example of how the ductility of metal can be useful.
   c. Inferring What property of metals led to the use of plastic or wood handles on many metal cooking utensils? Explain.
2. **a. Identifying** What family of elements in the periodic table contains the most reactive metals?
   b. Applying Concepts What area of the periodic table is the best place to look for a metal that could be used to coat another metal to protect it from corrosion?

c. **Predicting** If scientists could produce element 120, what predictions would you make about its reactivity?
3. **a. Describing** Describe the general process by which new elements are synthesized.
   b. Applying Concepts How is plutonium made?

Lab zone At-Home Activity

Everyday Metals Make a survey of compounds in your home that contain metals. Look at labels on foods, cooking ingredients, dietary supplements, medicines, and cosmetics. Also look for examples of how metals are used in your home, such as in cookware and wiring. Identify for your family the ways that the properties of metals make them useful in daily life.

Lab zone At-Home Activity

Everyday Metals **L1** Students' answers should list metals in many household items and should describe how the metals' properties make them useful.

Lab zone Chapter Project

Keep Students on Track Encourage students to think about properties to observe in their metals. They might include properties such as shininess, hardness, and color. Also, encourage them to plan how to test other properties of metals such as corrosion, magnetism, electrical and heat conductivity, density, and reactivity with acids and oxygen. Review their experimental designs and make sure they have addressed safety issues.

Monitor Progress _____ L2

Answers
Figure 18 Sample answer: What high-energy particles does curium produce, and how are the particles used?

✓ **Reading Checkpoint** Below the lanthanides; in Period 7

✓ **Reading Checkpoint** Elements with atomic numbers higher than 92, because they are not found naturally on Earth

Assess

Reviewing Key Concepts

1. **a.** Conductivity—the ability of an object to transfer heat or electricity to another object; ductility—the ability of a material to be pulled out into a wire **b.** Sample answer: Copper's ductility allows copper to be drawn into wires that carry electricity. **c.** Metals are good conductors of heat. Plastic or wood handles, which do not conduct heat, protect hands from the heat.
2. **a.** Group 1, or alkali metals **b.** Groups 13–15 **c.** Element 120 would likely have reactivity similar to that of the alkaline earth metals.
3. **a.** New elements are synthesized when atomic nuclei are forced to crash into the nuclei of other elements with enough energy to combine into a single nucleus.
   b. Plutonium is made by bombarding nuclei of uranium-238 with neutrons in a nuclear reactor.

Reteach **L1**

Give students a black-and-white copy of the periodic table. Have them color-code the locations of the six metal groups. Then have them make a key that identifies the locations and properties of each group.

Performance Assessment **L2**

Oral Presentation Have students choose one metal from Groups 1 to 13, then describe themselves as if they were that metal, including their position in the periodic table and their properties.

All in One Teaching Resources
• Section Summary: *Metals*
• Review and Reinforce: *Metals*
• Enrich: *Metals*

Copper or Carbon? That Is the Question L2

Prepare for Inquiry

Key Concept
The properties of elements determine their uses.

Skills Objectives
After this lab, students will be able to
- observe properties of copper and carbon.
- classify substances as metals or nonmetals.
- control variables in an experiment.
- draw conclusions about the best uses of substances based on their properties.

 Prep Time 15 minutes

Time 30 minutes

Advance Planning
The diameters of the copper wire and graphite should be about the same. Consider assembling the conductivity testers in advance.

Alternative Materials
Any heat resistant container may be used in place of the beaker.

Safety
 Caution students to keep water away from the electrical apparatus, electrical outlets, and the hot plate. Make sure students turn off the hot plate before conducting the experiment. Review the safety guidelines in Appendix A.

All in One Teaching Resources
- Lab Worksheet: *Copper or Carbon? That Is the Question*

Guide Inquiry

Invitation
Invite students to give examples of items made of metal. (*Sample answers: tools, cookware, airplanes, cars*) Ask: **What characteristics do these items have in common?** (*Sample answer: They are hard, shiny, and strong.*) Display a piece of sulfur, graphite, or other nonmetal. Invite students to describe its characteristics and compare them to those of metals.

Copper or Carbon? That Is the Question

Problem
Materials scientists work to find the best materials for different products. In this lab, you will look for an answer to the following problem: How do the properties of copper and graphite determine their uses? You will compare the properties of a copper wire and a pencil lead. Pencil lead is made mostly of graphite, a form of the nonmetal element carbon.

Skills Focus
observing, classifying, controlling variables, drawing conclusions

Materials
- 1.5-V dry cell battery
- 250-mL beaker • stopwatch
- flashlight bulb and socket
- 3 lengths of insulated wire
- thin copper wire with no insulation, about 5–6 cm long
- 2 graphite samples (lead from a mechanical pencil), each about 5–6 cm long
- hot plate
- water

Procedure
1. Fill a 250-mL beaker about three-fourths full with water. Heat it slowly on a hot plate. Let the water continue to heat as you complete Part 1 and Part 2 of the investigation.

PART 1 Physical Properties

2. Compare the shininess and color of your copper and graphite samples. Record your observations.

3. Bend the copper wire as far as possible. Next, bend one of the graphite samples as far as possible. Record the results of each test.

PART 2 Electrical Conductivity

4. Place a bulb into a lamp socket. Use a piece of insulated wire to connect one pole of a dry cell battery to the socket, as shown in the photo below.

5. Attach the end of a second piece of insulated wire to the other pole of the dry cell battery. Leave the other end of this wire free.

6. Attach the end of a third piece of insulated wire to the other pole of the lamp socket. Leave the other end of this wire free.

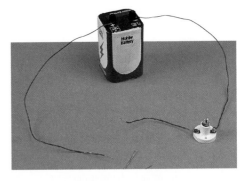

7. Touch the free ends of the insulated wire to the ends of the copper wire. Record your observations of the bulb.

8. Repeat Step 7 using a graphite sample instead of the copper wire.

Introduce the Procedure
Before students begin the procedure, refer them to the photograph of the conductivity tester. Demonstrate how to assemble and use the tester. Also demonstrate how to test for heat conductivity. Emphasize the importance of using equal lengths of copper and graphite. Then, ask: **What element is graphite a form of?** (*Carbon*)

Troubleshooting the Experiment
- Have plenty of graphite pencil leads available, as they break easily.
- In the conductivity test, make sure students do not touch the wires together or place them too close to each other on the copper or graphite as the light might illuminate inadvertently.

Expected Outcome
Copper is shinier, more malleable, and conducts heat and electricity better than graphite.

PART 3 Heat Conductivity

9. Turn off the hot plate.

10. Hold one end of a graphite sample between the fingertips of one hand. Hold one end of the copper wire between the fingertips of the other hand. **CAUTION:** *Be careful not to touch the beaker.*

11. Dip both the graphite and copper wire into the hot water at the same time. Allow only about 1 cm of each piece to reach under the water's surface. From your fingertips to the water, the lengths of both the graphite sample and the copper wire should be approximately equal.

12. Time how long it takes to feel the heat in the fingertips of each hand. Record your observations.

Analyze and Conclude

1. **Observing** Compare the physical properties of copper and graphite that you observed.

2. **Classifying** Based on the observations you made in this lab, explain why copper is classified as a metal.

3. **Controlling Variables** In Step 11, why was it important to use equal lengths of copper wire and graphite?

4. **Drawing Conclusions** Which of the two materials, graphite or copper, would work better to cover the handle of a frying pan? Explain your choice.

5. **Communicating** Write a paragraph explaining why copper is better than graphite for electrical wiring. Include supporting evidence from your observations in this lab.

More to Explore

Research other uses of copper in the home and in industry. For each use, list the physical properties that make the material a good choice.

Analyze and Conclude

1. Copper is shiny, hard, and flexible. Graphite is dull, relatively soft (shown in its ability to leave a mark on paper), and easily broken (brittle).

2. Copper is classified as a metal because it is hard, shiny, ductile, and a good conductor of heat and electricity.

3. The manipulated variable in the experiment is the identity of the substance: carbon versus copper. All other factors, including the length of the sample and the temperature of the water, must be kept constant.

4. Graphite would work better to cover the handle of a frying pan because it has a lower heat conductivity than does copper.

5. Students' paragraphs should emphasize properties such as more flexibility, ductility, and greater electrical conductivity that would make copper the better choice for electrical wiring.

Extend Inquiry

More to Explore Students may list a variety of uses for copper. For each use listed, make sure students assign a relevant property that is consistent with the material.

Objectives

After this lesson, students will be able to

K.3.4.1 Describe the properties of nonmetals.

K.3.4.2 Tell how metalloids are useful.

Target Reading Skill

Using Prior Knowledge Explain that using prior knowledge helps students connect what they already know to what they are about to read.

Answers

Sample answers:

What You Know

1. Nonmetals are not shiny.
2. Nonmetals are not magnetic.

What You Learned

1. Nonmetals are dull and brittle.
2. Metalloids have characteristics of metals and nonmetals.

All in One Teaching Resources

• Transparency K28

Preteach

Build Background Knowledge   L2

Experience With Chlorine

Ask: **What do you know about chlorine?** *(Sample answer: Chemical used in swimming pools, part of bleach)* Encourage students to build on their experiences with chlorine in swimming pools and share their observations. Point out the position of chlorine in the periodic table. Invite students to share any knowledge they may have about elements near chlorine.

98 • K

Reading Preview

Key Concepts

• What are the properties of nonmetals?

• How are the metalloids useful?

Key Terms

• nonmetal
• diatomic molecule • halogen
• noble gas • metalloid
• semiconductor

↻ Target Reading Skill

Using Prior Knowledge Before you read, write what you know about the properties of nonmetals and metalloids in a graphic organizer like the one below. As you read, write what you learn.

What You Know
1. Nonmetals are not shiny.
2.

What You Learned
1.
2.

These bears, the grass behind them, and all life on Earth is based on carbon, a nonmetal. ▶

98 ◆ K

Lab zone Discover **Activity**

What Are the Properties of Charcoal?

1. Break off a piece of charcoal and roll it between your fingers. Record your observations.

2. Rub the charcoal on a piece of paper. Describe what happens.

3. Strike the charcoal sharply with the blunt end of a fork. Describe what happens.

4. When you are finished with your investigation, return the charcoal to your teacher and wash your hands.

Think It Over

Classifying Charcoal is a form of the element carbon. Would you classify carbon as a metal or a nonmetal? Use your observations from this activity to explain your answer.

Life on Earth depends on certain nonmetal elements. The air you and other animals breathe contains several nonmetals, including oxygen. And all living organisms are made from compounds of the nonmetal carbon. Yet, while many compounds containing nonmetals are useful to life, some nonmetals by themselves are poisonous and highly reactive. Still other nonmetals are completely unreactive. Compared to metals, nonmetals have a much wider variety of properties. However, nonmetals do have several properties in common.

Lab zone Discover **Activity**

Skills Focus Classifying   L1

Materials activated charcoal, paper, fork

Time 5 minutes

Tips Activated charcoal is available where aquarium supplies are sold. You may substitute charcoal briquettes, but tell students that the charcoal has been mixed with clay to keep its shape.

Expected Outcome The charcoal breaks easily, rubs off on fingers and paper, and shatters when hit with a fork.

Think It Over Sample answer: Carbon is brittle, dull, not malleable, and not lustrous. Carbon is not a metal.

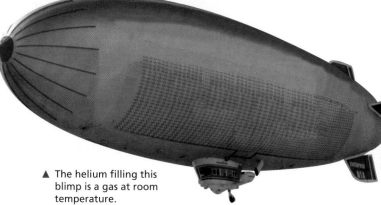

FIGURE 20
Physical Properties of Nonmetals

Nonmetals have properties that are the opposite of metals. **Comparing and Contrasting** *Contrast the properties of these nonmetals with those of metals.*

▲ The helium filling this blimp is a gas at room temperature.

◄ Sulfur crumbles into a powder.

Nonmetals are good insulators. Carbon compounds are found in the plastic insulating these copper wires. ▶

Properties of Nonmetals

A **nonmetal** is an element that lacks most of the properties of a metal. **Most nonmetals are poor conductors of electricity and heat and are reactive with other elements. Solid nonmetals are dull and brittle.** Look at the periodic table in Section 2. All of the elements in green-tinted boxes are nonmetals. Many of the nonmetals are common elements on Earth.

Physical Properties Ten of the 16 nonmetals are gases at room temperature. The air you breathe is mostly a mixture of two nonmetals, nitrogen (N) and oxygen (O). Other nonmetal elements, such as carbon (C), iodine (I), and sulfur (S), are solids at room temperature. Bromine (Br) is the only nonmetal that is liquid at room temperature.

Look at examples of nonmetals in Figure 20. In general, the physical properties of nonmetals are the opposite of those of the metals. Solid nonmetals are dull, meaning not shiny, and brittle, meaning not malleable or ductile. If you hit most solid nonmetals with a hammer, they break or crumble into a powder. Nonmetals usually have lower densities than metals. And nonmetals are also poor conductors of heat and electricity.

Chapter 3 K ◆ 99

Differentiated Instruction

English Language Learners/ Beginning `L1`
Comprehension: Key Concept Rewrite the boldfaced sentences on this page as a list of nonmetal properties. Have students construct a cluster diagram with "Properties of Nonmetals" in the center and each property connected to it by a line. Allow students to list properties using

English synonyms or native words.
learning modality: visual

English Language Learners/ Intermediate `L2`
Comprehension: Key Concept Have students complete the activity at left, but do not allow them to use native words.
learning modality: visual

Instruct

Properties of Nonmetals

Teach Key Concepts `L2`
Contrasting Nonmetals and Metals

Focus Tell students that nonmetals are most often described as anything that is not a metal.

Teach List the properties of metals discussed in *Metals*. Then, list properties of nonmetals, opposite the corresponding metal property. Ask: **Are nonmetals good conductors of heat and electricity?** *(No)* **In what state are most nonmetals found at room temperature?** *(Most are gases, some are solids, only one is a liquid.)* Explain that most solid nonmetals are brittle. Ask: **What properties of metals are the opposite of brittle?** *(Malleable and ductile)*

Apply Ask: **What properties of oxygen make it a nonmetal?** *(Sample answer: It is a gas at room temperature and a poor conductor of electricity and heat.)* **learning modality: verbal**

Independent Practice `L2`

All in One Teaching Resources
• Guided Reading and Study Worksheet: *Nonmetals and Metalloids*

🅞 **Student Edition on Audio CD**

Monitor Progress _____ `L2`

Writing Instruct students to write down one characteristic that most nonmetals have.

Answer
Figure 20 Sulfur is brittle, helium is a gas, and plastics do not conduct electricity. Metals are bendable, good conductors of electricity, and usually solid at room temperature.

K ● 99

Focus Remind students that metals react with other elements by losing electrons and nonmetals gain or share electrons.

Teach Direct students to look at Figure 21. Ask: **Which element will gain an electron?** (*Chlorine*) **Which element will lose an electron?** (*Sodium*)

Apply Explain that the reactivity of elements depends on electrons. Ask: **Why do the nonmetals in Group 18 rarely react with other elements to form compounds?** (*They do not readily lose or share electrons.*)

learning modality: visual

Families of Nonmetals

Teach Key Concepts L2

Nonmetal Groups

Focus Point out that Group 18 is the one group that consists only of nonmetals. However, nonmetals in mixed groups do share similar properties with the metals in their group.

Teach Begin a table on the board with properties of nonmetals as you did with metals. Again, keep track of the properties of each nonmetal family as students study them. Record the properties of that group, including the number of electrons lost when reacting with other elements. Also include examples of each.

Apply Ask: **What property do elements in mixed groups share?** (*They all gain, lose, or share the same number of electrons.*)

learning modality: visual

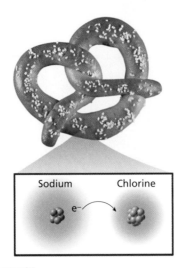

| Sodium | Chlorine |

FIGURE 21
Reactions of Nonmetals
The table salt on a pretzel is mined from deposits found on Earth. The same compound can also be formed from a reaction between the metal sodium and the nonmetal chlorine.

14

6
C
Carbon
14
Si
Silicon
32
Ge
Germanium
50
Sn
Tin
82
Pb
Lead

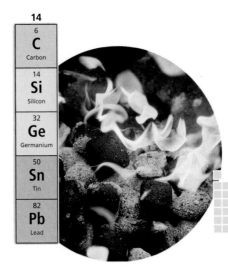

Chemical Properties Most nonmetals are reactive, so they readily form compounds. In fact, fluorine (F) is the most reactive element known. Yet, Group 18 elements hardly ever form compounds.

Atoms of nonmetals usually gain or share electrons when they react with other atoms. When nonmetals and metals react, electrons move from the metal atoms to the nonmetal atoms, as shown by the formation of salt, shown in Figure 21. Another example is rust—a compound made of iron and oxygen (Fe_2O_3). It's the reddish, flaky coating you might see on an old piece of steel or an iron nail.

Many nonmetals can also form compounds with other nonmetals. The atoms share electrons and become bonded together into molecules.

Reading Checkpoint In which portion of the periodic table do you find nonmetals?

Families of Nonmetals

Look again at the periodic table. Notice that only Group 18 contains elements that are all nonmetals. In Groups 14 through 17, there is a mix of nonmetals and other kinds of elements.

The Carbon Family Each element in the carbon family has atoms that can gain, lose, or share four electrons when reacting with other elements. In Group 14, only carbon is a nonmetal. What makes carbon especially important is its role in the chemistry of life. Compounds made of molecules containing long chains of carbon atoms are found in all living things.

Most of the fuels that are burned to yield energy contain carbon. Coal, for example, is mostly the element carbon. Gasoline is made from crude oil, a mixture of carbon compounds with chains of 5 to 50 or more carbon atoms in their molecules.

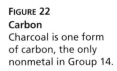

FIGURE 22
Carbon
Charcoal is one form of carbon, the only nonmetal in Group 14.

The Nitrogen Family Group 15, the nitrogen family, contains two nonmetals, nitrogen and phosphorus. These nonmetals usually gain or share three electrons when reacting with other elements. To introduce yourself to nitrogen, take a deep breath. The atmosphere is almost 80 percent nitrogen gas (N_2). Nitrogen does not readily react with other elements, so you breathe out as much nitrogen as you breathe in.

Nitrogen is an example of an element that occurs in nature in the form of diatomic molecules, as N_2. A **diatomic molecule** consists of two atoms. In this form, nitrogen is not very reactive. Although living things need nitrogen, most of them are unable to use nitrogen from the air. However, certain kinds of bacteria can use this nitrogen to form compounds. This process is called nitrogen fixation. Plants can then take up these nitrogen compounds formed in the soil by the bacteria. Farmers also add nitrogen compounds to the soil in the form of fertilizers. Like all animals, you get the nitrogen you need from the food you eat—from plants, or from animals that ate plants.

Phosphorus is the other nonmetal in the nitrogen family. Phosphorus is much more reactive than nitrogen, so phosphorus in nature is always found in compounds. A compound containing phosphorus is used to make matches, because it can react with oxygen in the air.

FIGURE 23
The Nitrogen Family
Nitrogen and phosphorus are grouped in the same family of the periodic table, Group 15. Making Generalizations *How do atoms of both these elements change when they react?*

▼ Nitrogen is a key ingredient of fertilizers.

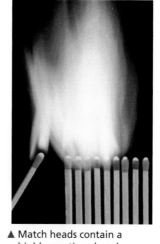

▲ Match heads contain a highly reactive phosphorus compound that ignites easily.

Vocabulary: Word Part Analysis Write the word *diatomic* on the board and ask: **What is the root word of this word?** (*Atom*) Explain that the prefix *di-* means "two" or "double." The suffix *-ic* means "of," or "pertaining to." Say that this suffix changes a noun to an adjective. Ask: **Since you know that an atom is the smallest particle of matter, what does "diatomic molecule" mean?** (*A molecule of two atoms*)

Lab zone Build Inquiry [L2]

Reading Fertilizer Bags

Materials labels from various types of fertilizers

Time 15 minutes

Focus Tell students that nitrogen and phosphorus are two of the key ingredients in fertilizers.

Teach Have students find the guaranteed analysis of chemicals on the fertilizer label. Ask: **In what form is the nitrogen present in the fertilizer?** (*Sample answer: Nitrates and ammonium compounds*) **In what form is the phosphorus?** (*Sample answer: Phosphates*)

Apply Ask: **Why aren't nitrogen and phosphorus present as pure elements in the fertilizer?** (*As part of a compound, nitrogen and phosphorus are more stable and in a form that plants can easily use.*) **learning modality: verbal**

Differentiated Instruction

Gifted and Talented [L3]
Understanding the Bends Explain that even though humans cannot get the nitrogen they need by breathing nitrogen from the air, some inhaled nitrogen gas can dissolve in the blood. Under increased pressure, such as that experienced by deep-sea divers, even more nitrogen dissolves. If a diver surfaces too quickly, the dissolved nitrogen comes out of solution (the blood) too quickly and decompression sickness occurs. Invite students to find out how nitrogen causes decompression sickness (or the bends) to occur. Challenge them to use their knowledge of the gas laws to explain why nitrogen gas can dissolve in the blood at higher pressures. **learning modality: verbal**

Monitor Progress [L2]

Oral Presentation Have students give the number of electrons that elements in the carbon family and elements in the nitrogen family usually lose, gain, or share.

Answers
Figure 23 Both gain or share three electrons.

Reading Checkpoint To the right of the metalloids

Build Inquiry

L2

Finding Nonmetals

Materials none

Time 15 minutes

Focus Tell students that nonmetals have many different uses.

Teach Invite student groups to look for nonmetals in the classroom and around the school building and grounds. Have them list the nonmetals they observe and describe their uses. When students return the classroom, make a class list of the observed nonmetals. Then, challenge students to identify the nonmetal elements.

Apply Ask: **Why are most nonmetals found as part of a compound?** *(Sample answer: Nonmetals are very reactive.)*
learning modality: visual

Try This Activity

Show Me the Oxygen
How can you test for the presence of oxygen?

1. Pour about a 3-cm depth of hydrogen peroxide (H_2O_2) into a test tube.
2. Add a pea-sized amount of manganese dioxide (MnO_2) to the test tube.
3. Observe the test tube for about 1 minute.
4. When instructed by your teacher, set a wooden splint on fire.
5. Blow the splint out after 5 seconds and immediately plunge the glowing splint into the mouth of the test tube. Avoid getting the splint wet.

Observing Describe the change in matter that occurred in the test tube. What evidence indicates that oxygen was produced?

FIGURE 24
The Oxygen Family
Oxygen and sulfur are the most common of the three nonmetals in Group 16.
Interpreting Tables *What is the atomic number of each Group 16 element?*

◄ The rubber in these tires contains sulfur.

102 ◆ K

The Oxygen Family Group 16, the oxygen family, contains three nonmetals—oxygen, sulfur, and selenium. These elements usually gain or share two electrons when reacting with other elements.

You are using oxygen right now. With every breath, oxygen travels into your lungs. There, it is absorbed into your bloodstream, which distributes it all over your body. You could not live without a steady supply of oxygen. Like nitrogen, the oxygen you breathe is a diatomic molecule (O_2). In addition, oxygen sometimes forms a triatomic (three-atom) molecule, which is called ozone (O_3). Ozone collects in a layer in the upper atmosphere, where it screens out harmful radiation from the sun. However, ozone is a dangerous pollutant at ground level because it is highly reactive.

Because oxygen is highly reactive, it can combine with almost every other element. It also is the most abundant element in Earth's crust and the second-most abundant element in the atmosphere. (The first is nitrogen.)

Sulfur is the other common nonmetal in the oxygen family. If you have ever smelled the odor of a rotten egg, then you are already familiar with the smell of some sulfur compounds. Sulfur is used in the manufacture of rubber for rubber bands and automobile tires. Most sulfur is used to make sulfuric acid (H_2SO_4), one of the most important chemicals used in industry.

▲ Some of the oxygen needed by a frog enters through its skin.

16
8
O
Oxygen

16
S
Sulfer

34
Se
Selenium

52
Te
Tellurium

84
Po
Polonium

Try This Activity

Skills Focus Observing **L2**

Materials 3% hydrogen peroxide solution, manganese dioxide, test tube, wooden splint, matches, safety goggles

Time 15 minutes

Tips Substitute wooden coffee stirrers for splints.

Expected Outcome The H_2O_2 bubbles after the addition of MnO_2. The glowing splint relights and burns brightly. Sample answer: Oxygen in the form of a solid and a liquid changes to a gas. The splint relit, indicating the presence of oxygen.

Extend Test for the presence of carbon dioxide. Add a small amount of hydrochloric acid to a test tube containing crushed shells or limestone (calcium carbonate). After the reaction, light a splint and insert it into the test tube. It will be extinguished by the carbon dioxide gas. **learning modality: visual**

The Halogen Family Group 17 contains fluorine, chlorine, bromine, iodine, and astatine. These elements are also known as the **halogens,** which means "salt forming." All but astatine are nonmetals, and all share similar properties. A halogen atom typically gains or shares one electron when it reacts with other elements.

All of the halogens are very reactive, and the uncombined elements are dangerous to humans. Fluorine is so reactive that it reacts with almost every other known substance. Even water and powdered glass will burn in fluorine. Chlorine gas is extremely dangerous, but it is used in small amounts to kill bacteria in water supplies.

Even though the halogen elements are dangerous, many of the compounds that halogens form are quite useful. Compounds of carbon and fluorine make up the nonstick coating on cookware. Small amounts of fluorine compounds are added to the water supply to help prevent tooth decay. Chlorine is one of the two elements in ordinary table salt (the other is sodium). Another salt of chlorine is calcium chloride, which is used to help melt snow. Bromine reacts with silver to form silver bromide, which is used in photographic film.

Go Online
SciLINKS NSTA

For: Links on nonmetals
Visit: www.SciLinks.org
Web Code: scn-1134

Go Online
SciLINKS NSTA

For: Links on nonmetals
Visit: www.SciLinks.org
Web Code: scn-1134

Download a worksheet that will guide students' review of Internet resources on nonmetals.

Lab zone Build **Inquiry** L3

Contrasting Halogens and Noble Gases

Materials art supplies, paper

Time 15 minutes

Focus Tell students that halogens are highly reactive and noble gases are very unreactive.

Teach Challenge students to create a cartoon that contrasts the reactivity of halogens and noble gases. Cartoons can be a single panel or a short series, color or black and white. Encourage students to be creative.

Apply Ask: **What causes the difference between the reactivity of halogens and noble gases?** (*Halogens easily gain or share one electron when reacting with other elements. Noble gases do not usually gain, lose, or share any electrons.*) **learning modality: kinesthetic**

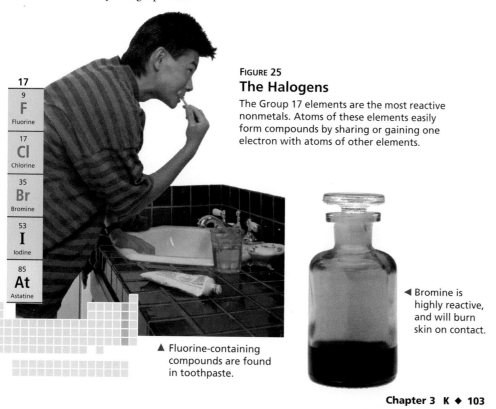

FIGURE 25
The Halogens
The Group 17 elements are the most reactive nonmetals. Atoms of these elements easily form compounds by sharing or gaining one electron with atoms of other elements.

◀ Bromine is highly reactive, and will burn skin on contact.

▲ Fluorine-containing compounds are found in toothpaste.

Chapter 3 K ◆ 103

Monitor Progress L2

Oral Presentation Call on students at random to give the group number and one characteristic of the oxygen family and the halogens.

Answer
Figure 24 Oxygen, 8; sulfur, 16; selenium, 34; tellurium, 52; and polonium, 84

The Metalloids

Teach Key Concepts L2
Properties of Metalloids

Focus Show students the location of metalloids in the periodic table.

Teach Ask: **What are some properties of metalloids?** *(They have some properties of both metals and nonmetals. They are all solids at room temperature. They are brittle, hard, and somewhat reactive.)* **What is the most useful property of metalloids?** *(Their varying ability to conduct electricity)*

Apply Explain that silicon and germanium are metalloids used to make semiconductors. Ask: **What is a semiconductor?** *(A substance that can conduct electricity under some conditions but not under others.)* **What are semiconductors used for?** *(To make computer chips, transistors, and lasers)* **learning modality: verbal**

Integrating Physics L2

Have students find silicon on the periodic table. Ask: **Is silicon a metal, nonmetal, or metalloid?** *(Metalloid)* Explain that besides being used to make computer chips, silicon is also used to make solar cells. When light strikes the junction between two semiconductors or between a metal and a semiconductor, an electron moves from one atom to another. Ask: **What is the charge of an atom that has gained an electron?** *(Negative)* **What is the charge of an atom that has lost an electron?** *(Positive)* Explain that this transfer of charge can power a small appliance or charge a battery. **learning modality: verbal**

FIGURE 26
The Noble Gases
Electricity makes the Group 18 elements glow brightly inside glass tubes. **Applying Concepts** *Why are neon and the other noble gases so unreactive?*

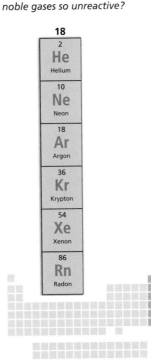

The Noble Gases The elements in Group 18 are known as the **noble gases.** They do not ordinarily form compounds because atoms of noble gases do not usually gain, lose, or share electrons. As a result, the noble gases are usually unreactive. Even so, scientists have been able to form some compounds of the heavy noble gases (Kr, Xe) in the laboratory.

All the noble gases exist in Earth's atmosphere, but only in small amounts. Because they are so unreactive, the noble gases were not discovered until the late 1800s. Helium was discovered by a scientist who was studying not the atmosphere but the sun.

Have you made use of a noble gas? You have if you have ever purchased a floating balloon filled with helium. Noble gases are also used in glowing electric lights. These lights are commonly called neon lights, even though they are often filled with argon, xenon, or other noble gases.

Hydrogen Alone in the upper left corner of the periodic table is hydrogen—the element with the simplest and smallest atoms. Each hydrogen atom has one proton and one electron. Some hydrogen atoms also have neutrons. Because the chemical properties of hydrogen differ very much from those of the other elements, it really cannot be grouped into a family. Although hydrogen makes up more than 90 percent of the atoms in the universe, it makes up only 1 percent of the mass of Earth's crust, oceans, and atmosphere. Hydrogen is rarely found on Earth as a pure element. Most hydrogen is combined with oxygen in water (H_2O).

Reading Checkpoint Why were the noble gases undiscovered until the late 1800s?

FIGURE 27
Importance of Hydrogen
Water is a compound of hydrogen and oxygen. Without liquid water, life on Earth would be impossible.

The Metalloids

Along the border between the metals and the nonmetals are seven elements called metalloids. These elements are shown in the purple squares in the periodic table in Section 2. The **metalloids** have some characteristics of both metals and nonmetals. All are solids at room temperature. They are brittle, hard, and somewhat reactive.

The most common metalloid is silicon (Si). Silicon combines with oxygen to form silicon dioxide (SiO_2). Ordinary sand, which is mostly SiO_2, is the main component of glass. A compound of boron (B) and oxygen is added during the process of glassmaking to make heat-resistant glass. Compounds of boron are also used in some cleaning materials.

The most useful property of the metalloids is their varying ability to conduct electricity. Whether or not a metalloid conducts electricity can depend on temperature, exposure to light, or the presence of small amounts of impurities. For this reason, metalloids such as silicon, germanium (Ge), and arsenic (As) are used to make semiconductors. **Semiconductors** are substances that can conduct electricity under some conditions but not under other conditions. Semiconductors are used to make computer chips, transistors, and lasers.

 Reading Checkpoint What is the most common metalloid, and where is it found?

FIGURE 28
Silicon
A silicon computer chip is dwarfed by an ant, but the chip's properties as a semiconductor make it a powerful part of modern computers.

14
Si
Silicon

Section 4 Assessment

Target Reading Skill Using Prior Knowledge Review your graphic organizer about nonmetals and metalloids, and revise it based on what you learned in the section.

Reviewing Key Concepts

1. a. **Reviewing** What physical and chemical properties are found among the nonmetals?
   b. **Making Generalizations** What happens to the atoms of most nonmetals when they react with other elements?
   c. **Comparing and Contrasting** How do the physical and chemical properties of the halogens compare with those of the noble gases?

2. a. **Identifying** Where in the periodic table are the metalloids found?
   b. **Describing** What are three uses of metalloids?
   c. **Applying Concepts** What property makes certain metalloids useful as "switches" to turn a small electric current on and off?

Lab zone **At-Home Activity**

Halogen Hunt Identify compounds in your home that contain halogens. Look at labels on foods, cooking ingredients, cleaning materials, medicines, and cosmetics. The presence of a halogen is often indicated by the words *fluoride, chloride, bromide,* and *iodide* or the prefixes *fluoro-, chloro-, bromo-,* and *iodo-.* Show your family these examples and describe properties of the halogens.

Lab zone **At-Home Activity**

Halogen Hunt L1 Suggest students make a chart to list halogens they find. Examples include toothpaste (fluorine), table salt (chlorine), flour (bromine), tincture of iodine (iodine), and pesticides (fluorine and chlorine). Students might know about halogen light fixtures. Caution students not to touch pesticides or halogen light bulbs.

Lab zone **Chapter Project**

Keep Students on Track Allow students to begin testing their metal samples after you have approved their experimental plans. Suggest that students use descriptive means (e.g., *well, somewhat, poorly, not at all*) to rate a property if they cannot measure it exactly. When students test for conductivity, they might also test nonmetals (e.g., plastics, wood) for comparison.

Monitor Progress L2

Answers

Figure 26 Atoms of noble gases do not usually gain, lose, or share electrons.

✓ **Reading Checkpoint** Because they are unreactive and scarce

✓ **Reading Checkpoint** Silicon; in sand

Assess

Reviewing Key Concepts

1. **a.** Some nonmetals are gases at room temperature, while others are dull, brittle solids. In general, nonmetals have lower densities than metals and are poor conductors of heat and electricity. Except for Group 18 elements, most nonmetals react readily to form compounds. **b.** Atoms of nonmetals usually gain or share electrons when they react with other elements. **c.** At room temperature, fluorine and chlorine are gases, bromine is a liquid, iodine and astatine are solids, and all the noble gases are gases. While all the halogens are very reactive, the noble gases are usually stable and unreactive.

2. **a.** The metalloids are found along the border between the metals and nonmetals in the periodic table. **b.** Sample answer: As components of glass, cleaning materials, computer chips, transistors, and lasers **c.** Some metalloids, called *semiconductors,* conduct electricity under some conditions but not under other conditions.

Reteach L1

Have students make a table that compares and contrasts the properties of nonmetals and metalloids.

Performance Assessment L2

Writing Have students write a paragraph that explains why some metalloids are used to make semiconductors.

All in One Teaching Resources

- Section Summary: *Nonmetals and Metalloids*
- Review and Reinforce: *Nonmetals and Metalloids*
- Enrich: *Nonmetals and Metalloids*

Alien Periodic Table L2

Prepare for Inquiry

Key Concept
In the periodic table, elements are classified according to their properties.

Skills Objective
After this lab, students will be able to
- draw conclusions about the Earth names of the alien elements based on atomic number.
- classify elements based on their properties.
- interpret data on the properties of elements.
- infer the position of the elements on the periodic table.

Prep Time 5 minutes

Class Time 30 minutes

Advance Planning
Remind students to bring their textbooks to lab.

Alternative Materials
Give students index cards to rearrange the elements until they find the correct order. Or provide extra copies of the alien periodic table.

All in One Teaching Resources
- Lab Worksheet: *Alien Periodic Table*

Guide Inquiry

Invitation
Challenge students to find specific elements on the periodic table using clues. Ask: **What metal in Period 3 is slightly heavier than sodium?** *(Magnesium)*

Introduce the Procedure
Refer students to the data for the alien elements and suggest that they work on the clues in order. Emphasize that they will need more than one clue to identify some elements.

Troubleshooting the Experiment
- Suggest that students work in pencil.
- Allow students to work in pairs.

Expected Outcome
See the sample data table on the next page.

Alien Periodic Table

Problem
Imagine that inhabitants of another planet send a message to Earth that contains information about 30 elements. However, the message contains different names and symbols for these elements than those used on Earth. Which elements on the periodic table do these "alien" names represent?

Skills Focus
drawing conclusions, classifying, interpreting data, inferring

Materials
- ruler
- periodic table from text for reference

Procedure
1. Copy the blank periodic table on page 107 into your notebook.
2. Listed below are data on the chemical and physical properties of the 30 elements. Place the elements in their proper position in the blank periodic table.

Alien Elements

 The noble gases are **bombal (Bo)**, **wobble (Wo)**, **jeptum (J)**, and **logon (L)**. Among these gases, wobble has the greatest atomic mass and bombal the least. Logon is lighter than jeptum.

 The most reactive group of metals are **xtalt (X)**, **byyou (By)**, **chow (Ch)**, and **quackzil (Q)**. Of these metals, chow has the lowest atomic mass. Quackzil is in the same period as wobble.

 Apstrom (A), **vulcania (V)**, and **kratt (Kt)** are nonmetals whose atoms typically gain or share one electron. Vulcania is in the same period as quackzil and wobble.

 The metalloids are **ernst (E)**, **highho (Hi)**, **terriblum (T)**, and **sississ (Ss)**. Sississ is the metalloid with the greatest atomic mass. Ernst is the metalloid with the lowest atomic mass. Highho and terriblum are in Group 14. Terriblum has more protons than highho. **Yazzer (Yz)** touches the zigzag line, but it's a metal, not a metalloid.

 The lightest element of all is called **pfsst (Pf)**. The heaviest element in the group of 30 elements is **eldorado (El)**. The most chemically active nonmetal is apstrom. Kratt reacts with byyou to form table salt.

 The element **doggone (D)** has only 4 protons in its atoms.

 Floxxit (Fx) is important in the chemistry of life. It forms compounds made of long chains of atoms. **Rhaatrap (R)** and **doadeer (Do)** are metals in the fourth period, but rhaatrap is less reactive than doadeer.

 Magnificon (M), **goldy (G)**, and sississ are all members of Group 15. Goldy has fewer electrons than magnificon.

 Urrp (Up), **oz (Oz)**, and **nuutye (Nu)** all gain 2 electrons when they react. Nuutye is found as a diatomic molecule and has the same properties as a gas found in Earth's atmosphere. Oz has a lower atomic number than urrp.

 The element **anatom (An)** has atoms with a total of 49 electrons. **Zapper (Z)** and **pie (Pi)** lose two electrons when they react. Zapper is used to make lightweight alloys.

Analyze and Conclude
1. See the column on the next page.

2. Yes. Some clues identified a characteristic belonging to only one element, such as doggone having 4 protons, pfsst being the lightest element, and anatom having 49 electrons.

3. Some clues apply to several elements, such as clues about a group, so you need more information to identify specific elements.

4. Although there are some exceptions to the pattern, the atomic mass of elements usually increases as the atomic number increases.

5. The alien periodic table does not include transition metals, lanthanides, actinides, and elements beyond atomic number 50. Sample answer: It is not likely that certain groups of elements would be missing in a place where so many other elements are present.

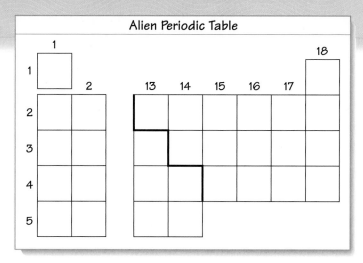

Alien Periodic Table

1							18
1	**2**	**13**	**14**	**15**	**16**	**17**	
2							
3							
4							
5							

Analyze and Conclude

1. **Drawing Conclusions** List the Earth names for the 30 alien elements in order of atomic number.

2. **Classifying** Were you able to place some elements within the periodic table with just a single clue? Explain using examples.

3. **Interpreting Data** Why did you need two or more clues to place other elements? Explain using examples.

4. **Inferring** Why could you use clues about atomic mass to place elements, even though the table is now based on atomic numbers?

5. **Communicating** Write a paragraph describing which groups of elements are not included in the alien periodic table. Explain whether or not you think it is likely that an alien planet would lack these elements.

More to Explore

Notice that Period 5 is incomplete on the alien periodic table. Create names and symbols for each of the missing elements. Then, compose a series of clues that would allow another student to identify these elements. Make your clues as precise as possible.

▼ Radio telescopes in New Mexico

K ◆ 107

1.

Earth	Alien Planet
hydrogen	pfsst
helium	bombal
lithium	chow
beryllium	doggone
boron	ernsst
carbon	floxxit
nitrogen	goldy
oxygen	nuutye
fluorine	apstrom
neon	logon
sodium	byyou
magnesium	zapper
aluminum	yazzer
silicon	highho
phosphorus	magnificon
sulfur	oz
chlorine	kratt
argon	jeptum
potassium	quackzil
calcium	doadeer
gallium	rhaatrap
germanium	terriblum
arsenic	sississ
selenium	urrp
bromine	vulcania
krypton	wobble
rubidium	xtalt
strontium	pie
indium	anatom
tin	eldorado

Extend Inquiry

More to Explore Sample answer: Democritus (De), boyle (Bo), avogadro (Av), and heisenberg (Hb) could be the names and symbols of the missing elements (though students will likely choose others). Sample clues: All the missing elements are in the fifth period. Hb and Bo are both metalloids, but Hb has a smaller mass. De is an unreactive gas. Av tends to gain one electron when it reacts.

Elements From Stardust

Objectives
After this lesson, students will be able to
K.3.5.1 Explain how elements are created in stars.
K.3.5.2 Identify the results of fusion in large stars.

Target Reading Skill
Sequencing Explain that organizing information from beginning to end helps students understand a step-by-step process.

Answers
Sample flowchart:

Formation of Elements
Hydrogen nuclei fuse, forming helium.
Helium nuclei fuse, forming beryllium.
Fusion continues in smaller stars, forming elements up to oxygen.
Fusion in larger stars produces heavier elements up to iron.
The heaviest elements form during supernova explosions of the most massive stars.

All in One Teaching Resources
• Transparency K29

Preteach

Build Background Knowledge L2
Relating Stars to Particle Accelerators
Remind students how larger elements are made synthetically in particle accelerators. Ask: **How do particle accelerators work?** (*The nuclear particles of atoms are forced to crash into each other.*) Tell students that in this section they will learn how stars work like particle accelerators to form elements.

Elements From Stardust

Reading Preview
Key Concepts
• How are elements created in stars?
• What are the results of fusion in large stars?

Key Terms
• plasma • nuclear fusion
• nebula • supernova

Target Reading Skill
Sequencing As you read, make a flowchart like the one below that shows how elements are formed in stars. Write the steps in separate boxes in the flowchart in the order in which they occur.

Formation of Elements

| Hydrogen nuclei fuse, forming helium. |

↓

| Helium nuclei fuse, forming beryllium. |

↓

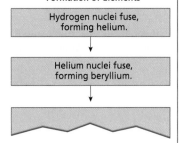

FIGURE 29
The Sun
Hot plasma streams into space from the surface of the sun.

Lab zone Discover Activity

Can Helium Be Made From Hydrogen?
1. A hydrogen atom has a nucleus of 1 proton surrounded by an electron. Most hydrogen nuclei do not contain neutrons, but one isotope of hydrogen contains 1 neutron, and another isotope contains 2 neutrons. Draw models of each of the three isotopes of hydrogen.
2. All helium atoms have 2 protons and 2 electrons, and almost all have 2 neutrons. Draw a model of a typical helium atom.

Think It Over
Developing Hypotheses How might the hydrogen atoms you drew combine to form a helium atom? Draw a diagram to illustrate your hypothesis. Why would hydrogen nuclei with neutrons be important for this process?

Have you wondered where the elements come from, or why some elements are common here on Earth, while others are much more rare? To answer questions such as these, scientists have looked in a place that might surprise you: stars. They have looked not only at distant stars, but also at the nearest star, the sun. By studying the sun and other stars, scientists have formed some interesting models of how the stars shine and theories about the origins of matter here on Earth.

How Elements Form in Stars
Like many other stars, the sun is made mostly of one element—hydrogen. This hydrogen exists at tremendously high pressures and hot temperatures. How hot is it? The temperature in the sun's core is about 15 million degrees Celsius.

Lab zone Discover Activity

Skills Focus Developing hypotheses L3
Materials none
Time 10 minutes
Tips Refer students to Figure 3 in *Introduction to Atoms* for a diagram showing the nuclei of isotopes. Remind them to draw only the nuclei of the atoms, not the electrons.

Think It Over Students might hypothesize that the atoms combine because the nuclei have lots of energy, are traveling at great speeds, or are under great pressure. Students' diagrams should show two hydrogen nuclei colliding with one another, forming a helium nucleus. The hydrogen nuclei must have neutrons because helium atoms have neutrons.

Plasma At the extreme temperatures found in the sun and other stars, matter does not exist as a solid, a liquid, or a gas. Instead, it exists in a state called plasma. The **plasma** state of matter consists of a gas-like mixture of free electrons and atoms stripped of electrons. Plasmas don't exist just in stars. A comet's tail is made partly of plasma. Plasmas also can be produced by high-voltage electricity or even an electric spark. A plasma forms inside a fluorescent light when it is switched on. Plasmas are also used to generate light inside flat-panel TV screens that you can hang on a wall. The difference between a plasma in a fluorescent light and plasma in the sun is that the sun's plasma is under extremely high pressure.

When Nuclei Combine Remember that atomic nuclei contain protons, which means that nuclei are positively charged. Usually, positively charged nuclei repel one another. But in stars, the pressure is so high that nuclei are squeezed close together and collide with one another.

As in particle accelerators, when colliding nuclei have enough energy, they can join together, as shown in Figure 31. **Nuclear fusion** is a process in which two atomic nuclei combine to form a larger nucleus, releasing huge amounts of energy in the process. **Nuclear fusion, which occurs in stars on a huge scale, combines smaller nuclei into larger nuclei, creating heavier elements.**

FIGURE 31
Nuclear Fusion
During nuclear fusion, two atomic nuclei collide and fuse. *Applying Concepts* *Why does nuclear fusion result in the production of a different element?*

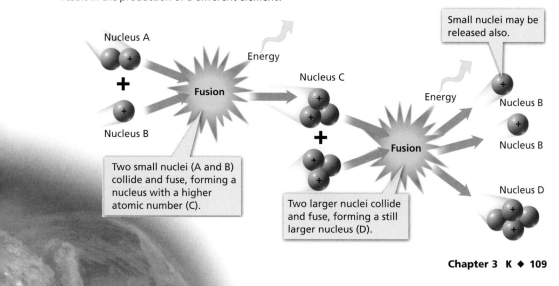

Two small nuclei (A and B) collide and fuse, forming a nucleus with a higher atomic number (C).

Two larger nuclei collide and fuse, forming a still larger nucleus (D).

Small nuclei may be released also.

Chapter 3 K ◆ 109

Instruct

How Elements Form in Stars

Teach Key Concepts　　L2
Nuclear Fusion and New Elements

Focus Tell students that in stars the electrons have escaped from the nucleus.

Teach Ask: **What occurs during nuclear fusion?** (*Two atomic nuclei combine to form a larger nucleus, with the release of energy.*) **How does nuclear fusion create new elements?** (*Smaller nuclei combine to form larger nuclei, creating new, heavier elements.*)

Apply Ask: **Why does nuclear fusion occur in stars?** (*The pressure is so high that nuclei are squeezed together.*) **learning modality: verbal**

Use Visuals: Figure 31　　L2
Steps in Nuclear Fusion

Focus Have students study Figure 31.

Teach Ask: **What particles make up nucleus A?** (*One proton and one neutron*) **What results from the fusion of nucleus A and nucleus B?** (*A larger nucleus and the release of energy*)

Apply Ask: **If this nuclear fusion reaction were occurring in the sun, what elements are A, B, C, and D?** (*A, isotope of hydrogen; B, isotope of hydrogen; C, isotope of helium; D, isotope of helium*) **learning modality: visual**

All in One Teaching Resources
• Transparency K30

Independent Practice　　L2
All in One Teaching Resources
• Guided Reading and Study Worksheet: *Elements From Stardust*

◉ **Student Edition on Audio CD**

Monitor Progress _____ L2

Writing Have students explain why matter must be in the form of plasma and why the nuclei must be under high pressure for nuclear fusion to occur.

Answer
Figure 31 The number of protons in the resulting nucleus is different.

⌐ Differentiated Instruction

Gifted and Talented　　L3
Tracing the Path of Element Formation
Challenge students to diagram the pathway of element formation in nuclear fusion reactions by starting with hydrogen and ending with iron. Suggest that students develop a method of organizing information to help them see the progression. **learning modality: logical/mathematical**

Less Proficient Readers　　L1
Asking Questions Have students listen to *Elements From Stardust* on the **Student Edition on Audio CD**. Before they listen, have them draw 3 columns (*What I Know, What I Want to Know, What I Learned*) and fill in what they already know about the inside of stars. Next, have them list questions. As they listen, they can answer their questions. **learning modality: verbal**

Elements and the Periodic Table

Show the Video Field Trip to let students understand the death of a star and how elements form. Discussion question: **How are elements formed when stars die?** *(As the layers of the star burn, the nuclei fuse into heavier elements.)*

Lab zone **Build Inquiry** L2

Modeling Element Formation

Materials 2 colors of modeling clay

Focus Remind students that electrons are not involved in fusion.

Teach Invite students to model the formation of helium, beryllium, carbon, and oxygen. Suggest that they use Figure 31 as a guide.

Apply Ask: **What factor determines which element an atom is?** *(The number of protons in the nucleus)* **learning modality: kinesthetic**

Go Online
SCiLINKS™ NSTA

For: Links on nuclear fusion
Visit: www.SciLinks.org
Web Code: scn-1135

Download a worksheet that will guide students' review of Internet resources on nuclear fusion.

Elements From Large Stars

Teach Key Concepts L2
Elements From Supernovas

Focus Tell students that stars larger than Earth's sun can produce heavier elements.

Teach Ask: **What is a supernova?** *(A huge explosion that breaks apart a massive star)* **How does a supernova create the heaviest elements?** *(Sample answer: It provides energy for the nuclear fusion reactions to occur.)*

Apply Ask: **Where did the matter in our sun and its planets come from?** *(From a gigantic supernova that occurred billions of years ago)* **learning modality: verbal**

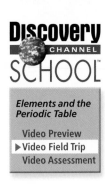

Discovery
CHANNEL
SCHOOL™

Elements and the
Periodic Table

Video Preview
▶ Video Field Trip
Video Assessment

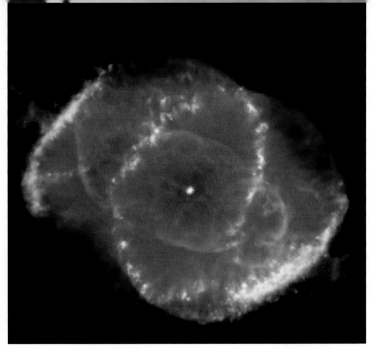

FIGURE 32
Planetary Nebula
The Cat's Eye Nebula is the remains of a star similar to the sun. Energy from the star causes the gases to glow.

Go Online
SCiLINKS™ NSTA

For: Links on nuclear fusion
Visit: www.SciLinks.org
Web Code: scn-1135

New Elements From Fusion What are the steps of nuclear fusion in the sun and other stars? In the sun, different isotopes of hydrogen fuse, producing nuclei of helium. This reaction produces a huge amount of energy and is the most important source of the energy in the sun. In other words, hydrogen is the fuel that powers the sun. Scientists estimate that the sun has enough hydrogen to last another 5 billion years.

As more and more helium builds up in the core, the sun's temperature and volume change. New fusion reactions occur. Over time, two or more helium nuclei can fuse, forming nuclei of heavier elements. For example, two helium nuclei combine, forming a nucleus of beryllium. Another helium nucleus can fuse with the beryllium nucleus, resulting in a carbon nucleus. Yet another helium nucleus and a carbon nucleus can fuse, forming oxygen. But stars the size of the sun do not contain enough energy to produce elements heavier than oxygen. Eventually, a star like the sun shrinks and its elements blow away. It forms a **nebula**—or cloudlike region of gases—similar to the one shown in Figure 32.

 Reading Checkpoint **What elements can be produced by stars the size of the sun?**

Elements From Large Stars

As they age, larger stars become even hotter than the sun. These stars have enough energy to produce heavier elements, such as magnesium and silicon. In more massive stars, fusion continues until the core is almost all iron.

Find iron on the periodic table in Section 2. You can see that there are many other elements heavier than iron. How are elements heavier than iron produced? In the final hours of the most massive stars, scientists have observed an event called a supernova. A **supernova** is a huge explosion that breaks apart a massive star, producing temperatures up to 1 billion degrees Celsius. **A supernova provides enough energy for the nuclear fusion reactions that create the heaviest elements.** The elements are blown off into space as the star burns out.

Most astronomers agree that the matter in the sun and the planets around it, including Earth, originally came from a gigantic supernova that occurred billions of years ago. If so, this means that the matter all around you was created in a star, and all matter on Earth is a form of stardust.

 Reading Checkpoint Where are elements heavier than iron produced?

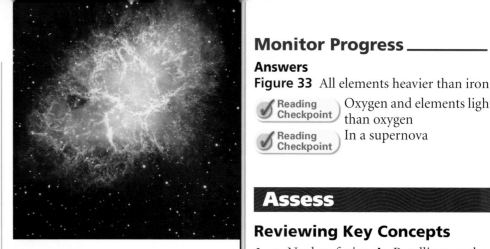

FIGURE 33
Supernova
The Crab Nebula is the supernova of a massive star first observed on Earth in the year 1054 by Chinese astronomers.
Making Generalizations *What elements may have formed in this supernova that would not have formed in a smaller star?*

Section 5 Assessment

Target Reading Skill Sequencing Refer to your flowchart about the formation of elements in stars as you answer Question 1.

Reviewing Key Concepts
1. a. **Identifying** What is the process that produces elements in stars?
   b. **Explaining** How are the elements beryllium, carbon, and oxygen produced in stars like the sun?
   c. **Applying Concepts** Why can elements be produced in the sun but not in Earth's atmosphere?
2. a. **Defining** What is a supernova?
   b. **Describing** What conditions of a supernova cause elements that are heavier than iron to form?
   c. **Developing Hypotheses** Earth has abundant amounts of iron, but also has many elements heavier than iron. Form a hypothesis to explain the presence of these heavier elements.

Writing in Science

How-to Paragraph Suppose you are the science officer on a spaceship. Your mission is to collect and analyze samples of matter from various sites as the ship travels around the Milky Way Galaxy. You and your assistants are able to identify the elements present in a sample. You want to know whether the sample could have come from a star like the sun, a more massive star, or a supernova. Write a set of instructions telling your assistants how to decide on the origin of the samples.

Chapter 3 K ◆ 111

Monitor Progress ____ [L2]

Answers
Figure 33 All elements heavier than iron
✓ **Reading Checkpoint** Oxygen and elements lighter than oxygen
✓ **Reading Checkpoint** In a supernova

Assess

Reviewing Key Concepts

1. a. Nuclear fusion b. Beryllium, carbon, and oxygen are produced in stars when helium nuclei combine with other helium nuclei and with the nuclei of beryllium and carbon. c. The high pressures and temperatures that allow nuclear fusion to occur in the sun do not exist in Earth's atmosphere.
2. a. A huge explosion that breaks apart a massive star b. Temperatures up to one billion degrees Celsius and the energy created by the huge explosion c. Because Earth has elements heavier than iron, the matter that makes up Earth was probably formed in a gigantic supernova that occurred billions of years ago.

Reteach [L1]
Have students diagram how two helium nuclei can form beryllium.

Performance Assessment [L2]
Writing Invite students to write a paragraph explaining how stars function as element factories.
Writing Students can save their paragraphs in their portfolios.

All in One Teaching Resources
- Section Summary: *Elements From Stars*
- Review and Reinforce: *Elements From Stars*
- Enrich: *Elements From Stars*

Writing in Science

Writing Mode Exposition/How-to
Scoring Rubric
4 Exceeds criteria; includes complete and highly accurate instructions for differentiating among the three origins of the samples
3 Meets criteria

2 Includes adequate instructions for differentiating between at least two of the origins and/or contains minor errors
1 Includes adequate instructions for at least one of the origins and/or contains serious errors

nteractive Textbook

- Complete student edition
- Section and chapter self-assessments
- Assessment reports for teachers

Help Students Read   L2

Building Vocabulary

Word/Part Analysis Tell students that they can use what they know about word parts to figure out the meaning of words. Instruct students to separate the word parts from *nonmetal* and *metalloid*. Suggest that they look at the word *metal* if they have difficulty. Then, have them look up each word part and write the definitions of these words using the definitions they found for the word parts. (Non- *means "not" and -oid means "having the appearance of" or "resembles."*)

Paraphrasing By writing the definitions of key terms in their own words, students can relate meaning to their own experiences. You might have students paraphrase all the key terms, or allow them to choose the terms that are most troublesome. Then have them read the text associated with the terms and find the terms in a dictionary or encyclopedia. From these definitions, challenge students to write another definition in their own words.

Connecting Concepts

Concept Maps Help students develop one way to show how the information in this chapter is related. Elements are organized in the periodic table according to their properties. These properties result from the properties of atoms. Have students brainstorm to identify the key concepts, key terms, details, and examples. Then write each item on a self-stick note and attach it at random to chart paper or to the board.

Tell students that this concept map will be organized in hierarchical order and to begin at the top with the key concepts. Ask students these questions to guide them to categorize the information on the self-stick notes: **What are atoms? How are elements organized? What are the properties of**

① Introduction to Atoms

Key Concepts

- Atoms are made of even smaller particles called protons, neutrons, and electrons.
- An element can be identified by the number of protons in the nucleus of its atoms.
- Because atoms are so small, scientists create models to describe them.

Key Terms

nucleus
proton
neutron
electron
atomic number
isotope
mass number
model

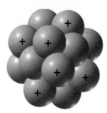

② Organizing the Elements

Key Concepts

- Mendeleev noticed that a pattern of properties appeared when he arranged the elements in order of increasing atomic mass.
- Each square in the periodic table includes the element's atomic number, chemical symbol, name, and atomic mass.
- The properties of an element can be predicted from its location in the periodic table.

Key Terms

atomic mass	period
periodic table	group
chemical symbol	

③ Metals

Key Concepts

- The physical properties of metals include shininess, malleability, ductility, and conductivity.
- The reactivity of metals tends to decrease as you move from left to right across the periodic table.
- Elements that follow uranium in the periodic table are made—or synthesized—when nuclear particles are forced to crash into one another.

Key Terms

metal	alkali metal
malleable	alkaline earth metal
ductile	transition metal
conductivity	alloy
reactivity	particle accelerator
corrosion	

④ Nonmetals and Metalloids

Key Concepts

- Most nonmetals are poor conductors of heat and electricity and are reactive with other elements. Solid nonmetals are dull and brittle.
- The most useful property of the metalloids is their varying ability to conduct electricity.

Key Terms

nonmetal	noble gas
diatomic molecule	metalloid
halogen	semiconductor

⑤ Elements From Stardust

Key Concepts

- Nuclear fusion, which occurs in stars on a huge scale, combines smaller nuclei into larger nuclei, creating heavier elements.
- A supernova provides enough energy for the nuclear fusion reactions that create the heaviest elements.

Key Terms

plasma	nebula
nuclear fusion	supernova

metals, nonmetals, and metalloids? How do stars form elements?

Prompt students by using connecting words or phrases, such as "include," "are made up of," and "have properties of," to indicate the basis for the organization of the map. The phrases should form a sentence between or among a set of concepts.

Answer

Accept logical presentations by students.

All in One Teaching Resources

- Key Terms Review: *Elements and the Periodic Table*
- Connecting Concepts: *Elements and the Periodic Table*

Review and Assessment

Go Online
PHSchool.com
For: Self-Assessment
Visit: PHSchool.com
Web Code: cga-1030

Organizing Information

Concept Mapping Copy the concept map about the periodic table onto a sheet of paper. Then complete it and add a title. (For more on Concept Mapping, see the Skills Handbook.)

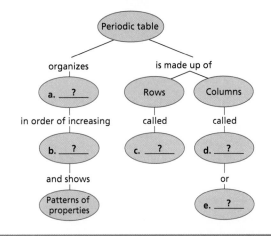

Reviewing Key Terms

Choose the letter of the best answer.

1. The atomic number of an atom is determined by the number of
   a. protons.   b. electrons.
   c. neutrons.   d. isotopes.

2. In the modern periodic table, elements are arranged
   a. according to atomic mass.
   b. according to atomic number.
   c. in alphabetical order.
   d. according to the number of neutrons in their nuclei.

3. Of the following, the group that contains elements that are the most reactive is the
   a. alkali metals.
   b. alkaline earth metals.
   c. carbon family.
   d. noble gases.

4. Unlike metals, many nonmetals are
   a. good conductors of heat and electricity.
   b. malleable and ductile.
   c. gases at room temperature.
   d. shiny.

5. At the hot temperatures of stars, electrons are stripped away from nuclei. This process forms a state of matter called
   a. a heavy element.   b. liquid.
   c. plasma.   d. supernova.

6. Inside the sun, nuclear fusion creates helium nuclei from
   a. oxygen nuclei.
   b. beryllium nuclei.
   c. carbon nuclei.
   d. hydrogen nuclei.

Writing in Science

News Report Imagine you are writing an article for a space magazine about the life cycle of a star. Which elements are produced in a star at different stages? How are these elements distributed into space?

Discovery CHANNEL SCHOOL

Elements and the Periodic Table
Video Preview
Video Field Trip
▶ Video Assessment

Review and Assessment

Organizing Information

Sample title: Organization of the Periodic Table
a. Elements
b. Atomic number
c. Periods
d. Families (or Groups)
e. Groups (or Families)

Reviewing Key Terms

1. a 2. b 3. a 4. c 5. c 6. d

Writing in Science

Writing Mode Description

Scoring Rubric

4 Exceeds criteria; includes a highly detailed and accurate description of the life cycle of a star, including what elements are formed and how they are dispersed

3 Meets criteria

2 Includes a brief description that contains a few errors and/or omissions

1 Includes a sketchy description that contains serious errors and/or omissions

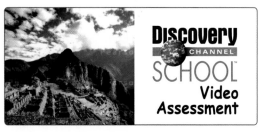
Discovery CHANNEL SCHOOL Video Assessment

Elements and the Periodic Table

Show the Video Assessment to review chapter content and as a prompt for the writing assignment. Discussion questions: **What must happen to a star in order for the heaviest elements to be created?** (*The star must explode.*) **How do elements from the stars continue to reach Earth?** (*From cosmic bodies such as meteorites striking Earth's surface*)

Go Online
PHSchool.com
For: Self-Assessment
Visit: PHSchool.com
Web Code: cga-1030

Students can take a practice test online that is automatically scored.

All in One Teaching Resources
- Transparency K31
- Chapter Test
- Performance Assessment Teacher Notes
- Performance Assessment Student Worksheet
- Performance Assessment Scoring Rubric

ExamView® Computer Test Bank CD-ROM

Checking Concepts

7. Two isotopes of an element have different numbers of neutrons in the nuclei of their atoms.

8. Phosphorus has an average atomic mass nearest to 31.

9. Sample answer: Fluorine and bromine have properties similar to those of chlorine.

10. Tin and lead are the two elements in Group 14 that are most likely to be malleable and good conductors of electricity.

11. Iodine is most likely to be a poor conductor of electricity and a brittle solid at room temperature.

12. Stars like the sun do not contain enough energy to produce elements heavier than oxygen.

Thinking Critically

13. Proton: mass—about one amu, location—nucleus; neutron: mass—about one amu, location—nucleus; electron: mass—about 1/2000 amu, location—outside the nucleus

14. (**A**) 28—atomic number; (**B**) Ni—chemical symbol; (**C**) Nickel—name; (**D**) 58.71—atomic mass

15. Particle accelerators cause nuclei to crash into the nuclei of other elements with enough energy to combine into nuclei of new elements.

16. The materials used in computer chips are semiconductors, which have the property of conducting electricity under some conditions and not under other conditions.

17. Because of their like (positive) charges, atomic nuclei repel one another strongly. The extremely high pressures found in stars squeeze the nuclei together.

Checking Concepts

7. How do two isotopes of an element differ from one another?

8. What element has an average atomic mass nearest to 31?

9. Use the periodic table to name two elements that have properties similar to those of chlorine (Cl).

10. Which two elements in Group 14 on the periodic table are most likely to be malleable and good conductors of electricity?

11. Of the elements oxygen (O), zinc (Zn), and iodine (I), which one would you predict to be a poor conductor of electricity and a brittle solid at room temperature?

12. Why are elements heavier than oxygen *not* produced in stars like the sun?

Thinking Critically

13. Comparing and Contrasting List the three kinds of particles that make up atoms, and compare their masses and their locations in an atom.

14. Applying Concepts Below is a square taken from the periodic table. Identify the type of information given by each labeled item.

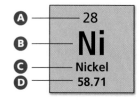

15. Applying Concepts Explain how particle accelerators are used to synthesize elements with atomic numbers above 95.

16. Inferring What property of the materials used in computer chips makes them useful as switches that turn electricity on and off?

17. Relating Cause and Effect Why is extremely high pressure required to cause atomic nuclei to crash into one another in stars?

Applying Skills

Use the table to answer Questions 18–22.

The table below list properties of five elements.

Element	Appearance	Atomic Mass	Conducts Electricity
A	Invisible gas	14.007	No
B	Invisible gas	39.948	No
C	Hard, silvery solid	40.08	Yes
D	Silvery liquid	200.59	Yes
E	Shiny, bluish-white solid	207.2	Slightly

18. Classifying Classify each element in the table as a metal or a nonmetal. Explain your answers.

19. Inferring Both elements B and C have an atomic mass close to 40. How is this similarity possible?

20. Drawing Conclusions Use the periodic table to identify the five elements.

21. Predicting Would you expect elements A and B to have similar chemical properties? Why or why not?

22. Predicting Would you expect to find element C uncombined in nature? Explain.

Lab zone Chapter **Project**

Performance Assessment Display the chart showing the metals you studied. Be ready to discuss which properties are common to all metals. Describe other properties of metals you could not test. List all the properties that could be used to find out whether an unknown element is a metal.

Lab zone Chapter **Project** L3

Performance Assessment In their class presentations, students should note any differences between expected and observed results and hypothesize reasons for these differences. Promote a cooperative spirit during presentations. Stress that there are many different properties to test, several ways to test each property, and properties (such as reactivities with many other elements) that could not be tested. Ask students to keep notes on the presentations, noting differences between experimental designs. Once all presentations have been made, lead a class discussion about which properties are common to all metals. One such property is electrical conductivity.

Standardized Test Prep

Test-Taking Tip

Reading All the Answer Choices

In answering a multiple-choice question, always read *every* answer choice before selecting the answer you think is correct. In some cases, all of the responses may be true statements, but only one answers the question correctly. In the sample question below, for example, you are asked why a carbon atom is heavier than the total mass of its protons and electrons. Each answer choice is a statement. If you look at each answer choice by itself, it expresses something that is correct. However, only one of the answer choices explains why a carbon atom is heavier than the total mass of its protons and electrons.

Sample Question

Why is the mass of a carbon atom greater than the total mass of its protons and electrons?

A The mass of a proton is greater than the mass of an electron.

B A proton is positively charged and an electron is negatively charged.

C Most of the atom's volume is the sphere-shaped cloud of electrons.

D One or more neutrons in the nucleus add mass to the atom.

Answer

The correct answer is **D**. With the exception of some hydrogen atoms, every atom contains one or more neutrons. The mass of a neutron is about the same as that of a proton. Choices **A**, **B**, and **C** are true statements about the subatomic particles that make up every atom. However, none of the statements answers the question.

Choose the letter of the best answer.

1. Elements that are gases at room temperature are likely to be classified as which of the following?
   A metals
   B nonmetals
   C metalloids
   D unreactive

2. Which property of aluminum makes it a suitable metal for soft drink cans?
   F It has good electrical conductivity.
   G It can be hammered into a thin sheet (malleability).
   H It can be drawn into long wires (ductility).
   J It can reflect light (shininess).

Use the table below to answer Questions 3–5.

8	9	10
O	**F**	**Ne**
Oxygen 15.999	Fluorine 18.998	Neon 20.179
16	17	18
S	**Cl**	**Ar**
Sulfur 32.06	Chlorine 35.453	Argon 39.948

3. Which element has an atomic number of 18?
   A hydrogen
   B oxygen
   C fluorine
   D argon

4. An atom of fluorine has 10 neutrons. What is the total number of other subatomic particles in this atom?
   F 9 protons and 9 electrons
   G 9 protons and 19 electrons
   H 10 protons and 10 electrons
   J 19 protons and 19 electrons

5. Which combination of elements represents part of a group, or family, of the periodic table?
   A oxygen, fluorine, and neon
   B sulfur, chlorine, and argon
   C fluorine and chlorine
   D oxygen and chlorine

Constructed Response

6. Describe the modern model of the atom. Your discussion should include the three main types of particles that make up an atom and the charge and location of each. Include an explanation of the overall charge on an atom.

Applying Skills

18. Elements A and B are most likely nonmetals because they are gases that do not conduct electricity. Elements C and D are most likely metals because they are silvery and conduct electricity. Element E is a weak conductor, but it is most likely a metal because of its appearance.

19. Almost all of the mass of an atom comes from its protons and neutrons. Although each element has a characteristic number of protons, the number of neutrons can vary and may cause two different elements to have similar atomic masses.

20. A: nitrogen; B: argon; C: calcium; D: mercury; E: lead

21. No. Element A (nitrogen) and element B (argon) are in different groups, or families.

22. No. Element C (calcium) is an alkaline earth metal. Elements in this group are not found as elements in nature.

Standardized Test Prep

1. B **2.** G **3.** D **4.** F **5.** C

6. The modern model of an atom includes three main types of atomic particles called protons, neutrons, and electrons. The protons and neutrons are clustered together in an atom's central core, or nucleus. Electrons move rapidly in the space outside the nucleus. Protons are positively charged, electrons are negatively charged, and neutrons have no charge. An atom has an equal number of protons and electrons, so its overall charge is neutral.

Chapter at a Glance

PRENTICE HALL
TeacherEXPRESS™
Plan · Teach · Assess

Chapter Project *Material Profiles*

Technology

Local Standards

All in One Teaching Resources
- Chapter Project Teacher Notes, pp. 236–237
- Chapter Project Student Overview, pp. 238–239
- Chapter Project Student Worksheets, pp. 240–241
- Chapter Project Scoring Rubric, p. 242

Discovery CHANNEL SCHOOL
Video Preview

Section 1

2–4 periods
1–2 blocks

Polymers and Composites
K.4.1.1 Explain how polymers form.
K.4.1.2 Tell what composites are made of.
K.4.1.3 Identify benefits and problems that relate to the use of synthetic polymers.

Discovery CHANNEL SCHOOL
Video Field Trip

Go Online
PHSchool.com

Go Online
PHSchool.com

Section 2

1 period
1/2 block

Metals and Alloys
K.4.2.1 Compare the properties of metals and alloys.
K.4.2.2 Describe how steels and other alloys are made and used.

Go Online
SciLINKS™ NSTA

Section 3

2 periods
1 block

Ceramics and Glass
K.4.3.1 Describe the properties of ceramics.
K.4.3.2 Describe the properties of glass.

Go Online
SciLINKS™ NSTA

Section 4

2–3 periods
1–1 1/2 blocks

Radioactive Elements
K.4.4.1 Describe how radioactivity was discovered.
K.4.4.2 Identify the types of particles and energy that radioactive decay can produce.
K.4.4.3 Describe how radioactive isotopes are useful.

Go Online
active art

Review and Assessment

Test Preparation

All in One Teaching Resources
- Key Terms Review, p. 275
- Transparency K39
- Performance Assessment Teacher Notes, p. 283
- Performance Assessment Scoring Rubric, p. 284
- Performance Assessment Student Worksheet, p. 285
- Chapter Test, pp. 286–289

Discovery CHANNEL SCHOOL
Video Assessment

Go Online
PHSchool.com

Test Preparation Blackline Masters

Chapter Activities Planner

For more activities
LAB ZONE
Easy Planner
CD-ROM

Student Edition	Inquiry	Time	Materials	Skills	Resources
Chapter Project, p. 117	Open-ended	Ongoing (2–3 weeks)	**All in One** Teaching Resources See p. 236	Classifying, designing experiments, comparing and contrasting, communicating	Lab zone Easy Planner **All in One** Teaching Resources Support pp. 236–237
Section 1					
Discover Activity, p. 118	Guided	10 minutes	White school glue, saturated solution of borax and water, paper cups, stirrers, large spoons	Observing	**Lab zone Easy Planner**
Skills Activity, p. 120	Directed	10 minutes	Calculator	Calculating	**Lab zone Easy Planner**
Technology Lab, pp. 126–127	Guided	Prep: 15 minutes Class: 40 minutes	Water, hand lens, weights (or books), scissors, packaging tape, thermometer, balance, clock or timer, containers (20 beakers, trays, or plastic cups), 10 mL 1% iodine solution, cookie (optional), polymers used in packaging (paper, Tyvek, plastic foam, ecofoam, cardboard, fabric, popcorn, sawdust, wood shavings, plastic)	Designing a solution, building a prototype, evaluating the design	**Lab zone Easy Planner Lab Activity Video** **All in One** Teaching Resources Technology Lab: *Design and Build a Polymer Package*, pp. 250–252
Section 2					
Discover Activity, p. 130	Guided	10 minutes, plus 1–2 day wait	Cut nail, wire nail, stainless steel bolt, paper towel, sealable plastic bag, saltwater solution	Developing hypotheses	**Lab zone Easy Planner**
At-Home Activity, p. 134	Guided	Home		Applying concepts, classifying	**Lab zone Easy Planner**
Section 3					
Discover Activity, p. 135	Guided	10 minutes	1 glazed and 1 unglazed flowerpot of the same size, sink or basin, water, balance	Inferring	**Lab zone Easy Planner**
Try This Activity, p. 137	Directed	15 minutes	Barrier material such as a notebook or cardboard, penlight flashlight, optical fibers	Observing	**Lab zone Easy Planner**
Section 4					
Discover Activity, p. 139	Guided	10 minutes	Round or cylindrical container such as a coffee can, ruler, scissors	Drawing conclusions	**Lab zone Easy Planner**
Skills Activity, p. 142	Directed	10 minutes	Calculator	Calculating	**Lab zone Easy Planner**
Skills Lab, p. 147	Directed	Prep: 5 minutes Class: 25 minutes	100 pennies, graph paper, container such as a jar or a box, colored pencils (optional)	Making models, graphing, interpreting data	**Lab zone Easy Planner Lab Activity Video** **All in One** Teaching Resources Skills Lab: *That's Half-Life!*, pp. 273–274

Section 1 **Polymers and Composites**

 3–4 periods, 1 1/2–2 blocks

ABILITY LEVELS
- **L1** Basic to Average
- **L2** For All Students
- **L3** Average to Advanced

Objectives

K.4.1.1 Explain how polymers form.

K.4.1.2 Tell what composites are made of.

K.4.1.3 Identify benefits and problems that relate to the use of synthetic polymers.

Key Terms
- polymer • monomer • plastic • composite

Local Standards

Preteach

Build Background Knowledge

Students identify items made of plastic.

 **Discover Activity** *What Did You Make?* **L1**

Targeted Print and Technology Resources

All in One Teaching Resources

L2 Reading Strategy Transparency K32: *Asking Questions*

⊙ **Presentation-Pro CD-ROM**

Instruct

Forming Polymers Use simple chemical formulas of proteins and sugars to explain how polymers form.

Polymers and Composites Lead a discussion about composites and how they relate to polymers.

Too Many Polymers? Use a chart to organize the benefits and problems of polymers.

 **Technology Lab** *Design and Build a Polymer Package* **L3**

Targeted Print and Technology Resources

All in One Teaching Resources

L2 Guided Reading, pp. 245–247

L2 Transparency K33

L3 Technology Lab: *Design and Build a Polymer Package,* pp. 250–252

📼 **Lab Activity Video/DVD**
Technology Lab: *Design and Build a Polymer Package*

PHSchool.com Web Code: cgd-1041

⊙ **Student Edition on Audio CD**

Assess

Section Assessment Questions

Have students use their completed graphic organizers to answer the questions.

Reteach

Students make a concept map that relates monomers, polymers, and composites.

Targeted Print and Technology Resources

All in One Teaching Resources

- Section Summary, p. 244
- **L1** Review and Reinforce, p. 248
- **L3** Enrich, p. 249

Section 2 **Metals and Alloys**

 2–3 periods, 1–1 1/2 blocks

Objectives

K.4.2.1 Compare the properties of metals and alloys.
K.4.2.2 Describe how steels and other alloys are made and used.

Key Terms

• alloy

Local Standards

Preteach

Build Background Knowledge

Tell students how 10-karat gold differs from 24-karat gold and have them infer why a jeweler might favor 10-karat gold.

 **Discover Activity** *Are They "Steel" the Same?* L1

Targeted Print and Technology Resources

 **Teaching Resources**

L2 Reading Strategy Transparency K34: *Outlining*

⊙ **Presentation-Pro CD-ROM**

Instruct

Comparing Metals and Alloys Define *alloy* and review metal properties in a discussion about the benefits of alloys.

Making and Using Alloys Ask questions in a discussion about alloys.

Targeted Print and Technology Resources

 **Teaching Resources**

L2 Guided Reading, pp. 255–256

www.SciLinks.org Web Code: scn-1142

⊙ **Student Edition on Audio CD**

Assess

Section Assessment Questions

 Have students use their completed outlines to answer the questions.

Reteach

Students compare and contrast the properties of metals and alloys in a table.

Targeted Print and Technology Resources

 **Teaching Resources**

• Section Summary, p. 254
L1 Review and Reinforce, p. 257
L3 Enrich, p. 258

Section 3 Ceramics and Glass

 1–2 periods, 1/2–1 block

ABILITY LEVELS
L1 Basic to Average
L2 For All Students
L3 Average to Advanced

Objectives

K.4.3.1 Describe the properties of ceramics.
K.4.3.2 Describe the properties of glass.

Key Terms

• ceramic • glass • optical fiber

Local Standards

Preteach

Build Background Knowledge

Students identify properties and uses of glass.

Lab zone Discover Activity *Does It Get Wet?* **L2**

Targeted Print and Technology Resources

All in One Teaching Resources

L2 Reading Strategy Transparency K35: *Identifying Main Ideas*

⊙ **Presentation-Pro CD-ROM**

Instruct

Ceramics Lead a discussion about the useful properties of ceramics.

Glass Ask questions about the properties of glass and how glass is made.

Targeted Print and Technology Resources

All in One Teaching Resources

L2 Guided Reading, pp. 261–262

www.SciLinks.org Web Code: scn-1143

⊙ **Student Edition on Audio CD**

Assess

Section Assessment Questions

Have students use their completed graphic organizers to answer the questions.

Reteach

Students write a definition for each key term.

Targeted Print and Technology Resources

All in One Teaching Resources

• Section Summary, p. 260
L1 Review and Reinforce, p. 263
L3 Enrich, p. 264

Section 4 Radioactive Elements

🕐 *3–4 periods, 1 1/2–2 blocks*

ABILITY LEVELS
L1 Basic to Average
L2 For All Students
L3 Average to Advanced

Objectives

K.4.4.1 Describe how radioactivity was discovered.

K.4.4.2 Identify the types of particles and energy that radioactive decay can produce.

K.4.4.3 Describe how radioactive isotopes are useful.

Key Terms

- nuclear reaction • radioactive decay • radioactivity • alpha particle
- beta particle • gamma radiation • half-life • radioactive dating • tracer

Local Standards

Preteach

Build Background Knowledge

Students share what they know about radioactivity.

 **Discover Activity** *How Much Goes Away?*   **L2**

Targeted Print and Technology Resources

All in One **Teaching Resources**

💿 **Presentation-Pro CD-ROM**

Instruct

Radioactivity Lead a discussion about the discovery of radioactivity.

Types of Radioactive Decay Ask questions to complete a table that compares and contrasts the three types of radioactive decay.

Using Radioactive Isotopes Lead students to list ways in which radioactive isotopes are used.

 Skills Lab *That's Half-Life!*   **L2**

Targeted Print and Technology Resources

All in One **Teaching Resources**
L2 Guided Reading, pp. 267–270
L2 Transparencies K36, K37, K38
L2 Skills Lab: *That's Half-Life!*, pp. 273–274

📼 **Lab Activity Video/DVD**
   Skills Lab: *That's Half-Life!*

PHSchool.com Web Code: cgp-1044

💿 **Student Edition on Audio CD**

Assess

Section Assessment Questions

↻ Have students use their definitions to answer the questions.

Reteach

Students diagram each form of radioactive decay.

Targeted Print and Technology Resources

All in One **Teaching Resources**
• Section Summary, p. 266
L1 Review and Reinforce, p. 271
L3 Enrich, p. 272

Go Online

NSTA–PD**LINKS**

For: Professional development support
Visit: www.SciLinks.org/PDLinks
Web Code: scf-1140

Professional Development

Section 1 **Polymers and Composites**

Polymerization Most polymerization reactions require a catalyst. A catalyst is a substance that increases the rate of a reaction by lowering the amount of energy required to get the reaction started. The catalyst itself is not used up in the reaction. Before catalysts were introduced into the polymerization reactions of synthetic polymers, these reactions could be accomplished only under very high heat and pressure.

Polymers form either by addition or condensation. The key to polymerization is the ability of monomer molecules to form repeating chains. For this to happen, each monomer must have at least two reactive sites. Addition polymers form when the double bonds of a molecule open up, making two sites available for bonding.

$$x\,CH_2=CH \quad \rightarrow \quad -(-CH_2CH-)-_x$$

$$\overset{\displaystyle CH_3}{|} \qquad\qquad \overset{\displaystyle CH_3}{|}$$

Propene (propylene) → Polypropylene

Condensation polymers are formed by the head-to-tail joining of monomer molecules. The reactive sites become available as –H and –OH split off respectively from two monomers. Water is produced along with the polymer.

Terephthalic acid   Ethylene glycol   Representative polymer unit of polyethylene terephthalate (PET)

Proteins in the body are formed by condensation reactions between amino acid monomers. Enzymes in body cells catalyze these reactions.

Section 2 **Metals and Alloys**

Manufacturing Steel Of the several different processes for manufacturing steel, the basic oxygen process is the most commonly used. In this process, liquid iron is poured into a cylindrical furnace lined with heat-resistant bricks. Scrap iron is also added, as well as specific amounts of the various metals required to produce a particular steel alloy. Oxygen that is at least 99.5 percent pure is blown into the furnace at an extremely high rate through a water-cooled pipe called a lance. The lance brings the oxygen below the surface of the molten steel. The oxygen causes a vigorous reaction that oxidizes carbon and silicon impurities. The oxidized carbon, which is carbon monoxide gas, is vented out of the furnace.

Limestone and dolomite fluxes are also added at the beginning of the process. These fluxes combine with oxidized silicon to form a slag which, in turn, absorbs any sulfur and phosphorus impurities. The slag is a liquid that is less dense than the molten steel and forms a layer on top of it. When the reaction is complete, the furnace is tipped and molten steel is poured out, leaving the slag behind. The molten steel is then cast or sent to another refining process.

⚑ **Address Misconceptions**

Some students may not understand why alloys are mixtures and not compounds. This misconception is addressed in Section 2, *Metals and Alloys*.

Oxygen Furnace

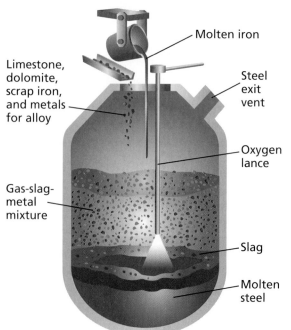

Molten iron

Limestone, dolomite, scrap iron, and metals for alloy

Steel exit vent

Oxygen lance

Gas-slag-metal mixture

Slag

Molten steel

Professional Development

Section 3 Ceramics and Glass

Manufacturing Glass The ingredients used to make glass are very similar to the ingredients used thousands of years ago. Silica sand, limestone (calcium carbonate), and soda ash (sodium carbonate) are mixed with recycled waste glass, or cullet. The use of cullet reduces the amount of natural gas required to melt the batch. These ingredients are carefully measured and mixed together in a large furnace that is fired to 1200–1300°C.

The molten glass flows out of the furnace directly into forming machines that form the glass into sheets or mold it into shapes. If glass sheets are being made, the molten glass is "floated" onto a bath of molten tin at a temperature of about 1000°C. The molten glass and tin do not mix, and the surface between the materials is perfectly smooth and flat. The glass forms into a very thin plate. When it is cool enough to be moved, the glass passes into an annealing chamber, called a lehr. Here the glass is gently warmed, then recooled slowly to remove any potential stress points.

If bottles or other shapes are being made, premeasured lumps of molten glass flow directly from the furnace into premolds, which form the basic shape of the bottle. The premolded shape moves into a second mold where compressed air blows the glass until it expands to completely fill the mold. The mold releases the newly formed bottle, which moves through a lehr for annealing. The finished glass containers are inspected and rejects are recycled as cullet.

Section 4 Radioactive Elements

Generating Power Some elements have radioisotopes that are fissionable, which means that the nuclei of these isotopes will split into smaller fragments when hit with neutrons. Uranium-235 and plutonium-239 are two such isotopes. When uranium-235 is hit by slow-moving neutrons, the nucleus breaks almost in half, producing krypton-91 and barium-142 nuclei. At the same time, it releases additional neutrons that react with other uranium-235 nuclei. This is a chain reaction that will continue as long as fissionable nuclei are present.

Nuclear fission releases huge amounts of energy, almost instantaneously, unless the reaction is controlled. In a nuclear reactor, heat energy produced by the fission reaction is used to generate steam, which drives a turbine that generates electricity. The fission reaction in a nuclear reactor is controlled in two ways. First, the neutrons are slowed down by either water or carbon in order to maintain a constant chain reaction. Secondly, some neutrons are trapped or absorbed to prevent the chain reactions from going too fast. Control rods made of cadmium are used to trap neutrons. The control rods can be extended almost all the way into the reactor core to slow fission down, or they can be pulled out to speed it up.

Help Students Read

Reciprocal Teaching
Modeling Strategies in Combination

Strategy Help students learn to apply the strategies of predict, question, clarify, and summarize. Teaching this strategy should take place over several days, beginning with the teacher modeling and leading students in discussion. The teacher gradually turns leadership over to students and becomes a facilitator, intervening only as needed. Choose a passage of several paragraphs from Section 1, *Polymers and Composites*.

Example
1. Read the paragraphs aloud or invite one student to read while the others follow along silently.
2. Discuss ways for students to apply each of the following:
   • Predict what will come next in the text. Students can use what they already know about a topic to make connections that will help them understand what comes next.
   • Ask "teacher-like" questions to check understanding and to think about what they need to find out.
   • Clarify the meanings of unfamiliar words or concepts.
   • Summarize what has been read.
3. Reread the paragraphs, modeling all four strategies.
4. Continue reading a few paragraphs at a time, discussing and modeling the strategies.
5. Repeat the process with different passages over a few days, gradually turning over the leadership role to students by having them lead the discussion of portions of the text.
6. When students are comfortable with the strategies, they can lead the entire discussion. Intervene only to get students back on track or to jump-start a discussion.

See *Polymers and Composites* for a script on how to use the Reciprocal Teaching strategy with students.

Interactive Textbook
- Complete student edition
- Video and audio
- Simulations and activities
- Section and chapter activities

Chapter 4

Exploring Materials

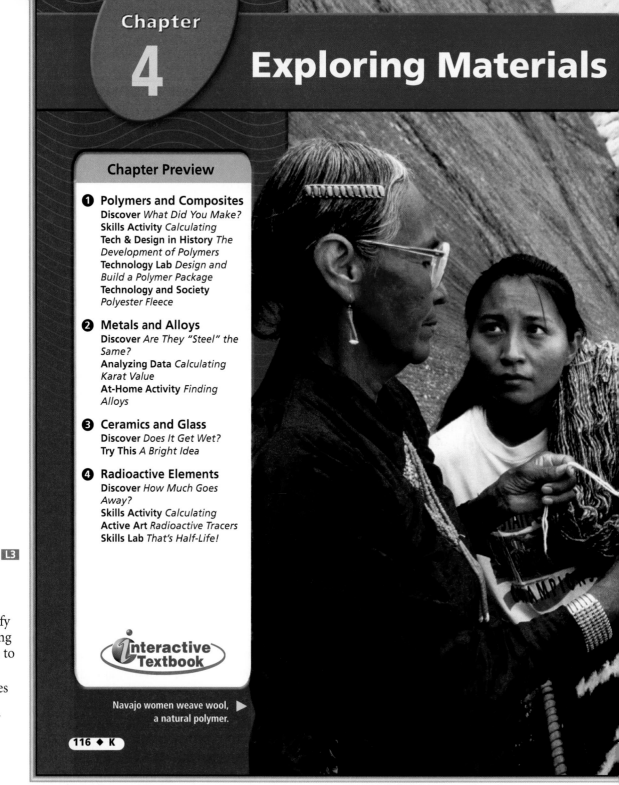

Chapter Preview

❶ Polymers and Composites
Discover *What Did You Make?*
Skills Activity *Calculating*
Tech & Design in History *The Development of Polymers*
Technology Lab *Design and Build a Polymer Package*
Technology and Society *Polyester Fleece*

❷ Metals and Alloys
Discover *Are They "Steel" the Same?*
Analyzing Data *Calculating Karat Value*
At-Home Activity *Finding Alloys*

❸ Ceramics and Glass
Discover *Does It Get Wet?*
Try This *A Bright Idea*

❹ Radioactive Elements
Discover *How Much Goes Away?*
Skills Activity *Calculating*
Active Art *Radioactive Tracers*
Skills Lab *That's Half-Life!*

Interactive Textbook

Navajo women weave wool, ▶ a natural polymer.

Chapter **Project** L3

Objectives
Students will classify material samples found from different locations and identify several properties of each. After completing this Chapter Project, students will be able to
- classify a variety of materials
- design experiments to test the properties of materials
- compare and contrast the properties of different materials
- communicate their findings about different materials to the class

Skills Focus
Classifying, designing experiments, comparing and contrasting, communicating

Project Time Line 2 to 3 weeks

All in One Teaching Resources
- Chapter Project Teacher Notes
- Chapter Project Worksheet 1
- Chapter Project Worksheet 2
- Chapter Project Scoring Rubric

Developing a Plan
Allow three or four days for students to collect materials. At the same time, students can write procedures for testing at least three properties of each material. Students should clearly identify the properties they will study, such as hardness, strength, density, elasticity, or solubility. Allow three days for students to conduct several trials of each test. For the final two days, students can analyze results and prepare presentations.

Possible Materials
Students will be collecting their own material samples. After reviewing students' testing procedures, gather materials students will need for testing various properties. For example, to study strength, students will need weights. To study density, students will need a balance and a graduated cylinder or meter stick.

Lab zone™ Chapter **Project**

Material Profiles

In this chapter, you will explore the properties of different types of materials. As you read this chapter, you will survey different materials found around you.

Your Goal To collect and investigate different materials found around you

To complete the project, you must

- collect at least eight material samples from at least three different locations
- identify several properties of each material
- create an informative display about these materials
- follow the safety guidelines in Appendix A

Plan It! With a group of classmates, brainstorm a list of the properties of various materials and how you might test these properties. You'll be working on this project as you study this chapter. When you finish Section 1, describe some polymers and composites you chose to collect and begin preparing a showcase. Add information when you finish Section 2, and complete your list of materials at the end of the chapter. Finally, present your completed showcase to the class.

DISCOVERY CHANNEL SCHOOL
Video Preview

Exploring Materials

Show the Video Preview to introduce the Chapter Project and provide an overview of chapter content. Discussion question: **What are some examples of polymers?** (Sample answer: Proteins, spider webs, cellulose, rubber, plastics)

Performance Assessment

The Chapter Project Scoring Rubric will help you evaluate how well students complete the Chapter Project. You may want to share the rubric with your students so they know what is expected. Students will be assessed on

- how well they identify materials based on their properties
- the thoroughness of their written procedures and experimental designs
- the completeness of their data tables, including outcomes of experiments and categorization of materials
- the thoroughness and clarity of their final presentations

Students can keep their written procedures and data tables in their portfolios.

Portfolio

Possible Shortcuts

Provide students with the materials, and tell them which properties to test. Small groups can test one material, and then class results can be combined.

Launching the Project

Show students several objects made of different materials such as plastics, metals, alloys, ceramics, and glass. Invite students to describe what they know about each material and why it was used to make that object. Ask: **What other materials could these objects be made of? What properties do these materials have that make them more suitable for making these objects?** List responses on the board to help students begin thinking about the properties of different materials.

Polymers and Composites

Objectives

After this lesson, students will be able to

K.4.1.1 Explain how polymers form.

K.4.1.2 Tell what composites are made of.

K.4.1.3 Identify benefits and problems that relate to the use of synthetic polymers.

Target Reading Skill

Asking Questions Explain that changing a head into a question helps students anticipate the ideas, facts, and events they are about to read.

Answer

Sample questions and answers:

How do polymers form? *(Polymers form when chemical bonds link large numbers of monomers in a repeating pattern.)*

How do polymers and composites compare? *(A composite often includes one or more polymers.)* **Why are there too many polymers?** *(It is often cheaper to throw some polymers away and make new ones than it is to reuse them, resulting in more trash.)*

All in One Teaching Resources

• Transparency K32

Preteach

Build Background Knowledge   L2

Experience With Plastics

Challenge students to name as many items as they can that are made of plastic. Then ask: **What advantage does plastic have over other materials that could be used to make these items?** *(Sample answer: Water-resistant, lightweight, flexible, comes in many colors)*

Polymers and Composites

Reading Preview

Key Concepts

• How do polymers form?
• What are composites made of?
• What benefits and problems relate to the use of synthetic polymers?

Key Terms

• polymer • monomer • plastic
• composite

Target Reading Skill

Asking Questions Before you read, preview the red headings. In a graphic organizer like the one below, ask a *how* or *why* question for each heading. As you read, write the answers to your questions.

Question	Answer
How do polymers form?	Polymers form when chemical bonds link . . .

Lab zone Discover **Activity**

What Did You Make?

1. Look at a sample of borax solution and write down the properties you observe. Do the same with white glue.
2. Put about 2 tablespoons of borax solution into a paper cup.
3. Stir the solution as you add about 1 tablespoon of white glue.
4. After 2 minutes, record the properties of the material in the cup. Wash your hands when you are finished.

Think It Over

Observing What evidence of a chemical reaction did you observe? How did the materials change? What do you think you made?

Delectable foods and many other interesting materials surround you every day. Have you ever wondered what makes up these foods and materials? You might be surprised to learn that many are partly or wholly polymers. A **polymer** (PAHL uh mur) is a large, complex molecule built from smaller molecules joined together in a repeating pattern.

The starches in pancakes and the proteins in meats and eggs are natural polymers. Many other polymers, however, are manufactured or synthetic. These synthetic polymers include polyester and nylon clothing, and plastics. Whether synthetic or natural, most polymers rely on the element carbon for their fundamental structures.

FIGURE 1
Polymers
The clothing, boots, goggles, and helmet worn by this climber are all made of polymers.

Lab zone Discover **Activity**

Skills Focus Observing   L1

Materials white school glue, saturated solution of borax and water, paper cups, stirrers, large spoons

Time 10 minutes

Tips Measure out the borax solution beforehand. Remind students to dispose of the product in the trash container; they should not wash the putty down the sink.

Expected Outcome A putty-like substance forms.

Think It Over A change in properties indicates a chemical reaction occurred. The two liquids combined to form a putty-like substance. Students may infer that they have made a polymer.

Forming Polymers

Food materials, living things, and plastic have something in common. All are made of carbon compounds. Carbon compounds contain atoms of carbon bonded to each other and to other kinds of atoms. Carbon is present in several million known compounds, and more carbon-containing compounds are being discovered or invented every day.

Carbon's Chains and Rings Carbon's unique ability to form so many compounds comes from two properties. First, carbon atoms can form four covalent bonds. Second, they can bond to each other in straight and branched chains and ring-shaped groups, as you can see in Figure 2. These structures form the "backbones" to which other atoms attach.

Hydrogen is the most common element found in compounds with carbon. Other elements include oxygen, nitrogen, phosphorus, sulfur, and the halogens—especially chlorine.

Carbon Compounds and Polymers Molecules of some carbon compounds can bond together, forming larger molecules, such as polymers. The smaller molecules from which polymers are built are called **monomers** (MAHN uh murz). **Polymers form when chemical bonds link large numbers of monomers in a repeating pattern.** A polymer may consist of hundreds or even thousands of monomers.

Many polymers consist of a single kind of monomer that repeats over and over again. You could think of these monomers as linked like the identical cars of a long passenger train. In other cases, two or three monomers may join in an alternating pattern. Sometimes links between monomer chains occur, forming large webs or netlike molecules. The chemical properties of a polymer depend on the monomers from which it is made.

Reading Checkpoint What are the patterns in which monomers come together to form polymers?

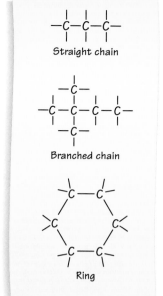

FIGURE 2
Carbon's Bonds
Carbon atoms can form structures like those shown above. In these drawings, lines represent covalent bonds. **Interpreting Diagrams** *How many covalent bonds are shown for each carbon atom?*

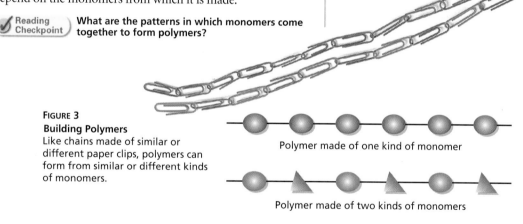
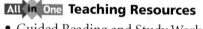

FIGURE 3
Building Polymers
Like chains made of similar or different paper clips, polymers can form from similar or different kinds of monomers.

Polymer made of one kind of monomer

Polymer made of two kinds of monomers

Differentiated Instruction

Special Needs   **L1**
Modeling Polymers Give students various modeling materials such as paper clips, plastic-foam balls, clay, toothpicks, string, beads, pipe cleaners, and washers. Invite students to make models of polymers by first choosing one, two, or three "monomers." Then, they can assemble their models by connecting the monomers in a repeating pattern. Ask: **What element is in all monomers?** *(Carbon)* **learning modality: kinesthetic**

Instruct

Forming Polymers

Teach Key Concepts   L2
Monomers and Polymers

Focus Tell students that polymers are large complex molecules.

Teach Show simple chemical formulas of proteins or sugars or diagrams like the ones in Figure 3. Ask: **What are the smaller molecules from which polymers are built?** *(Monomers)* **How do polymers form?** *(When chemical bonds link large numbers of monomers in repeating units)* Emphasize "repeating units." Describe the two basic patterns of repeating units found in polymers—a chain of a single, repeating monomers, or a chain of two or three different monomers in an alternating pattern. Show an example of each.

Apply Ask: **On what do the chemical properties of a polymer depend?** *(On the monomers from which it is made)* **learning modality: visual**

All in One Teaching Resources
• Transparency K33

Independent Practice   L2

All in One Teaching Resources
• Guided Reading and Study Worksheet: *Polymers and Composites*

⊙ **Student Edition on Audio CD**

Monitor Progress _____   L2

Writing Have students write a description of the ability of carbon atoms to form compounds.

Answers
Figure 2 Four

Reading Checkpoint Patterns of monomers in a polymer can be a single repeating monomer or a chain of two or three different monomers in an alternating pattern.

K ● 119

Polymers and Composites

Teach Key Concepts L2

Relating Polymers and Composites

Focus Tell students that chemists can create new materials by combining the useful properties of two or more substances.

Teach Ask: **What is a composite?** (*A material made by combining two or more substances to get the useful properties of each*) **How do polymers relate to composites?** (*Many composites are made from one or more polymers.*)

Apply Ask: **What is fiberglass made of?** (*Glass fibers woven together and strengthened with plastic.*) **Why is this composite useful?** (*It is a strong, hard solid that can be molded around a form to give it shape. It is lightweight and will not rust.*) **learning modality: verbal**

Help Students Read L1

Reciprocal Teaching Refer to the Content Refresher in this chapter, which provides guidelines for the Reciprocal Teaching strategy.

Have students apply the strategies of predicting, questioning, clarifying, and summarizing as they read Polymers and Composites. Before students read, ask: **How do you think polymers and composites are related?** (*Sample answer: Composites are usually made with at least one polymer.*) Then, have students read to verify their predictions. Clarify the meanings of any unfamiliar words and concepts. Ask students to summarize what has been read. As students become more familiar with this strategy, encourage them to assume the role of leader in these discussions.

FIGURE 4
Natural Polymers
Cellulose, the proteins in snake venom, and spider's silk are three examples of natural polymers.

▲ The cellulose in fruits and vegetables serves as dietary fiber that keeps the human digestive system healthy.

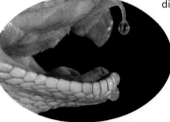

▲ Snake venom is a mixture containing approximately 90 percent proteins.

A spider's web is a silken polymer that is one of the strongest materials known. ▶

Lab zone Skills **Activity**

Calculating

Sit or stand where you have a clear view of the room you are in. Slowly sweep the room with your eyes, making a list of the objects you see. Do the same sweep of the clothes you are wearing. Check off those items on your list made (completely or partly) of natural or synthetic polymers. Calculate the percent of items that were *not* made with polymers.

Polymers and Composites

Polymers have been around as long as life on Earth. Plants, animals, and other living things produce many natural materials made of large polymer molecules.

Natural Polymers Cellulose (SEL yoo lohs) is a flexible but strong natural polymer found in the cell walls of fruits and vegetables. Cellulose is made in plants when sugar molecules are joined into long strands. Humans cannot digest cellulose. But plants also make digestible polymers called starches, formed from sugar molecules that are connected in a different way. Starches are found in pastas, breads, and many vegetables.

You can wear polymers made by animals. Silk is made from the fibers of the cocoons spun by silkworms. Wool is made from sheep's fur. These polymers can be woven into thread and cloth. Your own body makes polymers, too. For example, your fingernails and muscles are made of polymers called proteins. Within your body, proteins are assembled from combinations of monomers called amino acids. The properties of a protein depend on which amino acids are used and in what order. One combination builds the protein that forms your fingernails. Yet another combination forms the protein that carries oxygen in your blood.

120 ◆ K

Lab zone Skills **Activity**

Skills Focus Calculating

Materials calculator

Time 10 minutes

Tips After students list the items they observe, have them use the examples in this section to help them identify polymers.

Expected Outcome Percentages will vary based on students' observations.

L1 Percentages are calculated by dividing the number of items that are not polymers by the total number of items, then multiplying by 100.

Extend Have students make a circle graph that shows their results. They can divide their graphs into items made of natural polymers, made of synthetic polymers, and not made of polymers. **learning modality: logical/mathematical**

Synthetic Polymers Many polymers you use every day are synthesized—or made—from simpler materials. The starting materials for many synthetic polymers come from coal or oil. **Plastics**, which are synthetic polymers that can be molded or shaped, are the most common products. But there are many others. Carpets, clothing, glue, and even chewing gum can be made of synthetic polymers.

Figure 5 lists just a few of the hundreds of polymers people use. Although the names seem like tongue twisters, see how many you recognize. You may be able to identify some polymers by their initials printed on the bottoms of plastic bottles.

Compare the uses of polymers shown in the figure with their characteristics. Notice that many products require materials that are flexible, yet strong. Others must be hard or lightweight. When chemical engineers develop a new product, they have to think about how it will be used. Then they synthesize a polymer with properties to match.

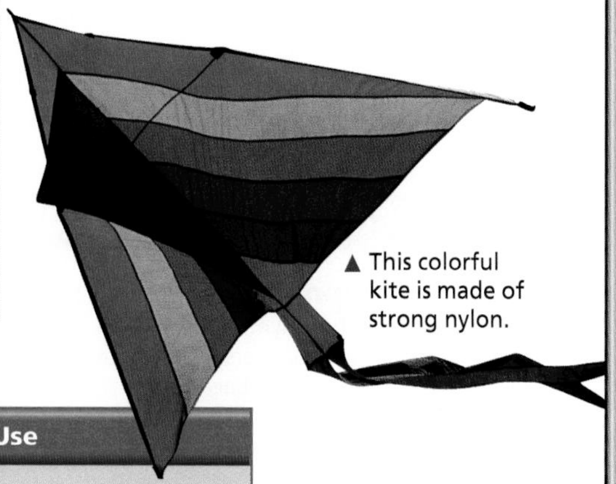

▲ This colorful kite is made of strong nylon.

Some Synthetic Polymers You Use

Name	Properties	Uses
Low-density polyethylene (LDPE)	Flexible, soft, melts easily	Plastic bags, squeeze bottles, electric wire insulation
High-density polyethylene (HDPE)	Stronger than LDPE; higher melting temperatures	Detergent bottles, gas cans, toys, milk jugs
Polypropylene (PP)	Hard, keeps its shape	Toys, car parts, bottle caps
Polyvinyl chloride (PVC)	Tough, flexible	Garden hoses, imitation leather, piping
Polystyrene (PS)	Lightweight, can be made into foam	Foam drinking cups, insulation, furniture, "peanut" packing material
Nylon	Strong, can be drawn into flexible thread	Stockings, parachutes, fishing line, fabric
Teflon (polytetrafluoroethylene)	Nonreactive, low friction	Nonstick coating for cooking pans

FIGURE 5
The properties of synthetic polymers make them ideal starting materials for many common objects.
Applying Concepts
Which synthetic polymer would you use to make a cover for a picnic table?

Chapter 4   K ◆ 121

Lab zone Build Inquiry   L1

Observing Synthetic Polymers

Materials plastic bag, empty milk jug, PVC pipe, polystyrene packing "peanuts"
Time 10 minutes

Focus Tell students that the properties of synthetic polymers make them useful for many objects and functions.

Teach Invite students to compare and contrast the characteristics of each material. Have them list the properties that make the polymers different from each other.

Apply Encourage students to look for markings on other types of plastics at home. Suggest they look at containers of food and household products. Have them identify and list the types of polymers used to make the items. **learning modality: visual**

Monitor Progress   L2

Skills Check Have students identify a characteristic that synthetic and natural polymers share.

Answer
Figure 5 Either nylon, polyvinyl chloride, or low-density polyethylene would make a suitable picnic table cover.

Discovery CHANNEL SCHOOL™
Video Field Trip

Exploring Materials

Show the Video Field Trip to let students learn about polymers and understand the differences between natural and synthetic polymers. Discussion question: **Why do scientists want to try to produce a synthetic polymer with the properties of spider silk?** *(Spider silk is the strongest natural fiber known. It is also lightweight, elastic, insoluble in water, and chemically unreactive.)*

• Tech & Design in History •

Focus Tell students that Charles Goodyear invented synthetic rubber in the same year that the first bicycle was invented. Remind students that horses were the primary mode of transportation at that time, although steam locomotives and steamboats were increasingly used to move cargo long distances. In 1869, the same year as the invention of celluloid, the transcontinental railroad was completed.

Teach After students have studied the timeline, ask: **Which materials in the timeline were developed as improvements on natural substances?** *(Celluloid, synthetic rubber)* Write the headings Strong, Flexible, and Lightweight on the board. Have students identify the polymers with these properties, then list them under the headings. Most polymers fit more than one category.

Writing in Science

Writing Mode Research
Scoring Rubric
4 Exceeds criteria; includes a succinct, informative headline and an engaging, fact-filled paragraph that tells how the invention will change people's lives
3 Meets criteria
2 Includes only brief but accurate information
1 Includes scant information and/or serious errors

Discovery CHANNEL SCHOOL™

Exploring Materials
Video Preview
▶ Video Field Trip
Video Assessment

Comparing Polymers Synthetic polymers are often used in place of natural materials that are too expensive or wear out too quickly. Polyester and nylon fabrics, for example, are frequently used instead of wool, silk, and cotton to make clothes. Laminated countertops and vinyl floors replace wood in many kitchens. Other synthetic polymers have uses for which there is no suitable natural material. Compact discs, computer parts, artificial heart valves, and even bicycle tires couldn't exist without synthetic polymers.

Composites Every substance has its desirable and undesirable properties. What would happen if you could take the best properties of two substances and put them together? A **composite** combines two or more substances in a new material with different properties.

• Tech & Design in History •

The Development of Polymers
The first synthetic polymers were made by changing natural polymers in some way. Later, crude oil and coal became the starting materials. Now, new polymers are designed regularly in laboratories.

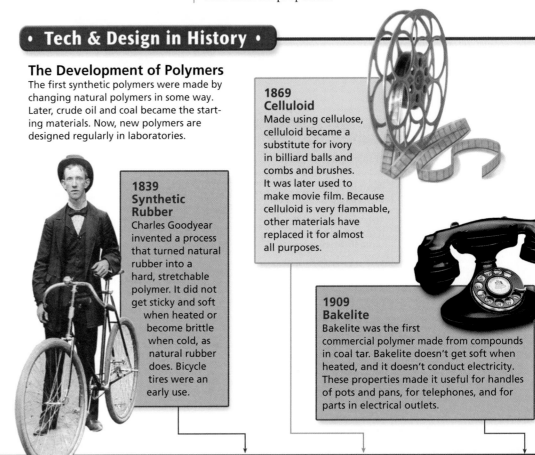

1839 Synthetic Rubber
Charles Goodyear invented a process that turned natural rubber into a hard, stretchable polymer. It did not get sticky and soft when heated or become brittle when cold, as natural rubber does. Bicycle tires were an early use.

1869 Celluloid
Made using cellulose, celluloid became a substitute for ivory in billiard balls and combs and brushes. It was later used to make movie film. Because celluloid is very flammable, other materials have replaced it for almost all purposes.

1909 Bakelite
Bakelite was the first commercial polymer made from compounds in coal tar. Bakelite doesn't get soft when heated, and it doesn't conduct electricity. These properties made it useful for handles of pots and pans, for telephones, and for parts in electrical outlets.

1800   1850   1900

Background

History of Science In 1834, Charles Goodyear tried to develop a way to make natural rubber hard, yet flexible, at all temperatures. While in prison for debt, he experimented with raw rubber and a rolling pin. Later, he, his wife, and their small children made up several hundred pairs of rubber overshoes, but the shoes melted before he could sell them. Goodyear and his family became so destitute that they had to live in an abandoned rubber factory. Even after he discovered and patented vulcanization, the process of heating rubber and sulfur together, legal battles and pressing debt led to the loss of his patents. In 1843, eight weeks before Goodyear filed a patent there, an English inventor developed the same process. In 1860, Goodyear died $200,000 in debt.

By combining the useful properties of two or more substances in a composite, chemists can make a new material that works better than either one alone. **Many composite materials include one or more polymers.** The idea of putting two different materials together to get the advantages of both was inspired by the natural world. Many synthetic composites are designed to imitate a common natural composite—wood.

Wood is made of long fibers of cellulose, held together by another plant polymer called lignin. Cellulose fibers are flexible and can't support much weight. Lignin is brittle and would crack under the weight of the tree branches. But the combination of the two polymers makes a strong tree trunk.

 Reading Checkpoint Why is wood a composite?

Writing in Science

Research and Write Find out more about the invention of one of these polymers. Write a newspaper headline announcing the invention. Then write the first paragraph of the news report telling how the invention will change people's lives.

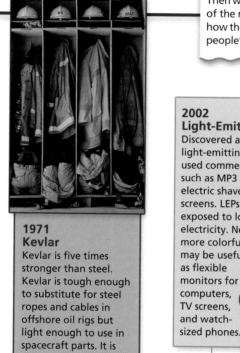

1934 Nylon
A giant breakthrough came with a synthetic fiber that imitates silk. Nylon replaced expensive silk in women's stockings and fabric for parachutes and clothing. It can also be molded to make objects like buttons, gears, and zippers.

1971 Kevlar
Kevlar is five times stronger than steel. Kevlar is tough enough to substitute for steel ropes and cables in offshore oil rigs but light enough to use in spacecraft parts. It is also used in protective clothing for firefighters and police officers.

2002 Light-Emitting Polymers
Discovered accidentally in 1990, light-emitting polymers (LEPs) are used commercially in products such as MP3 audio players and electric shavers with display screens. LEPs give off light when exposed to low-voltage electricity. Newer, more colorful LEPs may be useful as flexible monitors for computers, TV screens, and watch-sized phones.

| 1950 | 2000 | 2050 |

Chapter 4 K ◆ 123

Address Misconceptions L1

Composites Are Not Compounds

Focus Students may confuse composites with compounds because both are materials formed when two or more substances combine.

Teach Inform students that in composites, the individual components are still present and retain their original properties. Composites are formed by physical processes; the chemical properties of the materials are not changed.

Apply Ask: **How is this different from what happens when a compound forms?** *(When a compound forms, the elements react chemically to create a substance with different chemical properties.)* **learning modality: verbal**

Monitor Progress _____ L2

Oral Presentation Invite students to choose one composite or one synthetic polymer and describe how it has made a difference in their everyday lives.

Answer

Reading Checkpoint Wood is made of two plant polymers, cellulose and lignin.

Too Many Polymers?

Teach Key Concepts   L2
Advantages and Disadvantages of Polymers

Focus Ask: **Why have so many synthetic polymers been produced?** *(Sample answer: Each new polymer has properties that give it a specific use.)*

Teach Begin a chart on the board, labeled with the headings Benefits and Problems. Invite students to complete the chart by asking questions like: **What makes synthetic polymers beneficial?** *(They are inexpensive to make, strong, and last a long time.)* **What are some problems with synthetic polymers?** *(They increase the volume of trash because they are so inexpensive to produce that they are simply thrown away, and they do not naturally break down in the environment.)*

Apply Ask: **How can the problems with synthetic polymers be solved?** *(Sample answer: Use fewer materials made from synthetic polymers. Reuse products made from polymers. Recycle these materials into another useful product.)* **learning modality: verbal**

Go Online
PHSchool.com
For: More on polymers
Visit: PHSchool.com
Web Code: cgd-1041

Students can review polymers in an online activity.

FIGURE 6
Synthetic Composites
The composites in the fishing rod above make it flexible so that it will not break when reeling in a fish. Fiberglass makes the snowboard at right both lightweight and strong.

Uses of Composites The idea of combining the properties of two substances to make a more useful one has led to many new products. Fiberglass composites are one example. Strands of glass fiber are woven together and strengthened with a liquid plastic that sets like glue. The combination makes a strong, hard solid that can be molded around a form to give it shape. These composites are lightweight but strong enough to be used as a boat hull or car body. Also, fiberglass will not rust as metal does.

Many other useful composites are made from strong polymers combined with lightweight ones. Bicycles, automobiles, and airplanes built from such composites are much lighter than the same vehicles built from steel or aluminum. Some composites are used to make fishing rods, tennis rackets, and other sports equipment that needs to be flexible but strong.

 Reading Checkpoint **What are two examples of composites?**

Too Many Polymers?

You can hardly look around without seeing something made of synthetic polymers. They have replaced many natural materials for several reasons. **Synthetic polymers are inexpensive to make, strong, and last a long time.**

But synthetic polymers have caused some problems, too. Many of the disadvantages of using plastics come from the same properties that make them so useful. **For example, it is often cheaper to throw plastics away and make new ones than it is to reuse them. As a result, plastics increase the volume of trash.**

Go Online
PHSchool.com
For: More on polymers
Visit: PHSchool.com
Web Code: cgd-1041

Differentiated Instruction

Gifted and Talented   L3
Devising a Recycling Plan
Have students brainstorm a list of ways that plastic waste can be reduced at school or in their homes. To get them started, ask: **What are some ways to take advantage of the special characteristics of plastics without contributing to problems caused by too much waste?** *(Sample answer: Reuse plastic items such as sealable sandwich bags and grocery bags instead of throwing them away.)* Then, challenge students to use their lists to devise a plan for recycling, reducing, or reusing plastics. Suggest that they implement their plans at home. Consider implementing a school-wide plan. **learning modality: logical/ mathematical**

One of the reasons that plastics last so long is that most plastics don't react very easily with other substances. As a result, plastics don't break down—or degrade—into simpler materials in the environment. In contrast, natural polymers do. Some plastics are expected to last thousands of years. How do you get rid of something that lasts that long?

Is there a way to solve these problems? One solution is to use waste plastics as raw material for making new plastic products. You know this idea as recycling. Recycling has led to industries that create new products from discarded plastics. Bottles, fabrics for clothing, and parts for new cars are just some of the many items that can come from waste plastics. A pile of empty soda bottles can even be turned into synthetic wood. Look around your neighborhood. You may see park benches or "wooden" fences made from recycled plastics. Through recycling, the disposal problem is eased and new, useful items are created.

 Reading Checkpoint Why do plastic materials often increase the volume of trash?

FIGURE 7
Recycling Plastics
Plastics can be recycled to make many useful products. This boardwalk, for example, is made of recycled plastics. *Making Judgments What advantages or disadvantages does this material have compared to wood?*

Section 1 Assessment

Target Reading Skill Asking Questions Use your graphic organizer about the section headings to help answer the questions below.

Reviewing Key Concepts

1. a. **Defining** What are polymers made of?
   b. **Identifying** What properties enable carbon atoms to form polymers and so many other compounds?
   c. **Interpreting Diagrams** How do the two kinds of polymers modeled in Figure 3 differ?
2. a. **Reviewing** Distinguish between natural polymers, synthetic polymers, and composites.
   b. **Classifying** Make a list of polymers you can find in your home. Classify them as natural or synthetic.
   c. **Drawing Conclusions** Why are composites often more useful than the individual materials from which they are made?

3. a. **Listing** List two benefits and two problems associated with the use of synthetic polymers.
   b. **Making Judgments** Think of something plastic that you have used today. Is there some other material that would be better than plastic for this use?

Writing in Science

Advertisement You are a chemist. You invent a polymer that can be a substitute for a natural material such as wood, cotton, or leather. Write an advertisement for your polymer, explaining why you think it is a good replacement for the natural material.

Chapter 4 K ◆ 125

Writing in Science

Writing Mode Persuasion
Scoring Rubric
4 Exceeds criteria
3 Meets criteria
2 Includes a developed idea but contains some errors
1 Includes a sketchy idea and/or serious errors

Lab zone Chapter Project

Keep Students on Track As students collect their samples, remind them to record any information on labels or packages. They should also record where they found the material and what its function is. Suggest they use the table in Figure 5 and the examples in this section to help them identify the materials as natural or synthetic, polymer or composite.

Monitor Progress L2

Answers
Figure 7 Advantages: will not rot, uses recycled materials; disadvantages: not easily disposed of

 Reading Checkpoint Sample answer: Wood and fiberglass

Reading Checkpoint It is cheap and easy to throw plastics away, and they do not degrade.

Assess

Reviewing Key Concepts

1. a. Polymers are made of smaller molecules joined together in a repeating pattern. **b.** Carbon atoms can form four covalent bonds and bond to each other in straight and branched chains and ring-shaped groups. **c.** One is made of a single kind of monomer that repeats. The other is made of two monomers joined in an alternating pattern.
2. a. Natural polymers are formed in plants, animals, and other living things. Synthetic polymers are made by people from materials in coal and oil. Composites combine useful properties of two or more materials and often include one or more polymers. Composites can be natural or synthetic. **b.** Sample answer: Natural polymers include wool, hair, cellulose, and silk. Synthetic polymers include items made of plastic and nylon. **c.** Composites combine the desirable properties of the individual materials from which they are made.
3. a. Sample benefits: Strong, inexpensive, durable, lightweight, flexible, can be molded or shaped, don't react easily. Sample problems: Recycling used items may be more expensive than discarding them and making new ones; don't break down quickly in the environment. **b.** Sample answer: A reusable cloth bag can replace a plastic grocery bag.

Reteach L1
Students can make a concept map relating monomers, polymers, and composites.

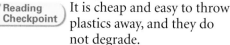 **Teaching Resources**

• Section Summary: *Polymers and Composites*
• Review and Reinforce: *Polymers and Composites*
• Enrich: *Polymers and Composites*

Design and Build a Polymer Package L3

Prepare for Inquiry

Key Concept
Both natural and synthetic polymers vary in their ability to provide cushioning that will protect breakable objects during shipping.

Skills Objective
After this lab, students will be able to
- design an inexpensive shipping package that will protect a breakable object
- build a testable prototype of a shipping package
- evaluate the design and redesign the shipping package, if necessary, for better performance

 **Prep Time** 15 minutes
Class Time 40 minutes

Advance Planning
Obtain samples of at least four different polymers used in packaging. Have a small supply of each sample available for each group.

Safety

Remind students to wear safety goggles and aprons throughout the activity. Students should use heat-resistant gloves when testing heat insulation properties. Caution students to take care when using the iodine solution as it is toxic and will also stain skin and clothing. Review the safety guidelines in Appendix A.

All in One Teaching Resources
- Lab Worksheet: *Design and Build a Polymer Package*

Guide Inquiry

Invitation
Ask: **What factors must be considered when choosing a packaging material?** (*Sample answer: Strength, resistance to tearing, and cushioning*) Invite students to imagine they are running a mail-order catalog company. Ask: **What factors would you consider in choosing packaging materials for your business?** (*Sample answer: Cost, cushioning, weight, resistance to pests, effect on environment*)

Design and Build a Polymer Package

Problem
Can you design and build packaging made of polymers that is suitable for mailing a breakable object to a friend?

Design Skills
designing a solution, building a prototype, evaluating the design

Materials
- water
- hand lens
- weights (or books)
- scissors
- packaging tape
- thermometer
- balance
- clock or timer
- containers (20 beakers, trays, or plastic cups)
- iodine solution, 1% solution (10 mL)
- cookies or hard-boiled eggs
- polymers used in packaging (paper, Tyvek, plastic foam, ecofoam, cardboard, fabric, popcorn, sawdust, wood shavings, plastic)

Procedure

PART 1 Research and Investigate

1. Make a list of all the ways you can think of to test the properties of polymers. Think about properties including:
   - ability to protect a fragile object
   - reaction to water • appearance
   - heat insulation • strength
   - reaction to iodine • mass
   Note: Iodine turns a dark blue-black color when starch is present. (Starch may attract insects or other pests.)

2. Select a property you wish to test. Choose a method that you think would be the best way to test that property.

3. Design a step-by-step procedure for the test. Do the same for each of the other properties you decide to investigate. Be sure that you change only one variable at a time. Include any safety directions in your procedure.

4. Predict which polymers you think will perform best in each test you plan.

5. After your teacher has approved your procedure, perform the tests on each polymer.

6. Record your observations in a table similar to the one shown.

Data Table				
Polymer	Brief Description of Test 1	Brief Description of Test 2	Brief Description of Test 3	Brief Description of Test 4
A				
B				
C				

Introduce the Procedure
Have students read the procedure. Ask: **What properties of each polymer will you test?** (*Sample answer: Ability to protect a fragile object, reaction to water, heat insulation, strength, reaction to iodine, mass, and appearance*) **What are the design criteria?** (*A strong, cheap, and environmentally friendly way to protect and enclose an object so that it will not break when dropped 1.5 m.*)

Troubleshooting the Experiment
- Guide students in controlling variables. Emphasize that only one property and one polymer should be tested at a time.
- Advise students to set up the heat insulation test first. Other tests may be performed while they wait for the time to pass until a second temperature measurement is taken.

PART 2 Design and Build

7. Using what you learned in Part 1, design packaging that
   - could be used to completely enclose a hard-boiled egg or cookie.
   - can drop a distance of 1.5 m without breaking the egg or cookie.
   - is strong and inexpensive to make.

8. Sketch your design on a sheet of paper, and list the materials you will need. Design an experiment to test the packaging.

9. Obtain your teacher's approval for your design. Then construct the packaging.

PART 3 Evaluate and Redesign

10. Test your packaging to evaluate how well the packaging meets the criteria in Step 7.

11. Based on the results of your tests, decide how you could improve your packaging. Then make any needed changes and test how the packaging performs again.

Analyze and Conclude

1. **Building a Prototype** What properties of polymers that you identified in Part 1 proved most useful when you designed your prototype in Part 2?

2. **Evaluating the Design** Did your packaging protect the object inside? What characteristics of your design do you think led to this result?

3. **Designing a Solution** How did your testing and evaluation of your prototype help you to redesign it?

4. **Evaluating the Impact on Society** How might people change their behavior if stronger and cheaper packaging material becomes available?

5. **Working With Design Constraints** Suppose the constraints on your design are changed. Now, your packaging must also be able to support a 10-kilogram weight. How would this affect your choice of materials and your design?

Communicate

Write an advertisement to market your packaging. In your ad, explain why your packaging does the best job of protecting the objects inside.

K ◆ 127

Expected Outcome

Students are expected to create packaging made of polymers. The packaging must be strong, cheap, and environmentally friendly. It must prevent an object from breaking when dropped a distance of 1.5 m. Students may need to redesign their device to meet the criteria.

Analyze and Conclude

1. Sample answer: Ability to protect a fragile object and strength are the properties that proved to be most useful.

2. Sample answer: The final packaging did not prevent the object from breaking. My design was not strong enough and did not prevent the egg from escaping the packaging.

3. Sample answer: The testing and evaluation of the design helped locate possible strength issues and areas where the egg might slip through the packaging.

4. People most likely would choose to use the improved packaging if they were convinced it would protect objects they want to ship and would cost them less to use.

5. Sample answer: To support the additional mass, a stronger polymer would have to be used, or more of the same polymer. Also, the mass of the polymer and cost of the polymer would now need to be considered.

Extend Inquiry

Communicate Advertisements should describe the benefits of the packaging. Benefits may include strength, ability to protect fragile objects, and low cost.

Technology and Society

Polyester Fleece

Key Concept
Plastic can be recycled to make polyester fleece, a warm, lightweight fabric.

Build Background Knowledge

Recalling Synthetic Polymers
Ask: **How are synthetic polymers made?** *(They are made from simpler materials that often come from oil or coal.)* **What are their benefits?** *(Sample answer: Synthetic polymers are cheaper than natural polymers and last longer. Many are also strong, flexible, and lightweight.)* **What are their disadvantages?** *(It is cheaper to throw them away than it is to reuse them. This increases the volume of trash.)*

Introduce the Debate
Ask: **How can the volume of plastics in the trash be reduced?** *(Sample answer: By using the waste plastics as raw materials for making new plastic products)* **How would a company that made polyester fleece decide whether to use recycled plastics or raw materials?** *(Sample answer: Assess the costs of reprocessing used plastics and processing raw materials for the fabric fibers. Also consider the impact on the environment.)*

Facilitate the Debate
Invite students to participate in a mock board meeting of a company that manufactures polyester fleece. Have them discuss the advantages and disadvantages of making polyester fibers from raw materials and from recycled plastics. Students can role-play engineers, accountants, environmentalists, and chemists. Students should consider material costs, energy costs, water use, worker safety, and effects on the environment.

After the debate, have students write a brief business plan describing whether the company chose to use raw materials or recycled plastics to manufacturer polyester fibers. They should include reasons that the company made that choice.

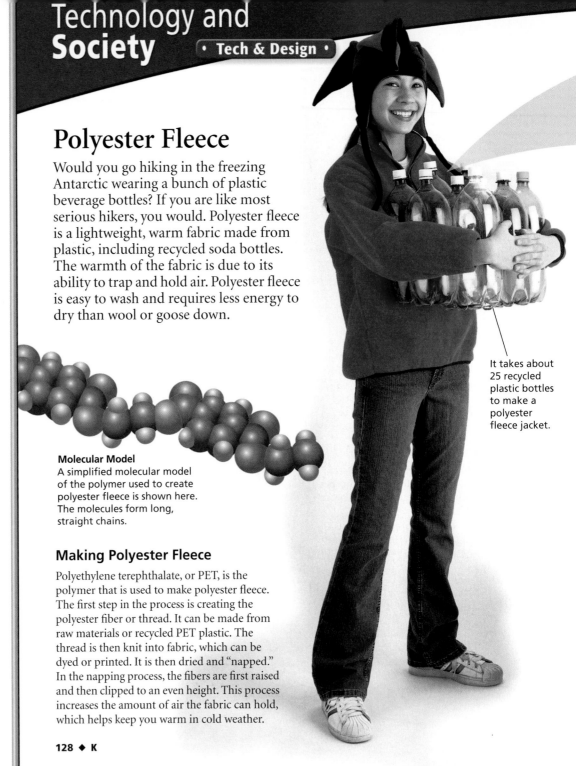

Polyester Fleece

Would you go hiking in the freezing Antarctic wearing a bunch of plastic beverage bottles? If you are like most serious hikers, you would. Polyester fleece is a lightweight, warm fabric made from plastic, including recycled soda bottles. The warmth of the fabric is due to its ability to trap and hold air. Polyester fleece is easy to wash and requires less energy to dry than wool or goose down.

Molecular Model
A simplified molecular model of the polymer used to create polyester fleece is shown here. The molecules form long, straight chains.

It takes about 25 recycled plastic bottles to make a polyester fleece jacket.

Making Polyester Fleece

Polyethylene terephthalate, or PET, is the polymer that is used to make polyester fleece. The first step in the process is creating the polyester fiber or thread. It can be made from raw materials or recycled PET plastic. The thread is then knit into fabric, which can be dyed or printed. It is then dried and "napped." In the napping process, the fibers are first raised and then clipped to an even height. This process increases the amount of air the fabric can hold, which helps keep you warm in cold weather.

Background

Facts and Figures Companies that manufacture polyester fibers are always looking for the most profitable method. It is often cheaper to make fibers directly from the chemical ingredients because chemical prices are low. The costs of using recycled bottles are less flexible because the costs of transporting, cleaning, and chopping into granules do not change much. Some companies address this problem by looking for the best deals in recycled plastic and buying them, whether they need the materials immediately or not. They warehouse the excess material until they need it. Other companies keep costs down by switching from one source of recycled material to another. Some companies use scrap plastic produced in the manufacturing process or from manufacturing mistakes.

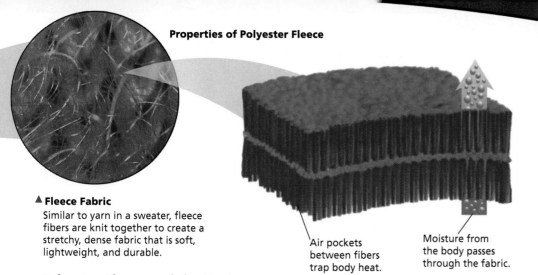

Properties of Polyester Fleece

▲ **Fleece Fabric**
Similar to yarn in a sweater, fleece fibers are knit together to create a stretchy, dense fabric that is soft, lightweight, and durable.

Air pockets between fibers trap body heat.

Moisture from the body passes through the fabric.

Polyester Fleece and the Environment

Making polyester fleece fabric uses water and energy, like other fabric-making processes. Using recycled materials to create polyester fleece saves energy and reduces wastes. One trade-off involves the safety of workers in the fleece factories. The clipping process creates dust particles in the air that workers then breathe. Some companies that produce fleece are developing technology that should reduce dust in the workplace, as well as technologies that conserve and reuse energy and water.

Plastic Bottle Granules
PET plastic bottles are chipped to create granules like those shown here. The granules can be used in making polyester fleece. ▼

Weigh the Impact

1. Identify the Need
What are some benefits of using polyester fleece to make clothing and blankets?

2. Research
Use the Internet to find companies that make or sell polyester fleece made from recycled plastic. Identify ways in which this form of recycling helps the environment.

3. Write
Create a pamphlet to encourage your classmates to recycle plastics. Describe how PET plastic can be used to create polyester fleece.

Go Online
PHSchool.com

For: More on polyester fleece
Visit: PHSchool.com
Web Code: cgh-1040

Weigh the Impact

1. Sample answer: Polyester fleece is a lightweight, warm fabric that is easy to wash and requires less energy than wool or goose down to dry. If recycled plastic is used to make fleece fibers, it can also save energy and reduce wastes.
2. Sample answer: This form of recycling reduces the volume of trash by reducing the amount of plastics. It also saves energy.
3. Encourage students to use illustrations in their pamphlets and to use clear, concise language when describing the process used to make fleece from PET plastic. Pamphlets should describe why recycling plastics is important and why reusing PET plastics to create polyester fleece is beneficial.

For: More on polyester fleece
Visit: PHSchool.com
Web Code: cgh-1040

Students can research this issue online.

Extend

Encourage students to learn about other products that are manufactured from recycled plastics. Instruct them to choose one product and tell what kind of plastic is reused to make it and how that product is beneficial.

Objectives

After this lesson, students will be able to

K.4.2.1 Compare the properties of metals and alloys.

K.4.2.2 Describe how steels and other alloys are made and used.

Target Reading Skill

Outlining Explain that using an outline format helps students organize information by main topic, subtopic, and details.

Answer

Metals and Alloys

  I. Comparing metals and alloys

    A. Properties of metals

    B. Properties of alloys

  II. Making and using alloys

    A. Steels

    B. Other alloys

All in One Teaching Resources

• Transparency K34

Preteach

Build Background Knowledge   L2

Pure Gold or a Mixture

Tell students that 24-karat gold is pure gold and 10-karat gold is less than half gold and more than half silver. Ask: **Why would a jeweler want to make a gold charm from 10-karat gold rather than 24-karat gold?** *(Students may say because it is less expensive, but some may know that 10-karat gold jewelry is stronger.)* Consider asking this question again later in the section.

Reading Preview

Key Concepts
• How do the properties of metals and alloys compare?
• How are steels and other alloys made and used?

Key Term
• alloy

Target Reading Skill

Outlining As you read, make an outline about metals and alloys that you can use for review. Use the red section headings for the main topics and the blue headings for the subtopics.

Metals and Alloys
I. Comparing metals and alloys
A. Properties of metals
B.
II. Making and using alloys
A.

▲ A brass euphonium

Lab zone Discover Activity

Are They "Steel" the Same?

1. Wrap a cut nail (low-carbon steel), a wire nail (high-carbon steel), and a stainless steel bolt together in a paper towel.
2. Place the towel in a plastic bag. Add about 250 mL of salt water and seal the bag.
3. After one or two days, remove the nails and bolt. Note any changes in the metals.

Think It Over

Developing Hypotheses What happened to the three types of steel? Which one changed the most, and which one changed the least? What do you think accounts for the difference?

More than 6,000 years ago, people learned to make copper tools that were sharper than stone tools. Later, people also used tin for tools. But copper and tin are soft, so they bend easily and are hard to keep sharp. About 5,000 years ago, metal makers discovered a way to make better tools.

Comparing Metals and Alloys

Copper and tin mixed together in the right amounts make a stronger, harder metal that keeps its sharp edge after long use. This discovery marked the beginning of the Bronze Age. It also was the invention of the first alloy. An **alloy** is a mixture made of two or more elements that has the properties of metal. In every alloy, at least one of the elements is a metal.

Properties of Metals You know a piece of metal when you see it. It's usually hard and shiny. At room temperature, all metallic elements (except mercury) are solids. Metals share other properties, too. You learned in Chapter 3 that metals can conduct electricity. They are ductile—that is, they can be drawn out into thin wire. For example, copper made into wire carries electric current to the outlets in your home. Metals are also malleable—that is, they can be hammered into a sheet. Aluminum, rolled flat, makes aluminum foil.

130 ◆ K

Lab zone Discover Activity

Skills Focus Developing hypotheses   L1

Materials cut nail, wire nail, stainless steel bolt, paper towel, sealable plastic bag, saltwater solution

Time 10 minutes, plus 1- or 2-day waiting period

Tips Cut nails have flat heads and are made of low-carbon steel; they are commonly used on hardwood floors. Wire nails are also called finishing nails. If possible, leave the nails and bolts in the bag for two days so students can see more dramatic changes.

Think It Over Both nails rusted; the bolt did not rust or rusted very little. The cut nail changed the most; the bolt changed the least. The materials in the nails determine how the nails react to salt water.

Properties of Alloys The properties of an alloy can differ greatly from those of its individual elements. Pure gold, for example, is soft and easily bent. For that reason, gold jewelry and coins are made of an alloy of gold with another metal, such as copper or silver. These gold alloys are much harder than pure gold but still let its beauty show. Even after thousands of years, objects made of gold alloys do not change. They still look exactly the same as when they were first made.

Alloys are used much more than pure metals because they are generally stronger and less likely to react with air or water. Iron, for example, is often alloyed with one or more other elements to make steel. And steel is used in many tools because of its superior strength and hardness. You have seen iron objects rust when they are exposed to air and water. But forks and spoons made of stainless steel can be washed over and over again without rusting. That's because stainless steel—an alloy of iron, carbon, nickel, and chromium—does not react with air and water as iron does.

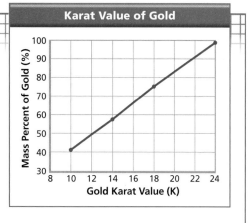

FIGURE 8
Gold and Steel
This necklace is made of gold alloys. The pipe wrench is made of steel.
Applying Concepts Why are alloys used to make these objects rather than pure metals?

 Reading Checkpoint Why is most jewelry made of gold alloys rather than pure gold?

Math ▶ **Analyzing Data**

Calculating Karat Value

Gold is often alloyed with other metals, such as silver, to improve its hardness and durability. The mass percent of gold in such an alloy is usually expressed by its karat value. Gold karat values and mass percent data are plotted on the graph shown here.

1. **Reading Graphs** Which axis has values that describe the mass of gold relative to the mass of the alloy?

2. **Reading Graphs** How does the mass percent of gold change as the karat value increases?

3. **Interpreting Data** What is the mass percent of gold for a 14-karat gold alloy?

Karat Value of Gold

[Line graph: x-axis "Gold Karat Value (K)" from 8 to 24; y-axis "Mass Percent of Gold (%)" from 30 to 100. Line rises from about 41% at 10K to about 99% at 24K.]

4. **Creating Data Tables** Create a data table that gives the approximate mass percent of gold for alloys with karat values of 10, 12, 14, 16, 18, 20, 22, and 24.

Differentiated Instruction

English Learners/Beginning L1
Comprehension: Asking Questions
After students have read Comparing Metals and Alloys, ask them very simple questions to assess their comprehension. Questions include: **What are metals like? What is an alloy? How are alloys different from metals? learning modality: verbal**

English Learners/Intermediate L2
Comprehension: Asking Questions
In addition to the questions above, ask students inferential questions such as: **What material would make a better cooking pan, iron or stainless steel? learning modality: verbal**

Instruct

Comparing Metals and Alloys

Teach Key Concepts L2
Contrasting Weight and Mass

Focus Write the definition of alloy on the board.

Teach Review the properties of metals. Ask: **Why are alloys used more often than pure metals?** *(Alloys are generally stronger and less likely to react with air or water.)*

Apply Ask: **What metals are alloyed to make stainless steel?** *(Iron, carbon, nickel, and chromium)* **Why is stainless steel used for forks and spoons instead or iron?** *(Stainless steel does not rust.)* **learning modality: verbal**

Math ▶ **Analyzing Data**

Math Skill Making and interpreting graphs

Focus Explain that a line graph can show the relationship between two different values.

Teach Have students study the graph. Ask: **Where is karat value plotted?** *(The x-axis)* **What is the highest gold karat value?** *(24K)*

Answers
1. The *y*-axis
2. The mass percent of gold increases.
3. About 58%
4. The table should show approximately the following relationships: 10-karat, 41%; 12-karat, 49%; 14-karat, 58%; 16-karat, 67%; 18-karat, 75%; 20-karat, 83%; 22-karat, 92%; 24-karat, 99%.

Independent Practice L2

All in One Teaching Resources

• Guided Reading and Study Worksheet: *Metals and Alloys*

⊙ **Student Edition on Audio CD**

Monitor Progress _____ L2

Answers
Figure 8 Alloys are stronger and less likely to react with air or water.

 Reading Checkpoint Gold alloys are harder and less easily bent than pure gold.

Making and Using Alloys

Teach Key Concepts   [L2]

Making and Using Alloys

Focus Tell students that many different alloys of steel exist.

Teach Ask: **How are many alloys made?** *(By melting the metals and mixing them together in specific amounts)* **What other elements are often alloyed with iron to make steel?** *(Sample answer: Carbon, chromium, manganese, and nickel)* Emphasize that the different alloys of steel have different properties based on which elements are added to iron and in what amounts.

Apply Ask: **What are some uses of steel?** *(Sample answer: Knives, nails, chains, bicycle frames, cookware, and train rails)* **learning modality: verbal**

For: Links on alloys
Visit: www.SciLinks.org
Web Code: scn-1142

Download a worksheet that will guide students' review of Internet sources on alloys.

▞ Address Misconceptions   [L1]

Alloys Are Mixtures

Focus Students may not understand why alloys are mixtures and not compounds.

Teach Explain that physical processes can be used to separate the metals in an alloy. For example, if brass is heated to a high temperature, the zinc will melt before the copper does. Explain that although some alloys, such as sterling silver, require specific amounts of each metal, others need only a range of amounts. For example, brass may have up to 50 percent zinc.

Apply Ask: **Why is an alloy not a compound?** *(The metals in the alloy do not react chemically.)* **learning modality: verbal**

For: Links on alloys
Visit: www.SciLinks.org
Web Code: scn-1142

Making and Using Alloys

Many alloys are made by melting metals and mixing them together in carefully measured amounts. Since the beginning of the Bronze Age, this technique has been used to make copper alloys. Some modern alloys are made by mixing the elements as powders and then heating them under high pressure. This process uses less energy because the metal powders blend at lower temperatures. The material then can be molded into the desired shape immediately. Using a more recent technique, titanium may be bombarded with nitrogen ions to make a strong alloy for artificial joints.

Steels When you want to describe something very hard or tough, you may use the expression "hard as steel." Steel is an alloy of iron with other elements. It is used for its strength, hardness, and resistance to corrosion. Without steel, automobiles, suspension bridges, skyscrapers, and surgical knives would not exist.

Not all steels are alike. Their properties depend on which elements are added to iron and in what amounts. Carbon steels are stronger and harder than wrought iron, which is almost pure iron.

FIGURE 9
Alloys have a wide variety of uses. **Making Generalizations** *How do the properties of bronze make it well-suited for its uses?*

Common Alloys			
Alloy	**Elements**	**Properties**	**Uses**
Brass	Copper, zinc	Strong, resists corrosion, polishes well	Musical instruments, faucets, decorative hardware, jewelry
Bronze	Copper, tin	Hard, resists corrosion	Marine hardware, screws, grillwork
Stainless steel	Iron, carbon, nickel, chromium	Strong, resists corrosion	Tableware, cookware, surgical instruments
Carbon steel	Iron, carbon	Inexpensive, strong	Tools, auto bodies, machinery, steel girders, rails
Plumber's solder	Lead, tin	Low melting point	Sealer for joints and leaks in metal plumbing
Sterling silver	Silver, copper	Shiny, harder than pure silver	Jewelry, tableware
Dental amalgam	Mercury, silver, tin, copper, zinc	Low melting point, easily shaped	Dental fillings
Pewter	Tin, antimony, copper; sometimes lead*	Bright or satin finish, resists tarnish	Tableware, decorative objects
Wood's metal	Bismuth, lead, tin, cadmium	Low melting point	Fire sprinklers, electric fuses

*Pewter containing lead cannot be used with food.

Solder

FIGURE 10
Alloys in Daily Life
Solder is used by plumbers to seal leaking pipes. Brass is found in decorative objects, such as this door knocker. Stainless steel is often found in cookware, and pewter is used in some tableware.

▲ Brass   ▲ Stainless steel

▲ Pewter

High-carbon steels contain 0.6 to 1.5 percent carbon. Tools, knives, and springs are just some of the uses for high-carbon steels. Low-carbon steels, with less than 0.2 percent carbon, are ductile and malleable and are used for nails, cables, and chains.

There are hundreds of different types of steels. Usually carbon is added to the iron plus one or more of the following metals: chromium, manganese, molybdenum, nickel, tungsten, and vanadium. Steels made with these metals are generally stronger, harder, and more corrosion-resistant than carbon steel. Depending on their properties, these steels may become bicycle frames, train rails, steel tubing, or construction equipment.

Other Alloys Bronze, brass, sterling silver, and solder (SAHD ur) are just a few examples of other kinds of alloys. Alloys are used to make items ranging from plumbing materials and sprinkler systems to tableware and doorknobs. Even your dentist uses alloys. Have you ever had a cavity in a tooth? A mixture of mercury with silver or gold (called an amalgam) makes a pasty solid. It hardens quickly, filling a hole in the tooth. Look at Figure 9 and see how many of the examples listed in the table are alloys you have seen or used.

 Reading Checkpoint Name three uses of high-carbon steels.

Lab zone Teacher **Demo**   L1

Demonstrating Properties of Solder

Materials soldering iron, solder, 2 wires, modeling clay, aluminum foil

Time 15 minutes

Focus Have students look at the table in Figure 9. Ask: **What metals are alloyed to make plumber's solder?** (*Lead and tin*)

Teach Cover the table top with foil. Press a lump of modeling clay on the foil and firmly fix one wire in the clay, leaving one end of the wire free. Place the second wire next to the free end of the wire in the clay. Use the soldering iron to heat up the solder and let it melt over the junction of the two wires. Allow the solder to cool and harden, then demonstrate that the two wires are joined.

Apply Ask: **What property of solder makes it useful to plumbers and electricians?** (*Sample answer: It has a low melting point, but is solid at room temperature.*) **learning modality: visual**

Differentiated Instruction

Gifted and Talented   L3
Finding Alloys in Coins Explain that most United States coins are made of alloys. Give students pennies and copper wire to compare. Ask: **How is the copper alloy different from pure copper?** (*It is

much stronger; it will not bend.) Invite students to research the composition and minting of coins. Have them find out the specific composition of each type of coin. **learning modality: verbal**

Monitor Progress   L2

Oral Presentation Have students name three uses for metal alloys.

Answers
Figure 9 Because bronze is hard and resists corrosion, it is useful in environments that are potentially corrosive, such as near or on the ocean, and where it will hold its shape, such as in hardware and screws.

Reading Checkpoint High-carbons steels are used for tools, knives, and springs.

Reviewing Key Concepts

1. a. Sample answer: Shiny, ductile, malleable **b.** Bronze is made of copper and tin. **c.** Alloys are generally stronger and less likely to react with air or water than pure metals.

2. a. Sample answer: Many alloys are made by melting metals and mixing them together in carefully measured amounts. **b.** The steel has a low carbon content; it is less than 0.2% carbon. **c.** In sterling silver, copper is alloyed with silver to make tableware that is shiny and harder than pure silver.

Reteach　　　　L1

Have students create a table to compare and contrast the properties of metals and alloys.

Performance Assessment　　L2

Writing Have students choose an item that is made of a metal alloy and write a paragraph describing what the alloy is made of and why it serves the function better than the original metals.

All in One Teaching Resources

- Section Summary: *Metals and Alloys*
- Review and Reinforce: *Metals and Alloys*
- Enrich: *Metals and Alloys*

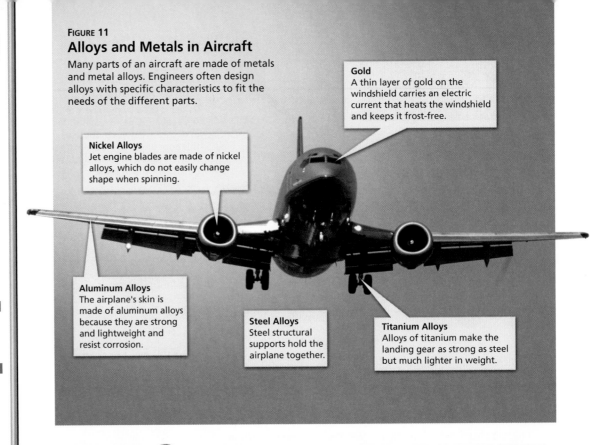

FIGURE 11
Alloys and Metals in Aircraft
Many parts of an aircraft are made of metals and metal alloys. Engineers often design alloys with specific characteristics to fit the needs of the different parts.

Gold
A thin layer of gold on the windshield carries an electric current that heats the windshield and keeps it frost-free.

Nickel Alloys
Jet engine blades are made of nickel alloys, which do not easily change shape when spinning.

Aluminum Alloys
The airplane's skin is made of aluminum alloys because they are strong and lightweight and resist corrosion.

Steel Alloys
Steel structural supports hold the airplane together.

Titanium Alloys
Alloys of titanium make the landing gear as strong as steel but much lighter in weight.

Section 2 Assessment

Target Reading Skill Outlining Use the information in your outline about metals and alloys to answer the questions.

Reviewing Key Concepts

1. a. Listing List three properties you would expect a pure metal object to have.
　b. Reviewing From what pure metals is bronze made?
　c. Comparing and Contrasting Compare and contrast the general properties of alloys and pure metals.
2. a. Describing Describe one way in which alloys are made.
　b. Inferring A steel suitable for making nails is malleable and ductile. What can you infer about the probable carbon content of the steel?
　c. Interpreting Tables Look at the table in Figure 9. What metal may be alloyed with silver to make tableware that is shiny and harder than pure silver?

Lab zone **At-Home Activity**

Finding Alloys Find items in your home that are made from metals or alloys. Look for cooking utensils, tools, toys, sports equipment, appliances, and other household items that are made with these materials. Discuss with members of your family how properties of the metals or alloys relate to the uses of the objects.

Lab zone **At-Home Activity**

Finding Alloys L1 Encourage students to use the table in Figure 9 to identify the alloys they find at home. Students should explain to their families that alloys have characteristics different from those of the metals they contain. For example, tableware or jewelry made of pure silver would dent more easily than the same things made of alloys.

Lab zone **Chapter Project**

Keep Students on Track By now, students will have devised the tests for the physical and chemical properties of their materials. They might test for hardness, fiber strength, flexibility, color, density, solubility in water, or reaction to corrosive chemicals. Review students' written procedures and data tables. Make sure students have samples they are permitted to test or have devised tests that will not damage the samples.

Reading Preview

Key Concepts
• What are the properties of ceramics?
• What are the properties of glass?

Key Terms
• ceramic • glass
• optical fiber

Target Reading Skill
Identifying Main Ideas As you read about ceramics, write the main idea in a graphic organizer like the one below. Then write three supporting details that give examples of the main idea.

Main Idea

Ceramics are useful because they resist moisture.

Detail	Detail	Detail

Lab zone Discover **Activity**

Does It Get Wet?

1. [icons] Find the masses of a glazed pottery flowerpot and an unglazed one of similar size. Record both values.
2. Place both pots in a basin of water for ten minutes.
3. Remove the pots from the water and gently blot dry with paper towels.
4. Find and record the masses of both flowerpots again.
5. Calculate the percent of change in mass for each pot.

Think It Over

Inferring Which pot gained the most mass? What can you infer about the effect that glazing has on the pot?

Have you ever heard the phrase "a bull in a china shop"? Imagine the damage! The phrase comes from the fact that ceramics and glass are brittle and can shatter when struck. In spite of this property, archaeologists have uncovered many ceramic and glass artifacts used by the Romans and other ancient civilizations. Because ceramics and glass resist moisture and don't react readily, some of these ancient objects remain in excellent condition even today.

Ceramics

Ceramics are hard, crystalline solids made by heating clay and other mineral materials to high temperatures. Clay is made of water and very small mineral particles containing mostly silicon, aluminum, and oxygen. Clay forms when the minerals in rock break down.

FIGURE 12
Homes Made of Clay
These homes in New Mexico were built with clay bricks hundreds of years ago.

Chapter 4 K ◆ 135

Lab zone Discover **Activity**

Skills Focus Inferring [L2]

Materials 1 glazed and 1 unglazed flowerpot of the same size, sink or basin, water, balance

Time 10 minutes

Tips Consider reviewing how to find the percent of change:

$$\frac{(\text{new mass} - \text{initial mass})}{\text{initial mass}} \times 100\%$$

Larger pots and pots soaked longer than 10 minutes will show more change.

Think It Over The unglazed pot gained the most mass. The glazing keeps water from soaking into the pot.

Objectives
After this lesson, students will be able to
K.4.3.1 Describe the properties of ceramics.
K.4.3.2 Describe the properties of glass.

Target Reading Skill

Identifying Main Ideas Explain that identifying main ideas and details helps students sort the facts from the information into groups. Each group can have a main topic, subtopics, and details.

Answer
Sample main idea: Ceramics are useful because they resist moisture.
Sample details: Many ceramics have a glassy, waterproof coating called glaze. Ceramic pottery has been used to store food. Ceramics are used as roofing tiles.

All in One Teaching Resources
• Transparency K35

Preteach

Build Background Knowledge [L2]
Observing Properties of Glass
Show students a clear drinking glass and ask: **What are some properties of this glass?** *(Sample answer: Clear, holds water, can break if dropped)* Then ask: **What are other uses for glass?** *(Sample answer: Windows, eyeglasses, television screens)*

Instruct

Ceramics

Teach Key Concepts [L2]
Properties of Ceramics

Focus Write the definition of ceramics.

Teach Ask: **What properties of ceramics make them useful?** *(Ceramics resist moisture, do not conduct electricity, withstand high temperatures.)*

Apply Ask: **What are some uses of ceramics?** *(Sample answer: Food storage, roofing tiles, bricks, sewer pipes)* **learning modality: verbal**

K ● 135

Making Ceramics

Materials potter's clay, toothbrush, water, lab apron, kiln

Time 20 minutes, plus 5 minutes after firing

Focus Explain that one way to make a clay pot is to wrap coils of clay on top of a clay base.

Teach Demonstrate how to make a clay coil. Then have each student make one coil. Tell students to carefully roll the coils to ensure that all air bubbles are removed. Have a volunteer cut a circular base for the pot from a flat piece of clay. To assemble the coils on the base, dip the toothbrush in water and lightly score the surface on which the coil will rest and the side of the coil that will lie on the base. Continue assembly by dipping the toothbrush in water and lightly scoring the top of the coil on the pot and the bottom of the coil being added. Allow each student to add his or her coil to the pot. Make sure students wash hands after handling the clay. Then, fire the pot and have students observe how the pot changed. Ask: **What happened to the pot during firing?** (*Water in the clay evaporated, causing the clay particles to stick together.*)

Apply Ask: **How could you make this pot colorful and waterproof?** (*By glazing the pot with silicon dioxide glaze and firing it again*)
learning modality: kinesthetic

Go Online
SciLINKS NSTA

For: Links on glass
Visit: www.SciLinks.org
Web Code: scn-1143

Download a worksheet that will guide students' review of Internet sources on glass.

Independent Practice   L2

All in One Teaching Resources

- Guided Reading and Study Worksheet: *Ceramics and Glass*

⊙ Student Edition on Audio CD

Go Online
SciLINKS NSTA

For: Links on glass
Visit: www.SciLinks.org
Web Code: scn-1143

Making Ceramics When a clay object is heated above 1,000°C, much of the water present in the clay evaporates, and the particles of clay stick together. This process forms hard ceramics such as bricks and flowerpots. These ceramics have tiny spaces in their structure that absorb and hold water. However, potters can cover a ceramic with a thin layer of silicon dioxide and heat it again. This process forms a glassy, waterproof coating called a glaze. You might see glazed pottery used to serve or store food. Potters often use colorful glazes to create artistic designs on their work.

Properties and Uses of Ceramics Despite their tendency to break, ceramics have several properties that make them useful. **Ceramics resist moisture, do not conduct electricity, and can withstand temperatures that would cause metals to melt.**

Ceramic pottery has been used for thousands of years to store food, protecting it from moisture and animals. Roofing tiles, bricks, and sewer pipes are all long-standing uses of ceramics. Ceramics also are used as insulators in electric equipment and light fixtures.

New uses for ceramics continue to be developed. Surgeons use bioceramic materials, for example, to replace human hips, knees, and other body parts. The catalytic converters in modern cars and trucks contain ceramics that help convert harmful exhaust gases to harmless carbon dioxide and water.

✓ Reading Checkpoint What are some uses of ceramics?

FIGURE 13
Making and Using Ceramics
Colorful glazes were used to decorate the ceramic plates below. **Predicting** *What will happen to the clay, right, when the potter heats it in a kiln, or hot oven?*

Differentiated Instruction

Special Needs   L1
Observing Glass Invite students to carefully examine various samples of glass such as colored bottles, eyeglasses, a baking dish, window glass, and a beaker. Ask: **Is all this glass the same?** (*No. The glass has* *different properties such as color, density, ability to bend light, and the ability to withstand heat.*) **What gives the glass different properties?** (*The materials that were mixed with the melting sand*) **learning modality: visual**

FIGURE 14
Figure 14
Ancient Glass
These glass objects, once used in ancient Rome, are on display at the Corning Museum in New York.

Glass

Thousands of years ago, people learned that sand mixed with limestone can be melted into a thick, hot liquid that flows like molasses. If this liquid cools quickly, it forms a clear, solid material with no crystal structure, called **glass**.

Making Glass Early glassmakers added calcium (in the form of limestone) and sodium (in the form of sodium carbonate) to the melting sand. This mixture melts at a lower temperature than sand alone, so it is easier to work with. Window glass, bottles, and jars are still made with this type of glass.

More than 2,000 years ago, glassmakers in ancient Syria invented glassblowing. A glassmaker would put a blob of melted glass on the end of an iron pipe. By blowing air through the pipe, the glassmaker could produce a hollow glass vessel. If the glass was blown inside a wooden mold, jars and vases in beautiful patterns and shapes could be created.

Properties and Uses of Glass Like ceramics, glass is brittle and can shatter when struck. Nonetheless, it has many useful properties. **Glass is clear, can be made in many shapes and colors, and can't be penetrated by liquids.**

Different materials may be added to glass to make it useful for particular purposes. Substituting lead oxide for limestone makes a glass that bends light in useful ways. This kind of glass is used to make lenses for eyeglasses, telescopes, and microscopes. Adding boron oxide creates a glass that resists heat better than ordinary glass. This type of glass is used for cookware and laboratory glassware that must be heated.

Lab zone Try This Activity

A Bright Idea
Model communication through glass.

1. Construct a barrier between you and a partner so that you cannot see each other.
2. Run a plastic optical fiber past the barrier. (Plastic fibers work similarly to glass fibers.)
3. Bring the bulb of a penlight flashlight close to your end of the fiber.
4. Using a single flash for "yes" and two flashes for "no," send your partner a message by responding to a series of yes and no questions he or she asks.
5. Change roles so that your partner has a chance to send signals in response to your questions.

Observing What happened when you and your partner sent signals to each other?

Lab zone Try This Activity

Skills Focus Observing

Materials barrier material such as a notebook or cardboard, penlight flashlight, optical fibers

Time 15 minutes

Tips For safety reasons, use only plastic optical fibers available from scientific supply houses. Suggest students ask questions about the identify of a small hidden object.

Expected Outcome The light travels through the fiber from one end to the other, carrying the flashes of light.

Extend Have students experiment to find out how efficient the optical fibers are over longer distances. **learning modality: kinesthetic**

Glass

Teach Key Concepts   L2
Properties of Glass

Focus Tell students that glass is a clear, solid material with no crystal structure.

Teach Ask: **How is glass made?** (*By melting sand mixed with limestone, calcium, or sodium and cooling it quickly*) **What are some properties of glass?** (*Sample answer: Brittle, can shatter when struck, clear, can be made in many shapes and colors, cannot be penetrated by liquids*)

Apply Ask: **What is glass used for?** (*Sample answer: Lenses in eyeglasses and telescopes, cookware, windows, optical fibers*) **learning modality: verbal**

Help Students Read   L1
Reciprocal Teaching Refer to the Content Refresher in this chapter, which provides guidelines for the Reciprocal Teaching strategy.

Have students read Glass with a partner. One partner reads a paragraph out loud. Then the other summarizes the paragraph's contents and explains the main concepts. The partners continue to switch roles with each new paragraph until finishing the section.

Monitor Progress   L2

Skills Check Have students make a flowchart that describes how a waterproof piece of pottery is made from clay.

Students can save their flowcharts in their portfolios.   **Portfolio**

Answers
Figure 13 The water will evaporate.

Reading Checkpoint Sample answer: Food storage, roofing tiles, bricks, sewer pipes, electrical insulators, replacements for hips and knees, and catalytic converters

Answer

Reading Checkpoint Sound is converted to light signals that travel through the fiber.

Assess

Reviewing Key Concepts

1. a. Ceramics are hard, brittle materials that resist moisture, do not conduct electricity, and can withstand high temperatures. **b.** Ceramics are electrical insulators. **c.** The earlier materials could be chewed by animals and could rot from exposure to sun and water. Ceramics are resistant to sun and water and protect food from animals.

2. a. Sand is the principal material used in making glass. **b.** Glass that contains lead oxide in place of limestone bends light in a way that makes the glass useful in lenses. **c.** Glass transmits light, can be drawn into fibers, and does not corrode.

Reteach **L1**

Have students write a definition for each key term.

Performance Assessment **L2**

Skills Check Have students compare a piece of pottery and a piece of glass, and then make a Venn diagram to show the similarities and differences between glass and ceramics.

All in One Teaching Resources

- Section Summary: *Ceramics and Glass*
- Review and Reinforce: *Ceramics and Glass*
- Enrich: *Ceramics and Glass*

FIGURE 15
Light in Optical Fibers
Even if optical fibers are twisted into a loop, the light moves within the fibers.

Communication Through Glass There's a good chance that the next time you make a phone call, your message will travel through glass. An **optical fiber** is a threadlike piece of glass (or plastic) that can be used for transmitting light. When you speak into a telephone, the signal created by your voice is converted to light signals that travel through the glass fiber. At the other end, the light may be converted into electronic signals that can then be converted to sound.

A pair of optical fibers, each the thickness of a human hair, can carry 625,000 phone calls at one time. One quarter pound of glass fiber can replace more than 2 tons of copper wire. This difference is a big advantage when installing long lines like those that carry messages under the ocean. Another benefit of glass fiber is its stability. Since the glass does not corrode as metals do, the lines are easier to maintain.

Reading Checkpoint In what form is a signal transmitted through an optical fiber?

Section 3 Assessment

🔁 **Target Reading Skill** Identifying Main Ideas Use your graphic organizer about ceramics to help you answer Question 1 below.

Reviewing Key Concepts

1. a. Listing What are the general properties of ceramics?
   b. Explaining Why are ceramics used in the manufacture of spark plugs and many other electrical devices?
   c. Inferring Before ceramics were invented, people stored food in containers such as baskets, leather bags, and wooden bowls. Why were ceramics an improvement as containers for food?

2. a. Reviewing What is the principal material used in making glass?
   b. Describing Describe how the composition of glass may be changed in order to make it useful in lenses.
   c. Applying Concepts What properties of glass make it particularly useful for communication via optical fibers?

Writing in Science

Letter It's Upper Egypt and the year is about 5000 B.C. You notice something strange that happens when your pottery furnace overheats. The presence of limestone containing sand and soda produces shiny coatings on your ceramic pots. Amazingly, the coatings render the pots waterproof! Write a letter to a relative describing your discovery.

Writing in Science

Writing Mode Description
Scoring Rubric
4 Exceeds criteria; includes a highly descriptive letter that accurately describes the discovery
3 Meets criteria
2 Description is weak and/or includes some errors
1 Includes inaccuracies and/or omissions

Reading Preview

Key Concepts
- How was radioactivity discovered?
- What types of particles and energy can radioactive decay produce?
- In what ways are radioactive isotopes useful?

Key Terms
- nuclear reaction
- radioactive decay
- radioactivity
- alpha particle
- beta particle
- gamma radiation
- half-life
- radioactive dating
- tracer

 **Target Reading Skill**

Building Vocabulary A definition states the meaning of a word or phrase by explaining its most important feature or function. After you read the section, reread the paragraphs that contain definitions of Key Terms. Use all the information you have learned to write a definition of each Key Term in your own words.

 Discover Activity

How Much Goes Away?

1. Make a circle about 8–10 centimeters in diameter on a piece of paper. You can do this by tracing the rim of a round container.
2. Use a straightedge to draw a line dividing the circle in half. Then divide one half into quarters, then into eighths, and so on, as shown in the diagram.
3. With scissors, cut out your circle. Now cut away the undivided half circle. Next, cut away the undivided quarter circle. Continue until you are left with one segment.
4. Place the segments on your desktop in the order you cut them.

Think It Over

Drawing Conclusions How is the piece of paper changing each time? Suppose the original circle was a model for a sample of radioactive material, and the paper you cut away is material that became nonradioactive. What would eventually happen?

What if you could find a way to turn dull, cheap lead metal into valuable gold? More than a thousand years ago, many people thought it was a great idea, too. They tried everything they could think of. Of course, nothing worked. There is no chemical reaction that converts one element into another. Even so, elements do sometimes change into other elements. A uranium atom can become a thorium atom. Atoms of carbon can become atoms of nitrogen. (But lead never changes into gold, unfortunately!) How is it possible for these changes to happen?

FIGURE 16
Trying to Make Gold From Lead
This painting from 1570 shows people trying to change lead into gold. No such chemical reaction was ever accomplished.

Section
4 Radioactive Elements

Objectives
After this lesson, students will be able to
K.4.4.1 Describe how radioactivity was discovered.
K.4.4.2 Identify the types of particles and energy that radioactive decay can produce.
K.4.4.3 Describe how radioactive isotopes are useful.

Target Reading Skill

Building Vocabulary Explain that knowing the definitions of key-concept words helps students understand what they read.

Answer
Suggest that students construct a crossword puzzle using the key terms. Have students exchange puzzles and solve them.

Preteach

Build Background Knowledge   L2

Experience With Radioactivity
Ask: **What do you know about radioactivity?** (*Sample answer: It is dangerous. It can give you cancer.*) Tell students that they will learn how atoms change when they are radioactive and how radioactivity is useful in science, medicine, and industry.

 Discover Activity

Skills Focus Drawing conclusions   L2

Materials round or cylindrical container such as a coffee can, ruler, scissors

Time 10 minutes

Tips Draw a sample circle on the board to show students how to make the correct divisions on their paper circles.

Expected Outcome Students will cut away half their paper each time.

Think It Over The piece of paper decreases by half each time. Sample answer: The radioactive material would continue to decrease by half until it became so small that it would be impossible to remove more.

Radioactivity

Teach Key Concepts [L2]

The Discovery of Radioactivity

Focus Explain that Marie Curie, her husband Pierre, and Henri Becquerel were the first scientists to study radioactivity.

Teach Ask: **What element was in the mineral that Henri Becquerel was studying?** *(Uranium)* **What did he observe?** *(The mineral sample left an image on a photographic plate in sunlight and in the dark.)* **What did the Curies conclude the source of the energy to be?** *(The nucleus of the atom was unstable and gave off energy spontaneously.)*

Apply Ask: **What two radioactive elements did the Curies isolate?** *(Polonium and radium)* **learning modality: verbal**

Modeling Nuclear Reactions

Materials modeling clay in 3 colors

Time 15 minutes

Focus Tell students that nuclear reactions do not involve electrons, only protons and neutrons.

Teach Instruct students to construct an atom of any element, using different colored clay balls for the appropriate number of protons, neutrons, and electrons. Have them assume the atom is unstable (though it actually may not be), and have them then model radioactive decay.

Apply Ask: **What is the new identity of your atom after radioactive decay?** *(Sample answer: Carbon became lithium.)* **learning modality: kinesthetic**

Independent Practice [L2]

All in One Teaching Resources

• Guided Reading and Study Worksheet: *Radioactive Elements*

 **Student Edition on Audio CD**

FIGURE 17
Radiation From Uranium
As with Becquerel's discovery, radiation from the uranium-containing mineral has exposed the photographic film.

Radioactivity

You learned in Chapter 14 that the number of protons in the nucleus of an atom determines its identity. Since chemical change involves only an atom's electrons, a chemical reaction can't convert one element into a different element. Such a change happens only during **nuclear reactions** (NOO klee ur)—reactions involving the particles in the nucleus of an atom.

Remember that atoms with the same number of protons and different numbers of neutrons are called isotopes. Some isotopes are unstable; that is, their nuclei do not hold together well. In a process called **radioactive decay,** the atomic nuclei of unstable isotopes release fast-moving particles and energy.

Discovery of Radioactivity In 1896, the French scientist Henri Becquerel discovered radioactive decay quite by accident while studying a mineral containing uranium. He observed that with exposure to sunlight, the mineral gave off a penetrating energy that could expose film. Becquerel assumed that sunlight was necessary for the energy release. So, when the weather turned cloudy, he put away his materials in a dark desk drawer, including a sample of the mineral placed next to a photographic plate wrapped in paper. Later, when Becquerel opened his desk to retrieve these items, he was surprised to discover an image of the mineral sample on the photographic plate. Sunlight wasn't necessary after all. Becquerel hypothesized that uranium spontaneously gives off energy, called radiation, all the time. But if so, what was the source of the energy?

Becquerel presented his findings to a young researcher, Marie Curie and her husband, Pierre. After further study, the Curies concluded that a reaction was taking place within the uranium nuclei. **Radioactivity** is the name that Marie gave to this spontaneous emission of radiation by an unstable atomic nucleus.

 Reading Checkpoint **How is a nuclear reaction different from a chemical reaction?**

FIGURE 18
Marie Curie
Marie Curie, her husband Pierre, and Henri Becquerel, pioneered the study of radioactive elements.

140 ◆ K

Differentiated Instruction

Less Proficient Readers [L1]
Vocabulary Building Write each key term and pronounce it for students. Invite them to repeat after you. Discuss the meaning of each term, and then have students begin a glossary of terms for the section. Help students write a definition of each term using words that are meaningful to them. Encourage them to use diagrams whenever possible. Then have students read the section along with the **Student Edition on Audio CD.** Instruct them to add any words they do not know to their glossaries.
learning modality: verbal

Polonium and Radium Marie Curie was surprised to find that some minerals containing uranium were even more radioactive than pure uranium. Suspecting that the minerals contained small amounts of other, highly radioactive elements, the Curies set to work. They eventually isolated two new elements, which Marie named polonium and radium.

Types of Radioactive Decay

There are three major forms of radiation produced during the radioactive decay of an unstable nucleus. **Natural radioactive decay can produce alpha particles, beta particles, and gamma rays.** The particles and energy produced during radioactive decay are forms of nuclear radiation.

Alpha Decay An **alpha particle** consists of two protons and two neutrons and is positively charged. It is the same as a helium nucleus. The release of an alpha particle by an atom decreases the atomic number by 2 and the mass number by 4. For example, a thorium-232 nucleus decays to produce an alpha particle and a radium-228 nucleus.

Beta Decay Some atoms are unstable because they have too many neutrons. During beta decay, a neutron inside the nucleus of an unstable atom changes into a negatively charged beta particle and a proton. A **beta particle** is a fast-moving electron given off by a nucleus during radioactive decay. The new proton remains inside the nucleus. That means that the nucleus now has one less neutron and one more proton. Its mass number remains the same but its atomic number increases by 1. For example, a carbon-14 nucleus decays to produce a beta particle and a nitrogen-14 nucleus.

Gamma Radiation Alpha and beta decay are almost always accompanied by gamma radiation. **Gamma radiation** consists of high-energy waves, similar to X-rays. Gamma radiation (also called gamma rays) has no charge and does not cause a change in either the atomic mass or the atomic number.

FIGURE 19
Radioactive Decay
Radioactive elements give off particles and energy during radioactive decay.
Interpreting Diagrams *Which type of radioactive decay produces a negatively charged particle?*

Alpha Decay

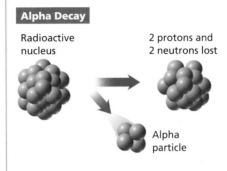

Radioactive nucleus

2 protons and 2 neutrons lost

Alpha particle

Beta Decay

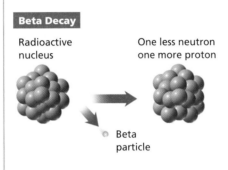

Radioactive nucleus

One less neutron one more proton

Beta particle

Gamma Decay

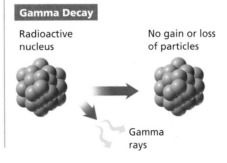

Radioactive nucleus

No gain or loss of particles

Gamma rays

Types of Radioactive Decay

Teach Key Concepts L2
Comparing Types of Radioactive Decay

Focus Tell students that three forms of radiation are produced during radioactive decay.

Teach Begin a compare/contrast table for the three types of radioactive decay. Use the diagrams in Figure 19 to discuss each type. Ask questions such as: **What particle is released during alpha decay?** *(Alpha particle)* **What is the electric charge of this particle?** *(Positive)* **How does this type of decay change the atom?** *(Reduces atomic number by 2 and atomic mass by 4)* **Is the resultant atom a different element?** *(Yes)* Repeat these questions with beta decay and gamma radiation. (When students study Figure 20 on the next page, have them add information to the table about what material can block each kind of radiation and what kind of injury the radiation can cause.)

Apply Ask: **Does radioactive decay occur in the nuclei of all atoms?** *(No. Only in the nuclei of unstable atoms)* **learning modality: visual**

All in One **Teaching Resources**
• Transparency K36

Monitor Progress L2

Skills Check Have students compare and contrast alpha, beta, and gamma decay.

Answers
Figure 19 Beta decay produces a negatively charged particle.

✓ Reading Checkpoint A nuclear reaction involves protons and neutrons of atoms and can change atoms of one element into atoms of another kind of element. A chemical reaction involves only electrons and cannot change the identity of an atom.

Use Visuals: Figure 20 **L2**

The Energy of Nuclear Radiation

Focus Have students study the diagram in Figure 20 and read the caption.

Teach Ask: **Which type of radiation is the least penetrating?** *(Alpha radiation)* **Which particle has the largest mass?** *(Alpha particles)* Point out that because of their large mass and large charge, alpha particles are easily blocked. Ask: **Why might gamma rays have such high penetrating power?** *(They have no mass and no charge.)*

Apply Remind students that Henri Becquerel wrapped the photographic plate in paper. Ask: **Which type of nuclear radiation was blocked from exposing the film?** *(Alpha particles; they are blocked by a sheet of paper.)* **learning modality: visual**

All in One Teaching Resources

• Transparency K37

Address Misconceptions **L1**

Atoms That Cause Decay

Focus Some students may think that all atoms produce nuclear radiation.

Teach Emphasize that only unstable atoms undergo radioactive decay, producing nuclear radiation. Remind students of isotopes. Draw the nucleus of carbon-12 (6 protons and 6 neutrons) and the nucleus of carbon-14 (6 protons and 8 neutrons). Explain that carbon-12 is a stable isotope of carbon. Its nucleus does not decay. Carbon-14 is an unstable isotope. It has an unstable nucleus because there are too many neutrons relative to the number of protons.

Apply Ask: **What is the relationship between carbon–12 and carbon–14?** *(Carbon–12 and carbon–14 are isotopes of the same element. Carbon–12 is a stable atom of 6 protons and 6 neutrons. Carbon–14 is an unstable atom because it has 8 neutrons instead of 6.)* **learning modality: verbal**

---

142 ◆ K

FIGURE 20
The Penetrating Power of Nuclear Radiation
The three types of nuclear radiation were named based on how easily each one could be blocked. Alpha, beta, and gamma are the first three letters of the Greek alphabet.
Inferring Which type of nuclear radiation is the most penetrating?

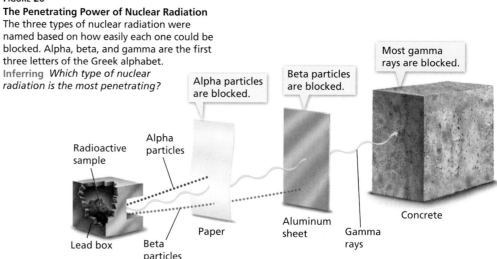

Radioactive sample
Lead box
Alpha particles
Beta particles
Paper
Alpha particles are blocked.
Aluminum sheet
Beta particles are blocked.
Gamma rays
Most gamma rays are blocked.
Concrete

Effects of Nuclear Radiation Although alpha particles move very fast, they are stopped by collisions with atoms. In Figure 20, you can see that alpha particles are blocked by a sheet of paper. Alpha radiation can cause an injury much like a bad burn.

Beta particles are much faster and more penetrating than alpha particles. They can pass through paper, but they are blocked by an aluminum sheet 5 millimeters thick. Beta particles can also travel into the human body and damage its cells.

Gamma rays are the most penetrating type of radiation. You would need a piece of lead several centimeters thick or a concrete wall about a meter thick to stop gamma rays. They can pass right through a human body, delivering intense energy to cells and causing severe damage.

 Reading Checkpoint How can alpha radiation affect the body?

Using Radioactive Isotopes

The decay of radioactive isotopes makes them useful in many ways. **Uses include determining the ages of natural materials on Earth, tracing the steps of chemical reactions and industrial processes, diagnosing and treating disease, and providing sources of energy.** These uses stem from two key properties of radioactive isotopes: First, radioactive isotopes change into different kinds of matter, and second, they give off detectable radiation.

Lab zone Skills **Activity**

Calculating
Carbon-14 has a half-life of 5,730 years. Data from several newly discovered fossils shows that carbon-14 has undergone decay in the fossils for five half-lives. Calculate the age of the fossils.

Lab zone Skills **Activity**

Skills Focus Calculating **L2**

Materials calculator

Time 10 minutes

Tips If students have difficulty determining which operation to perform, help them assign units to each number. The units will guide them through the calculation.

Expected Outcome 5 half-lives × 5,730 years/half-life = 28,650 years. The fossils are 28,650 years old.

Extend Challenge students to calculate how much older the fossil could have been before its age would have had to be found using a different isotope. *(60,000 years − 28,650 years = 31,350 years. If the fossil had been 31,350 years older, carbon-14 could not be used to find its age.)* **learning modality: logical/mathematical**

Radioactive Dating When the atoms of a radioactive isotope decay, they can change into other kinds of atoms. However, not all the atoms of a radioactive sample decay at once. They decay randomly, one at a time. Although you can't predict when any particular nucleus will decay, the time it takes for half the atoms to change can be measured. The **half-life** of an isotope is the length of time needed for half of the atoms of a sample to decay. The half-life is different for each isotope. As you can see in Figure 21, half-lives can range from less than a second to billions of years!

Fossils are the traces or remains of living things that have been preserved. The half-lives of certain radioactive isotopes are useful in determining the ages of rocks and fossils. For example, as plants grow they use carbon dioxide (CO_2) from the air. Some carbon dioxide contains carbon-14, which becomes part of the plant's structures the same way carbon-12 does. After the plant dies, it stops taking in carbon dioxide. If the plant's remains are preserved as a fossil, the amount of carbon-14 present can be measured. From the data, scientists can calculate how many half-lives have passed since the plant was alive. In this way, they can estimate the age of the fossil and its surrounding rock. This process is called **radioactive dating**.

Because the half-life of carbon-14 is only 5,730 years, it cannot be used to find the ages of objects older than about 60,000 years. Other isotopes, such as potassium-40 and uranium-238, are used to study older fossils, rocks, and objects used by early humans.

FIGURE 21
The half-lives of radioactive isotopes vary greatly.

Half-Lives of Some Radioactive Isotopes	
Element	**Half-Life**
Polonium-216	0.16 second
Sodium-24	15 hours
Iodine-131	8.07 days
Phosphorus-32	14.3 days
Cobalt-60	5.26 years
Radium-226	1,600 years
Carbon-14	5,730 years
Chlorine-36	400,000 years
Uranium-235	710 million years
Uranium-238	4.5 billion years

FIGURE 22
Radioactive Dating
Using the known half-lives of certain radioactive isotopes, such as uranium-238, scientists can determine the age of ancient objects. This saber-toothed cat lived about 25 million years ago.

K ◆ 143

Teach Key Concepts   L2
Comparing Types of Radioactive Decay

Focus Tell students that the decay of radioactive isotopes has many uses.

Teach Begin a list on the board of the uses of radioactivity. Ask: **What are some ways radioactive isotopes are used?** (*To determine the ages of natural materials on Earth, trace the steps of chemical reactions, diagnose and treat disease, and provide energy*) Elicit from students details about each use and add them to the list.

Apply Ask: **Why are radioactive materials dangerous?** (*Radiation can cause illness, disease, or death because it penetrates tissues, interfering with chemical reactions in cells.*)

Extend The active art will show students how radioactive tracers are used to study plant processes. **learning modality: visual**

Integrating Earth Science   L2
Ask: **What kinds of objects can be dated using carbon-14?** (*Only objects that originally contained carbon, such as plants, animals, and objects made from living things, and objects that are not more than 60,000 years old.*) Begin a list of class suggestions of what an archaeologist might find. Ask students to review the list and identify objects that could not be dated using carbon-14. **learning modality: verbal**

Monitor Progress _____   L2

Drawing Have students draw a diagram to model the half-life of a radioactive element.

Students can save their diagrams in their portfolios.

Answers
Figure 20 Gamma radiation is the most penetrating.

Reading Checkpoint Alpha radiation can cause an injury much like a bad burn.

Use Visuals: Figure 23

L2

Following Radioactive Tracers

Focus Invite students to examine Figure 23.

Teach Ask: **What radioactive isotope is used as the tracer?** (*Phosphorus-32*) **In this experiment, what are researchers trying to learn?** (*Where and how plants use phosphorus*) **Why does this experiment work?** (*Plants use the radioactive isotope of phosphorus just as they do the nonradioactive form.*)

Apply Ask: **Where does the radioactive phosphorous finally go in the plant?** (*To the leaves*) **learning modality: visual**

 **Teaching Resources**

• Transparency K38

L2

Designing Experiments Using Radioactive Tracers

Materials none

Time 15 minutes

Focus Remind students that a good experiment begins with a hypothesis. A good experimental design has identified variables, a complete procedure, and a well-organized data table.

Teach Direct student groups to design an experiment in which a radioactive tracer is used to determine whether plant seeds contain phosphorus from the soil.

Apply Ask: **What is the hypothesis of your experiment?** (*Sample answer: Seeds will contain phosphorus absorbed from the soil.*) **learning modality: logical/mathematical**

Go Online
active art

For: Radioactive Tracers activity
Visit: PHSchool.com
Web Code: cgp-1044

Students can examine how radioactive tracers move through a plant.

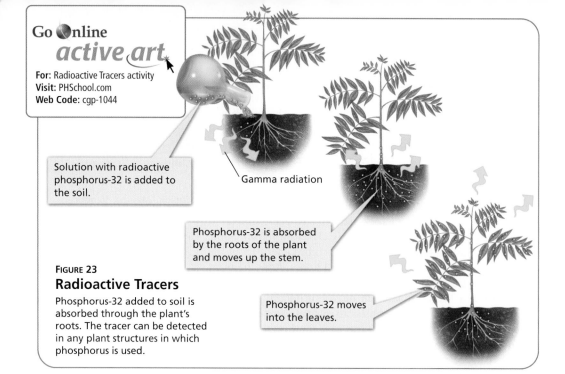

Go Online
active art

For: Radioactive Tracers activity
Visit: PHSchool.com
Web Code: cgp-1044

Solution with radioactive phosphorus-32 is added to the soil.

Gamma radiation

Phosphorus-32 is absorbed by the roots of the plant and moves up the stem.

FIGURE 23
Radioactive Tracers
Phosphorus-32 added to soil is absorbed through the plant's roots. The tracer can be detected in any plant structures in which phosphorus is used.

Phosphorus-32 moves into the leaves.

Uses in Science and Industry Like a lighthouse flashing in the night, a radioactive isotope "signals" where it is. **Tracers** are radioactive isotopes that can be followed through the steps of a chemical reaction or industrial process. Tracers behave the same way as nonradioactive forms of an element. Scientists can follow tracers, using equipment that detects radiation. This technique is helpful for studying reactions in living organisms, as shown in Figure 23. Phosphorus is used by plants in small amounts for healthy growth. A plant will absorb radioactive phosphorus-32 added to the soil just as it does the nonradioactive form. Radiation will be present in any part of the plant that contains the isotope. In this way, biologists can learn where and how plants use phosphorus.

In industry, tracers are used to find weak spots in metal pipes, especially oil pipelines. When added to a liquid, tracers can easily be detected if they leak out of the pipes. Engineers use gamma radiation from radioactive isotopes to look for flaws in metal. Gamma rays can pass through metal and be detected on a photographic film. By looking at the gamma-ray images, structural engineers can detect small cracks in the metal of bridges and building frames. Without these images, a problem might not be discovered until a disaster occurs.

Differentiated Instruction

Gifted and Talented **L3**
Detecting Radiation Explain that detecting radiation is the first step in using it safely. Three methods are used to detect radiation, the Geiger counter, a scintillation counter, and a film badge. Have students determine which is the best detector to monitor exposure to radiation if they were a scientist studying how a plant takes up phosphorus. Students can write a summary of their findings that includes reasons that the selected detector is the best choice. **learning modality: verbal**

Uses in Medicine Doctors use radioactive isotopes to detect medical problems and to treat some diseases. Tracers injected into the body travel to organs and other structures where that chemical is normally used. Using equipment that detects radiation, technicians make images of the bone, blood vessel, or organ affected. For example, tracers made with technetium-99 are used to diagnose problems in the bones, liver, kidneys, and digestive system.

In a process called radiation therapy, radioactive elements are used to destroy unhealthy cells. For example, iodine-131 is given to patients with tumors of the thyroid gland—a gland in the neck that controls the rate at which nutrients are used. Because the thyroid gland uses iodine, the radioactive iodine-131 collects in the gland. Radiation from this isotope destroys unwanted cells in the gland without serious effects on other parts of the body.

Cancer tumors of different kinds often are treated from outside the body with high-energy gamma rays. Many hospitals use cobalt-60 for this purpose. When gamma radiation is directed toward a cancer tumor, it causes changes that kill the cancer cells.

Nuclear Power Some power plants use radioactive isotopes as fuel. The nuclei of certain radioactive isotopes are made to split into smaller fragments, releasing enormous amounts of energy. Carefully controlled reactions, most often using uranium-235, provide electric energy in many parts of the world. And nuclear reactions provide the energy for nuclear submarines and other types of ocean vessels.

 Reading Checkpoint What is the fuel source for nuclear power plants?

FIGURE 24
Radioactive Isotopes in Medicine
Front and back body scans of a healthy patient were made using a radioactive isotope.

Front   Back

FIGURE 25
Nuclear Power
By using nuclear power, this submarine can operate for years without refueling. **Inferring** *Why is this an advantage for an ocean vessel?*

Chapter 4 K ◆ 145

Integrating Health L2

Students may wonder how gamma rays can be targeted at cancer cells without affecting body cells. Explain that healthy cells are affected during radiation therapy but that doctors shield the surrounding areas from radiation and use equipment that can deliver strong doses of radiation to a concentrated area. Because cancer cells divide rapidly, they are more affected by radiation than other cells. However, the side effects of radiation, such as hair loss and skin disorders, often occur when the radiation affects healthy cells that usually divide rapidly. **learning modality: verbal**

Help Students Read
Relating Cause and Effect Explain that an effect is what happens because of a cause. Invite students to look at the body scans in Figure 24. Then have them read to find out how these body scans were made. Ask: **What causes the images of the bones?** (*Radioactive tracers, such as technetium-99, that were injected into the body*) Encourage students to write a detailed explanation of the cause.

Monitor Progress _____ L2

Writing Have students describe two uses for radioactive isotopes and explain the properties of the radioactive isotopes that make these uses possible.

Students can save their descriptions in their portfolios.

Answer
Figure 25 The ocean vessel does not need to return frequently to port for refueling.

 Uranium-235 is most often used as a fuel source for nuclear power plants.

K ● 145

Monitor Progress _____ L2

Answer

Reading Checkpoint Materials with low levels of radiation may be buried in landfills.

Assess

Reviewing Key Concepts

1. a. Becquerel observed that a mineral containing uranium produced an image on a photographic plate. **b.** Sample answer: Radiation produced by the uranium in the mineral caused an image on the film. **c.** When the Curies further explored Becquerel's findings, they discovered the new elements polonium and radium.
2. a. The three products of radioactive decay are alpha particles, beta particles, and gamma rays. **b.** Most penetrating—gamma; less penetrating—beta; least penetrating—alpha **c.** Aluminum-28 is formed.
3. a. Radioactive isotopes behave the same way as nonradioactive forms of an element. Scientists can follow tracers with equipment that detects radiation. **b.** Gamma radiation can cause changes in cancer cells that kill the cells.

Reteach L1

Have students draw a diagram to illustrate each form of radioactive decay.

Performance Assessment L2

Writing Have small groups prepare pamphlets to inform the school or community of the benefits and hazards of nuclear power. Pamphlets should include scientific descriptions of radioactive decay.

All in One Teaching Resources

- Section Summary: *Radioactive Elements*
- Review and Reinforce: *Radioactive Elements*
- Enrich: *Radioactive Elements*

146 • K

FIGURE 26
Radiation Protection
Clothing that protects against radiation must be worn by people working with highly radioactive materials.

Safe Use of Radioactive Materials Despite their usefulness, radioactive materials are dangerous. Radiation penetrates living tissue, knocking electrons from atoms. This process produces particles that then can interfere with chemical reactions in living cells. Illness, disease, and even death may result from overexposure to radiation.

The dangers of radioactive materials mean that their use must be carefully managed. People who work with these materials must wear protective clothing and use insulating shields. Radioactive wastes and contaminated equipment can't just be thrown away. These items must be disposed of properly.

Materials with low levels of radiation may be buried in landfills. Such landfills are carefully monitored to prevent contamination of the environment. Isotopes with long half-lives, however, will remain hazardous for hundreds or even thousands of years. One solution to this problem is to dispose of these kinds of materials in specially designed containers that are buried in very dry underground tunnels. In that way, the radioactive wastes can be isolated for many generations.

 Reading Checkpoint **What type of radioactive materials may be buried in landfills?**

Section 4 Assessment

Target Reading Skill Building Vocabulary Use your definitions to help answer the questions.

Reviewing Key Concepts

1. a. **Identifying** Under what circumstances did Becquerel first notice the effects of radioactivity?
   b. **Interpreting Photographs** Look at the photo in Figure 17. Explain in your own words what happened.
   c. **Applying Concepts** How did Becquerel's work lead to the discovery of two new elements?
2. a. **Listing** What are the three products of radioactive decay?
   b. **Comparing and Contrasting** Contrast the penetrating power of three major types of nuclear radiation.
   c. **Predicting** Predict the identity and mass number of the nucleus formed during the beta decay of magnesium-28.
3. a. **Explaining** How can radioactive isotopes be used as tracers?
   b. **Relating Cause and Effect** How is the use of radioactive isotopes in treating some forms of cancer related to certain properties of gamma radiation?

146 ◆ K

Writing in Science

Persuasive Speech N.I.M.B.Y. is short for the phrase "not in my backyard." It stands for the idea that people don't want unpleasant or possibly hazardous conditions near where they live. They would prefer to see radioactive wastes go elsewhere. Your local government has invited citizens to a meeting to discuss possible options for storing radioactive wastes from nearby medical or industrial sites. Write a one- or two-paragraph speech for the public meeting, expressing your opinion.

Lab zone Chapter Project

Keep Students on Track By now, students should be performing their tests. Allow time for students to obtain multiple sets of data. Students should compare the results of their tests to determine the properties of the different materials. Help students group their samples by relating material properties to material functions. For example, noncorrosive, insoluble PVC is well suited for its use as a water pipe.

Writing in Science

Writing Mode Persuasion
Scoring Rubric
4 Exceeds criteria
3 Meets criteria
2 Includes a brief speech that contains a few errors and/or poor examples
1 Includes a sketchy speech and/or serious errors

That's Half-Life!

Problem
How can you model the way a sample of radioactive waste decays to a nonhazardous level?

Skills Focus
making models, graphing, interpreting data

Materials
- 100 pennies
- graph paper
- container such as a jar or a box
- colored pencils (optional)

Procedure
1. Copy the data table into your notebook. Then place 100 pennies in a container.
2. Shake the pennies out onto the desktop. Separate the ones showing heads from those showing tails.
3. Count the number of pennies showing tails and count the number of pennies showing heads. Record both these values.
4. Put back only the pennies showing tails.
5. Repeat the process until there are two pennies or fewer left in the container.
6. Keep a tally of the total number of pennies removed from the container. Record this number after each trial.

Analyze and Conclude
1. **Making Models** What does each of the following represent: (a) each trial, (b) the pennies that came up heads, (c) the pennies that came up tails?
2. **Graphing** Make a graph of your data. Label the horizontal axis with the trial number. Label the vertical axis with the number of pennies left in the container after each trial. Connect the data points with a curved line. On the same set of axes, plot the total number of pennies removed from the container after each trial. Use a dotted line or different colored pencil to make this graph.
3. **Interpreting Data** What do the graphs show?
4. **Communicating** Suppose 2,560 grams of low-level radioactive waste is buried at a waste disposal site. Assume that 10 grams of radioactive material gives off an acceptable level of radiation and that one half-life is 5.26 years. Write a paragraph in which you explain to townspeople how much time must pass before there is an acceptable radiation level at the site.

More to Explore
How could you use this model to show the decay of a sample that has twice the mass as the sample you modeled in this lab? What would you do differently? Predict how you think the results would differ.

Data Table			
Trial	Tails Remaining	Heads Removed (each trial)	Total Pennies Removed
1			
2			
3			

That's Half-Life! [L2]

Prepare for Inquiry

Key Concept
The half-life of a substance is the amount of time it takes for one half of the sample to decay.

Skills Objective
After this lab, students will be able to
- model radioactive decay by a random scattering of coins
- graph the data collected from their models
- interpret data collected from their models

 **Prep Time** 5 minutes
Class Time 25 minutes

Advance Planning
Because each group needs at least 100 pennies, consider asking students to bring in pennies. Record the number of pennies each student has brought for ease of returning.

All in One Teaching Resources
- Lab Worksheet: *That's Half-Life!*

Guide Inquiry

Introduce the Procedure
Tell students the decay of an individual nucleus in a sample is a random event that can be modeled by a coin toss. Explain that about half of all coin tosses land on heads, even though an individual coin toss is random. Because students will be removing about half of the pennies after each trial, they are modeling the half-life of a radioactive substance.

Analyze and Conclude
1. a. One half-life **b.** Decayed nuclei
c. Undecayed nuclei
2. The line for remaining pennies is a curve that decreases from left to right. The line for pennies removed is a curve that increases from left to right.
3. The number of remaining pennies is reduced by approximately half for each trial. The number of pennies removed increases.
4. After each interval of 5.26 years, the mass of radioactive isotope will be reduced by half. It would take 8 half-lives, or just over 42 years, to reach a level of less than 10 grams.

Extend Inquiry

More to Explore Students should use twice as many pennies. Sample prediction: It will take one more half-life for a sample with twice the mass to decay to two or fewer nuclei.

Study Guide

interactive Textbook

- Complete student edition
- Section and chapter self-assessment
- Assessment reports for teachers

Help Students Read **L1**

Building Vocabulary

Word/Part Analysis Explain that many words in the English language use prefixes from Greek or Latin. In Greek, *mono-* means "one" and *poly-* means "many." Ask: **What do these prefixes tell you about certain molecules?** (*Sample answer: Monomers are one molecule. Polymers are made up of many molecules.*)

Word Origins Explain that radiation originates from the Latin word *radiare,* which means "to emit beams or rays." Ask: **Why do you think Marie Curie chose the word *radioactivity* to describe her observations of the reaction of uranium nuclei?** (*Sample answer: She observed that the uranium nuclei actively emitted beams of energy, or radiation.*)

Connecting Concepts

Concept Maps Help students develop one way to show how the information in this chapter is related. Elements and compounds combine in different ways to form various materials with specific properties. These specific properties give these materials useful functions. Have students brainstorm to identify the key concepts, key terms, details, and examples. Then write each item on a self-sticking note and attach it at random to chart paper or to the board.

Tell students that this concept map will be organized in hierarchical order and to begin at the top with the key concepts. Ask students these questions to guide them to categorize the information on the self-sticking notes: **What are polymers and composites used for? How do alloys compare to metals? How do ceramics and glass compare? How are radioactive elements used?**

1 Polymers and Composites

Key Concepts

- Polymers form when chemical bonds link large numbers of monomers in a repeating pattern.
- Many composite materials include one or more polymers.
- Synthetic polymers are strong, inexpensive to make, and last a long time.
- It is often cheaper to throw plastics away and make new ones than it is to reuse them. As a result, plastics increase the volume of trash.

Key Terms
polymer
monomer
plastic
composite

2 Metals and Alloys

Key Concepts

- Alloys are used much more than pure metals because they are generally stronger and less likely to react with air or water.
- Many alloys are made by melting metals and mixing them together in carefully measured amounts.

Key Term
alloy

3 Ceramics and Glass

Key Concepts

- Ceramics resist moisture, do not conduct electricity, and can withstand temperatures that would cause metals to melt.
- Glass is clear, can be made in many shapes and colors, and can't be penetrated by liquids.

Key Terms
ceramic
glass
optical fiber

4 Radioactive Elements

Key Concepts

- In 1896, the French scientist Henri Becquerel discovered radioactive decay quite by accident while studying a mineral containing uranium.
- Natural radioactive decay can produce alpha particles, beta particles, and gamma rays.
- Among the many uses of the decay of radioactive isotopes are determining the ages of natural materials on Earth, tracing the steps of chemical reactions and industrial processes, diagnosing and treating disease, and providing sources of energy.

Key Terms
nuclear reaction
radioactive decay
radioactivity
alpha particle
beta particle
gamma radiation
half-life
radioactive dating
tracer

Prompt students by using connecting words or phrases, such as "include," "are made by," and "are used for," to indicate the basis for the organization of the map. The phrases should form a sentence between or among a set of concepts.

Answer Accept logical presentations by students.

All in One Teaching Resources

- Key Terms Review: *Exploring Materials*
- Connecting Concepts: *Exploring Materials*

Review and Assessment

Go Online
PHSchool.com

For: Self Assessment
Visit: PHSchool.com
Web Code: cga-1040

Organizing Information

Comparing and Contrasting Copy the table about polymers, alloys, ceramics, and glass onto a separate sheet of paper. Then fill in the empty spaces and add a title. (For more on Comparing and Contrasting tables, see the Skills Handbook.)

Material	Made From	How Made	How Used
Polymers	Monomers (carbon compounds)	a. ___?___	b. ___?___
Alloys	c. ___?___	Metals heated and mixed	d. ___?___
Ceramics	Clay; other materials	e. ___?___	f. ___?___
Glass	g. ___?___	Melted, then cooled in desired shapes	h. ___?___

Reviewing Key Terms

Choose the letter of the best answer.

1. Any large molecule made of many monomers is called a
   a. plastic.
   b. polymer.
   c. protein.
   d. chain.

2. Fiberglass is a type of
   a. polymer.
   b. alloy.
   c. ceramic.
   d. composite.

3. The properties of alloys most resemble those of
   a. ceramics.
   b. glass.
   c. metals.
   d. polymers.

4. Clean sand is heated to its melting point to make
   a. ceramics.
   b. glass.
   c. alloys.
   d. composites.

5. Unstable atomic nuclei that release fast-moving particles and energy are
   a. radioactive.
   b. alloys.
   c. isotopes.
   d. alpha particles.

If the statement is true, write _true_. If it is false, change the underlined word or words to make the statement true.

6. <u>Oxygen</u> is the element that forms the backbone of most polymers.

7. Cellulose is an example of a <u>synthetic</u> polymer.

8. A useful alloy of copper and tin is <u>steel</u>.

9. Roofing tiles and bricks are made with <u>ceramics</u>.

10. Alpha, beta, and gamma radiation form as the result of <u>chemical</u> reactions.

Writing in Science

Comparison Paragraph Write a paragraph comparing and contrasting natural and synthetic polymers. Give two examples of each.

Discovery CHANNEL SCHOOL

Exploring Materials
Video Preview
Video Field Trip
▶ Video Assessment

Review and Assessment

Organizing Information
Sample title: Properties of Polymers, Alloys, Ceramics, and Glass
a. Chemical bonds link monomers in a repeating pattern.
b. Sample: Fabrics
c. Metals and other elements
d. Sample: Tools
e. Heated above 1,000°C
f. Sample: Sewer pipes
g. Sand and limestone and sometimes lead oxide or other materials
h. Sample: Windows

Reviewing Key Terms
1. b 2. d 3. c 4. b 5. a
6. Carbon
7. natural
8. bronze
9. true
10. nuclear

Writing in Science

Writing Mode Comparison
Scoring Rubric
4 Exceeds criteria; includes an accurate and complete comparison with two specific examples for each type of polymer
3 Meets criteria
2 Includes a few errors and/or omissions
1 Includes serious errors and/or no examples

Discovery CHANNEL SCHOOL Video Assessment

Exploring Materials

Show the Video Assessment to review chapter content and as a prompt for the writing assignment. Discussion questions: **How are natural polymers different from synthetic polymers?** (*Natural polymers are easier to destroy, but are more expensive and not as strong as synthetic polymers.*) **How are synthetic polymers used?** (*Sample answer: Plastics, fabrics, car tires*)

Go Online
PHSchool.com

For: Self-Assessment
Visit: PHSchool.com
Web Code: cga-1040

Students can take a practice test online that is automatically scored.

All in One Teaching Resources
- Transparency K39
- Chapter Test
- Performance Assessment Teacher Notes
- Performance Assessment Student Worksheet
- Performance Assessment Scoring Rubric

ExamView® Computer Test Bank CD-ROM

Checking Concepts

11. Sample answer: Wool from sheep, cotton from cotton plants, cellulose from plants, silk from silkworms, proteins from all living things

12. Synthetic polymers do not react easily with other substances, which prevents them from breaking down into simpler materials. This increases the volume of trash. It is often cheaper and easier to make new synthetic polymers than to reuse them.

13. Pure gold is too soft for jewelry. Alloys of gold with other metals are harder and stronger.

14. When a clay object is heated above 1,000°C, most of the water in the clay evaporates, and the clay particles stick together.

15. Each element is defined by the number of protons contained within the nuclei of its atoms. A chemical reaction involves an atom's electrons; it does not change the number of protons.

16. Radioactive isotopes change into different kinds of matter, and they give off detectable radiation.

Thinking Critically

17. Hammer—steel because it is hard, heavy, and strong; aquarium wall—glass because it is transparent, strong, cannot be penetrated by liquids, and does not corrode; egg carton—polystyrene foam because it is soft, flexible, and protective

18. Glazed pots are waterproof and will keep moisture away from the stored food.

19. Two half-lives have passed, so the tool is 11,460 years old.

20. One half-life has occurred in the decay of a sample radioactive isotope. Diagrams should show the results of the second half-life in which one-fourth of the sample is the radioactive isotope and three-fourths is the decay products.

Checking Concepts

11. Name some polymers that are produced in nature. Tell where they come from.

12. Explain why some advantages of using synthetic polymers can become disadvantages.

13. Why is gold mixed with other metals to make jewelry?

14. Describe the process that changes clay into ceramics.

15. Explain why a chemical reaction cannot change one element into another element.

16. What properties of radioactive isotopes make them useful?

Thinking Critically

17. **Comparing and Contrasting** Explain which material—steel, glass, or polystyrene foam—would be the best choice for each of the following uses: a hammer, the wall of a saltwater aquarium, an egg carton.

18. **Applying Concepts** The earliest ceramic pots absorbed moisture. Why are glazed pots better for storing food?

19. **Calculating** A wooden tool found in a cave has one fourth as much carbon-14 as a living tree. How old is the tool? (*Hint:* The half-life of carbon-14 is 5,730 years.)

20. **Interpreting Diagrams** Look at the diagram below. Identify what is happening. Then, draw a labeled diagram of how the next step in the process would look.

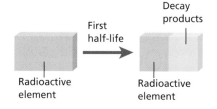

First half-life

Decay products

Radioactive element

Radioactive element

Applying Skills

Use the diagram to answer the questions.

The diagram below shows the first few steps of the radioactive decay of uranium-238.

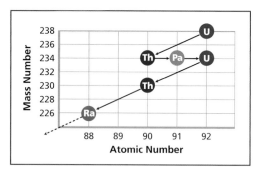

21. **Interpreting Data** How many elements are in the diagram? How many different isotopes of each element are there?

22. **Classifying** What type of radioactive decay resulted in uranium-238 becoming thorium-234? How do you know?

23. **Interpreting Diagrams** Describe how thorium-234 is changed into uranium-234.

24. **Inferring** How do you know from the diagram that thorium-230 is radioactive?

Lab zone Chapter **Project**

Performance Assessment Prepare a chart or poster to display the polymers you examined. Provide a sample of each polymer and include information such as its name, where it was found, what monomers it is made of (if known), and significant physical and chemical properties that you determined. Be prepared to compare the polymers with other types of materials such as glass, ceramics, and metals.

Lab zone Chapter **Project**   L3

Performance Assessment Provide class time for student presentations. In their presentations, students should explain how they were able to identify as polymers the items they collected. They should also be able to discuss various properties of these polymers and explain how these properties relate to the polymers' functions. Encourage students to relate any problems they may have had identifying or testing polymers, and suggest improvements they would like to make.

Standardized Test Prep

Test-Taking Tip

Interpreting a Data Table

When answering a question related to a data table, read the title of the table to see what type of data it contains. Next look at the headings of the columns and rows to see how the data are organized. For example, the data table below shows how the mass of a sample of Nitrogen-16 and the mass of its decay products change with time. Finally, read the question to determine which data you will need to answer the question.

Sample Question

Based on the data table below, how is the mass of Nitrogen-16 changing after each time period?

Decay of Radioactive Nitrogen-16

Time (s)	Mass of Nitrogen-16 (g)	Mass of Decay Products (g)
0.0	32	0
7.2	16	16
14.4	8	24
21.6	4	28

A It doubles.
B It decreases by half.
C It increases by 7.2 s.
D It stays the same.

Answer

The correct answer is **B**. The mass of nitrogen-16 decreases from 32 g to 16 g to 8 g to 4 g, so it decreases by half its mass each time. Answer **A** refers to the change in mass of the decay products. Answer **C** refers to the time interval, and answer **D** is not correct since the mass of nitrogen-16 changes after each time period.

Choose the letter of the best answer.

1. Which of the following is *not* an example of an alloy?

A brass   **B** bronze
C stainless steel   **D** iron

Use the information and data table below to answer Questions 2–3.

Polymer Identification

Test	Cotton	Wool	Polyester
Texture	Smooth	Rough	Smooth
Near flame	Does not bend or melt	Curls away from heat	Melts
In flame	Burns; smells like paper burning	Burns; smells like hair burning	Melts

2. A student has two pieces of fabric—one blue and one green. The student performs an investigation to identify the fabrics. What can the student conclude if the texture of both pieces of fabric is smooth?

F Both fabrics must be cotton.
G Both fabrics must be polyester.
H One fabric must be cotton and the other must be polyester.
J Neither piece is wool.

3. What should the student do before testing either piece of fabric near or in a flame?

A Put on safety goggles and an apron and tie back long hair.
B Crumple the fabric to make it burn more easily.
C Wash his or her hands.
D Determine the mass of the fabric

4. Radioactive isotopes give off radiation that can be detected. This property makes them useful in which of the following ways?

F as tracers in chemical reactions
G in detecting leaks in oil pipelines
H in diagnosing certain medical problems
J all of the above

Constructed Response

5. You are considering using either glass or disposable plastic to serve soft drinks at a party. Discuss how the beverage containers are similar and how they are different.

Applying Skills

21. Four elements; two isotopes of uranium (U-238, U-234), two isotopes of thorium (Th-234, Th-230), and one isotope each of protactinium and radium (Pa-234, Ra-226)

22. Alpha decay; the atomic number decreased by 2 and the mass number decreased by 4, which is what happens when an atom emits an alpha particle.

23. Thorium-234 undergoes beta decay to form protactinium-234, which undergoes beta decay to form uranium-234.

24. Thorium-230 must be radioactive because it decays into radium-226.

Standardized Test Prep

1. D   **2.** J   **3.** A   **4.** J

5. Both beverage containers will hold soft drinks without leaking. Glass containers may break if dropped, but can be washed and reused. Plastic containers will not break if dropped and can be thrown away. They may also be washed and reused.

Interdisciplinary Exploration

Gold—The Noble Metal

This interdisciplinary feature presents the central theme of gold as a metal by connecting four different disciplines: science, social studies, language arts, and mathematics. The four explorations are designed to capture students' interest and help them see how the content they are studying in science relates to other school subjects and to real-world events. Share with others for a team-teaching experience.

All in One Teaching Resources

- Interdisciplinary Exploration: *Science*
- Interdisciplinary Exploration: *Social Studies*
- Interdisciplinary Exploration: *Language Arts*
- Interdisciplinary Exploration: *Mathematics*

Build Background Knowledge
Properties of Metals

Help students recall what they learned in the chapter *Elements and the Periodic Table.* Ask: **What is a metal?** *(A metal is any element in a blue-tinted square and to the left of the zigzag line on the periodic table shown in this book.)* **What are some physical properties of metals?** *(Metals are shiny, malleable, ductile, conductive, and magnetic.)* **Chemical properties?** *(Metals usually react by losing electrons to other atoms.)*

Introduce the Exploration

Have students turn to the Periodic Table of the Elements in *Organizing the Elements,* and find gold. Ask: **What do you know about gold based on its location in the periodic table?** *(Sample answer: It is a transition metal and is less reactive than the metals in Groups 1 and 2.)* **What are some of the ways you know gold was used in the past and is used today?** *(Sample answer: Gold has been used in coins, jewelry, and ornaments. Gold is valuable and has been used like money.)*

◀ A gold crown is a symbol of royalty.

Gold—The Noble Metal

You can find it —

on people's wrists, in your computer, on dinner plates, satellites, and in spacesuits

Because gold is both rare and beautiful, people have prized it since ancient times. Gold was so valuable that it was used to make crowns for rulers and coins for trade. In some cultures, people wear gold bracelets and necklaces to show their wealth.

In spite of its many uses, gold is scarce. For every 23,000 metric tons of rock and minerals from the Earth's crust, you could produce only about 14 grams of gold, enough to make a small ring. Today, gold is found in many parts of the world. But even rich gold fields produce only small amounts of gold. In fact, if all the gold mined over the years were gathered and melted down, you would have a cube only about 15 meters on a side—about the size of a four-story square building.

Wearing Gold
This woman from Ghana in Africa displays her wealth in gold jewelry.

Gold Nugget
A nugget is gold in one of its natural forms.

Properties of Gold

Why is gold used for everything from bracelets to space helmets to medicine? You'll find the answers in this precious metal's unusual chemical and physical properties. Gold is deep yellow in color and so shiny, or lustrous, that its Latin name, *aurum,* means "glowing dawn." Gold's chemical symbol—Au—comes from that Latin word. Gold is very heavy—one of the densest metals.

Gold is very soft and malleable. That is, it's easy to bend or hammer into shapes without breaking. It can be pounded into very thin sheets called gold leaf. Gold is also the most ductile metal. You can draw out 30 grams of gold into a fine thread as long as 8 kilometers without breaking it.

Gold is very stable. Unlike iron, gold doesn't rust. It also doesn't tarnish in air as silver does. Ancient chemists thought that gold was superior to other metals. They classified it as one of the "noble" metals.

Ductile
Because gold is so ductile, it can be made into fine wires like the ones in this computer chip.

Malleable
A Korean delicacy is dried fish coated with gold leaf.

Stable and Lustrous
Hundreds of years ago, traders used these gold doubloons as money.

Science Activity

The gold hunters who flocked to California during the Gold Rush of 1849 were searching for gold in streams and rivers. Although they had very simple equipment, their technique worked because gold is so dense. Using pans, miners washed gold-bearing gravel in running water. Try your own gold panning.

Set up your own model of gold panning, using a large pan, a gravel mixture, and a very dense material as a substitute for gold. Use a sink trap. Under running water, shake and swirl the pan until the lighter materials wash away. What's left is your "gold."

• Why is "gold" left in the pan while other materials are washed away?

K ◆ 153

Background

Facts and Figures Because of gold's properties, the uses of gold have expanded greatly from its traditional uses in jewelry and coins. Gold is used in electronics because of its good conducting properties. Televisions, radios, and computers often have parts made of a gold alloy. Gold alloys are used in dental work, including crowns and fillings. Gold's reflective properties make gold film useful not only in space suits but also on the outside of spacecraft, as backing for mirrors in scientific equipment, and on the outside windows of office buildings. In addition, gold is used to make compounds to treat some medical conditions such as rheumatoid arthritis.

Explore Science Concepts

Discuss After students read about the properties of gold, ask: **What properties of gold are chemical properties?** (*Its stability; gold does not rust or tarnish.*) **Physical properties?** (*Its yellow color, luster, density, softness, malleability, and ductility*) Explain that gold also conducts heat and electricity, but it is not magnetic. Then ask: **What properties give gold its great value?** (*Sample answer: Color, luster, stability, and rarity*) **Are any properties of gold less than desirable?** (*Sample answer: Because gold is soft, objects made from gold can be easily bent.*)

Use Visuals Have students use the visuals in this feature to identify various uses of gold. For each use, invite students to name the property or properties of gold that make it suited for that function. Then ask: **What other uses does gold have that are not shown here?** (*Sample answer: Gold is used for dental fillings and crowns. A thin layer of gold on the windshield of an airplane conducts heat and keeps the windshield frost-free.*)

Science Activity

Materials large pan, sand and gravel mixture, dense material such as iron filings, sink trap, running water

Focus Ask: **When a mixture of sediments is mixed thoroughly in water and allowed to settle, which sediments are on the bottom?** (*The most dense sediments*)

Teach To prepare, mix a dense material, such as iron filings, in a bucket with sand and small gravel. As an alternative to using a sink, set up several large tubs filled with water. Show students what the "gold" is that they are looking for. Demonstrate how to swirl water in the pan filled with sand so that the lighter materials spill out with the water.

Expected Outcome "Gold" is the heaviest material in the pan, so it sinks to the bottom and remains in the pan when the other materials wash out.

Explore Social Studies Concepts

Use Maps Have students refer to the map on this page, and ask: **Where was the Kingdom of Ghana?** (*In West Africa, south of the Sahara*) **Where were there salt deposits, and where was salt needed?** (*Salt deposits were in the north, while salt was needed in Ghana.*) **Where were gold deposits, and where was gold desired?** (*Gold deposits were near Ghana, and gold was desired in the north.*)

Extend Discuss the concept of supply and demand in commerce. Ask: **In commerce, what is supply?** (*The amount of a material that is available to be traded or sold*) **What is demand?** (*The amount of a material that is desired by buyers*) **What happens to the value of a material if its supply is greater than its demand?** (*Its value decreases because the material is readily available and everyone has all of the material that they desire.*) **What happens to the value of a material if its demand is greater than its supply?** (*Its value increases because there is not enough material for everyone who desires it.*)

Social Studies Activity

Focus Remind students that they are simulating the values of salt and gold from over 1,000 years ago, not their current values.

Teach Divide the class into teams of four or five students each. Then give each team several sandwich bags, some teams have bags of salt and other teams have bags filled with objects like paper clips to represent gold. Tell groups to move to different parts of the room and discuss strategies for getting the best deals for their gold or salt. Next, invite traders to meet. At each meeting, announce a change in situation, such as the discovery of gold in Europe or an increased demand for salt in Africa.

Scoring Rubric

4 Exceeds criteria; team wholeheartedly adopts the roles of Salt Traders or Gold Miners and engages in spirited, yet silent trading and responds correctly to situations that affect the value of salt and gold
3 Meets criteria
2 Includes an understanding of how the value of a product is affected by its supply and demand
1 Includes misunderstandings of how supply and demand affect the value of goods

Golden Trade Routes

In West Africa nearly 1,000 years ago, salt was said to be worth its weight in gold. It may be hard to imagine how valuable this mineral was to people. But if you lived in a very hot, dry climate, you would need salt. It would be as valuable to you as gold. In West Africa, salt and gold were the most important goods traded.

Camel caravans crossed the desert going south, carrying slabs of salt from mines in the desert to trade centers, such as Jenne and Timbuktu. But several hundred kilometers south in the Kingdom of Ghana, salt was scarce and gold was plentiful. Salt traders from the north traveled into the forests of Ghana to trade salt for gold.

Around 1100, Arab travelers in Africa wrote about the fabulous wealth of the Kingdom of Ghana. The most popular tale was that the salt traders and gold miners never met, as a way of keeping secret the location of gold mines. Traders from the north left slabs of salt in an agreed-upon trading place, pounded their drums to indicate a trade, and then withdrew. Miners from the south arrived, left an amount of gold that seemed fair, and withdrew. The salt traders returned. If they thought the trade was fair, they took the gold and left. If they were not satisfied, the silent trade continued.

Salt Caravan
Camels carrying salt slabs travel to Timbuktu.

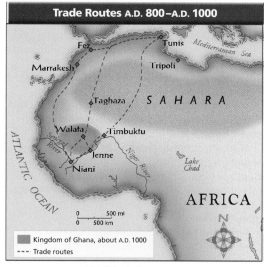

Gold Trade Routes
The map shows the busy north-south trade routes in West Africa about 1,000 years ago.

Social Studies Activity

How would you succeed as a gold or salt trader? Find out by carrying out your own silent trade. Work in teams of Salt Traders and Gold Miners. Before trading, each team should decide how much a bag of gold or a block of salt is worth. Then, for each silent trade, make up a situation that would change the value of gold or salt, such as, "Demand for gold in Europe increases."

• Suppose you are selling a product today. How would the supply of the product affect the value or sale price of the product?

Background

Facts and Figures The ancient Kingdom of Ghana flourished from about the seventh century to the thirteenth century A.D., in what is now southern Mauritania and Mali. This ancient kingdom has no direct connection with the modern country of Ghana. Trade was a major factor in the kingdom's early importance and subsequent growth. In about the fifth century, the camel was introduced to trans-Saharan trade. The gold fields were to the south of Ghana, on the Senegal River. After Ghana's decline in the mid-1200s, the Mali Empire dominated that region of West Africa until about 1500, when the Songhay Empire rose. Gold trade continued in those centuries. Both Timbuktu and Jenne (or Djenné) were associated with the later empires.

Go for the Gold

What do these sayings have in common?

"It's worth its weight in gold."

"Speech is silver, silence is golden."

"All that glitters is not gold."

"Go for the gold!"

All of these sayings use gold as a symbol of excellence, richness, and perfection—things that people want and search for. When writers use *gold* or *golden,* they are referring to something desirable, of value or worth. These words may also represent the beauty of gold.

In literature, writers and poets often use *gold* to make a comparison in a simile or metaphor. Similes and metaphors are figures of speech.

- A simile makes a comparison between two things, using *like* or *as* in the comparison. Here's an example: "An honest person's promise is as good as gold."

- A metaphor is a comparison without the use of like or as, such as, "When you're in trouble, true friends are golden."

Look for similes and metaphors in the poem by Florence Converse. What similes or metaphors has Converse made? What would this poem be like without the comparisons?

Rune of Riches*

I have a golden ball,
A big, bright, shining one,
Pure gold; and it is all
Mine—It is the sun.

I have a silver ball
A white and glistening stone
That other people call
The moon;—my very own!

The jewel things that prick
My cushion's soft blue cover
Are mine,—my stars, thick, thick,
Scattered the sky all over.

And everything that's mine
Is yours, and yours, and yours,—
The shimmer and the shine!—
Let's lock our wealth out-doors!

——Florence Converse

*A rune is a song or poem.

Explore Language Arts Concepts

Oral Presentation Call on volunteers to read aloud the examples given at the beginning of the exploration. Then ask: **What does the word gold mean in the saying "All that glitters is not gold"?** (*Something of the highest value*) Point out that in this use, the word can literally refer to gold, but it can also stand for anything of high value. **In your own words, what does this saying mean?** (*Sample answer: Not all attractive things are of great value.*) Then reinforce the difference between simile and metaphor by asking: **Which of the opening examples are similes?** (*None*) **What words in a phrase indicate that it is a simile?** (*Like or* as) Then invite volunteers to read each stanza of the poem. After each stanza, pause and invite the class to find similes or metaphors. Discuss any questions or misunderstandings students may have. At the end of the poem, ask: **What is this poem about?** (*Sample answer: The beauty of the night sky*) **Who does this beauty belong to?** (*Everyone*)

Organize Information Invite students to create a compare/contrast table to organize similes and metaphors that include the word gold or golden. Students may start with the sayings in the exploration, but encourage them to use a book of quotations to find other sayings. Suggest that students devise a way to classify sayings into different groups based on meaning.

Language Arts Activity

What does gold symbolize for you? Think of some comparisons of your own in which you use gold in a simile or metaphor. After jotting down all of your ideas, choose one (or more) and decide what comparison you will make. Write a short saying, a proverb, or a short poem that includes your own simile or metaphor.

- How does your comparison make your saying or poem more interesting?

K ◆ 155

Language Arts Activity

Focus Remind students of the difference between a simile and a metaphor.

Teach Invite the class to brainstorm a list of words that *gold* brings to mind, such as *wealth, beauty,* and *value.* Write the list on the board. Then encourage students to individually think of comparisons that include the word *gold.*

Scoring Rubric

4 Exceeds criteria; long list of ideas about gold from which a highly imaginative saying, proverb, or poem with an insightful comparison was made

3 Meets criteria

2 Includes one or two ideas and/or a weak comparison

1 Includes no ideas and/or an incomplete comparison

Background

Facts and Figures The word *metaphor* comes from a Greek word meaning "to transfer." In a metaphor, the meaning of one word or image is transferred to another, providing insight through a comparison between the two. With a metaphor, a writer can often convey a thought that would be difficult to convey in only a few words. But a good metaphor does not just suggest a similarity between unlike things. Rather, it causes the reader to call up images and emotions that enlarge the meaning. For example, the phrase "days of golden dreams," evokes in a reader complex feelings of happiness, well-being, and warmth by using the word *golden.*

Mathematics

Explore Mathematics Concepts

Use Math Skills Work through the steps of the example with students. Point out that in Step 1, a fraction is used because it is one way to express the parts of a whole. Ask: **Which number is the whole?** (*The denominator, or 24*) **Which number is the part?** (*The numerator, or 18*) For Step 2, explain that a percentage can be calculated by setting up a proportion. A proportion is a mathematical sentence that says two fractions are equal. Write the proportion.

$$\frac{18}{24} = \frac{x\%}{100\%}$$

Explain that to find the value of *x*, or the percentage of gold in the jewelry, the proportion is rewritten by cross-multiplying.

$100\% \times 18 = 24 \times x\%$

$x = 1800\% \div 24 = 75\%$

For Step 3, explain that to find the percent of copper, simply subtract 75 percent from 100 percent.

Review Remind students of what they learned about metals and alloys in *Metals and Alloys*. Ask: **What is an alloy?** (*An alloy is a solid mixture of two or more metals.*) **Why are alloys made?** (*To improve the usefulness of a metal by making it stronger or less reactive*)

Math Activity

Focus Remind students that pure gold is 24 K.

Teach Students may complete this activity on their own. Remind them that when rounding decimals to the nearest hundredth, they should round the second number to the right of the decimal point. If the third number to the right of the decimal point is 5 or above, round up; if it is below 5, keep the second number as it is.

Answers

The 14 K gold ring is 58 percent gold ($14 \div 24 = 0.583$).
Another metal is 42 percent of the ring ($100\% - 58\% = 42\%$).

The 12 K ring is 50 percent gold ($12 \div 24 = 0.5$).

The 20 K ring is 83 percent gold ($20 \div 24 = 0.833$).

Sample answer: I would like to own the 20 K gold ring because it contains more gold.

Mathematics

Measuring Gold

People often say that something is "worth its weight in gold." But modern-day jewelry is seldom made of pure gold. Because gold is so soft, it is usually mixed with another metal to form an alloy—a mixture of two or more metals. Most commonly the other metal in a gold alloy is copper, although alloys of gold can also contain silver, zinc, or other metals.

Suppose you are shopping for a gold chain. You see two chains that look the same and are exactly the same size. How do you decide which one to buy? If you look closely at the gold jewelry, you'll probably see in small print the numbers "20K," "18K," "14K," or "12K." The "K" is the abbreviation for karat, which is the measure of how pure an alloy of gold is. Pure gold is 24 karat. Gold that is 50 percent pure is $\frac{12}{24}$ gold, or 12 karat. The greater the amount of gold in a piece of jewelry, the higher the value.

You look again at the two gold chains and decide that your favorite is the 18-karat gold chain. It has copper in it. What percent of the 18 K gold chain is gold? What percent is copper?

Weighing Gold
A worker in the Federal Reserve Bank of the United States weighs dense ingots, or bars, of pure gold.

1 **Read and Understand**
You know that pure gold is $\frac{24}{24}$ gold, and an 18 karat chain is $\frac{18}{24}$ gold.

2 **Plan and Solve**
In order to find out what percent of an 18 K chain is gold, you need to write a proportion.

$$\frac{\text{Number of gold parts}}{\text{Number of parts in the whole}} \quad \begin{array}{l} \rightarrow \\ \rightarrow \end{array} \quad \frac{18}{24}$$

Then simplify the fraction and convert it to a percentage.

$$\frac{18}{24} = \frac{3}{4} = 75\%$$

3 **Look Back and Check**
If 75% of the chain is gold, then 25% of the chain must be copper.

156 ◆ K

Math Activity

How would you choose a gold ring? To decide, you might determine what percent of each ring is gold.

- What percent of a 14 K gold ring is gold? What percent is another metal? Round decimals to the nearest hundredth.

- What percent of a 12 K ring is gold? What percent of the 20 K ring is gold?

- Which ring would you like to own—the 12 K or the 20 K? Why?

Background

Facts and Figures The main purpose of adding elements to gold is to make the gold harder. The strongest alloy of gold and silver contains about 50 percent gold. But that alloy is a dull white color, and it easily tarnishes. "Green gold," an alloy often used in jewelry, is an alloy of gold and silver. "White gold" contains gold and nickel as well as small amounts of zinc and copper.

"Red gold," which contains varying amounts of gold and copper, has been widely used in making coins. Goldware, such as cups and bowls, is often made of "yellow gold," which contains gold, silver, and copper. "Solid gold" jewelry in the United States is mostly made with 10–21 karat gold.

Gold Mask
This gold mask was found in the tomb of a ruler of Mycenae, a city in ancient Greece. The mask is about 3,500 years old.

Tie It Together

Gold Producers

South Africa	United States	Russia
Australia	Canada	China

A Treasure Hunt

Work in small groups to make a World Treasure Map of one of the countries where gold is mined today. Use the library to learn about the gold-producing countries listed above.

On a large map of the world, use push pins to mark the locations of the gold sites. In the United States and Canada, mark the states and provinces that are the largest producers. Make up fact sheets to answer questions such as:

• Where are gold sites located in each country?

• When was gold first discovered there?

• Did a gold rush influence the history of that area?

If possible, collect photographs to illustrate gold products in each country. Post your pictures and fact sheets at the side of the World Treasure Map.

K ◆ 157

A Treasure Hunt

Time 1 week (3 days for research and collection of photographs, 2 days for making up the fact sheets and preparing the map)

Tips Have students work in groups of three or four. Encourage students to meet with their groups to agree on research strategies and then work individually or in pairs to gather the information.

• In the research stage, suggest that students first examine encyclopedia entrees and almanacs or atlases to make a list of countries, states, and provinces in which gold is produced. From that list, they can dig deeper in more specialized books and Internet sources.

• Have groups make their maps on poster board or a length of butcher paper. Advise them that their maps need not be exactly accurate. They can draw the continents, provinces, and states free form, using different pencil or marker colors for boundaries.

• If students are unsuccessful in collecting photos, they can make drawings from photographs they see in books and magazines.

Extend Groups can choose a country or continent on which to focus their attention and then prepare a more detailed report on the areas where gold is produced and the processes involved in production and trade.

Think Like a Scientist

The Skills Handbook is designed as a reference for students to use whenever they need to review inquiry, reading, or math skills. You can use the activities in this part of the Skills Handbook to teach or reinforce inquiry skills.

Observing

Focus Remind students that an observation is what they can see, hear, smell, taste, or feel.

Teach Invite students to make observations of the classroom. List these observations on the board. Challenge students to identify the senses they used to make each observation. Then, ask: **Which senses will you use to make observations from the photograph on this page?** (Sight is the only sense that can be used to make observations from the photograph.)

Activity

Some observations that students might make include that the boy is skateboarding, wearing a white helmet, and flying in the air. Make sure that students' observations are confined to only things that they can actually see in the photograph.

Inferring

Focus Choose one or two of the classroom observations listed on the board, and challenge students to interpret them. Guide students by asking why something appears as it does.

Teach Encourage students to describe their thought processes in making their inferences. Point out where they used their knowledge and experience to interpret the observations. Then invite students to suggest other possible interpretations for the observations. Ask: **How can you find out whether an inference is correct?** (By further investigation)

Activity

One possible inference is that the boy just skated off a ramp at a skate park. Invite students to share their experiences that helped them make the inference.

Predicting

Focus Discuss the weather forecast for the next day. Point out that this prediction is an inference about what will happen in the

---

Think Like a Scientist

Scientists have a particular way of looking at the world, or scientific habits of mind. Whenever you ask a question and explore possible answers, you use many of the same skills that scientists do. Some of these skills are described on this page.

Observing

When you use one or more of your five senses to gather information about the world, you are **observing.** Hearing a dog bark, counting twelve green seeds, and smelling smoke are all observations. To increase the power of their senses, scientists sometimes use microscopes, telescopes, or other instruments that help them make more detailed observations.

An observation must be an accurate report of what your senses detect. It is important to keep careful records of your observations in science class by writing or drawing in a notebook. The information collected through observations is called evidence, or data.

Inferring

When you interpret an observation, you are **inferring,** or making an inference. For example, if you hear your dog barking, you may infer that someone is at your front door. To make this inference, you combine the evidence— the barking dog—and your experience or knowledge—you know that your dog barks when strangers approach—to reach a logical conclusion.

Notice that an inference is not a fact; it is only one of many possible interpretations for an observation. For example, your dog may be barking because it wants to go for a walk. An inference may turn out to be incorrect even if it is based on accurate observations and logical reasoning. The only way to find out if an inference is correct is to investigate further.

Predicting

When you listen to the weather forecast, you hear many predictions about the next day's weather—what the temperature will be, whether it will rain, and how windy it will be. Weather forecasters use observations and knowledge of weather patterns to predict the weather. The skill of **predicting** involves making an inference about a future event based on current evidence or past experience.

Because a prediction is an inference, it may prove to be false. In science class, you can test some of your predictions by doing experiments. For example, suppose you predict that larger paper airplanes can fly farther than smaller airplanes. How could you test your prediction?

Activity

Use the photograph to answer the questions below.

Observing Look closely at the photograph. List at least three observations.

Inferring Use your observations to make an inference about what has happened. What experience or knowledge did you use to make the inference?

Predicting Predict what will happen next. On what evidence or experience do you base your prediction?

---

future based on observations and experience.

Teach Help students differentiate between a prediction and an inference. You might organize the similarities and differences in a Venn diagram on the board. Both are interpretations of observations using experience and knowledge, and both can be incorrect. Inferences describe current or past events. Predictions describe future events.

Activity

Students might predict that the boy will land and skate to the other side. Others might predict that the boy will fall. Students should also describe the evidence or experience on which they based their predictions.

Classifying

Could you imagine searching for a book in the library if the books were shelved in no particular order? Your trip to the library would be an all-day event! Luckily, librarians group together books on similar topics or by the same author. Grouping together items that are alike in some way is called **classifying.** You can classify items in many ways: by size, by shape, by use, and by other important characteristics.

Like librarians, scientists use the skill of classifying to organize information and objects. When things are sorted into groups, the relationships among them become easier to understand.

Activity

Classify the objects in the photograph into two groups based on any characteristic you choose. Then use another characteristic to classify the objects into three groups.

Activity

This student is using a model to demonstrate what causes day and night on Earth. What do the flashlight and the tennis ball in the model represent?

Making Models

Have you ever drawn a picture to help someone understand what you were saying? Such a drawing is one type of model. A model is a picture, diagram, computer image, or other representation of a complex object or process. **Making models** helps people understand things that they cannot observe directly.

Scientists often use models to represent things that are either very large or very small, such as the planets in the solar system, or the parts of a cell. Such models are physical models—drawings or three-dimensional structures that look like the real thing. Other models are mental models—mathematical equations or words that describe how something works.

Communicating

Whenever you talk on the phone, write a report, or listen to your teacher at school, you are communicating. **Communicating** is the process of sharing ideas and information with other people. Communicating effectively requires many skills, including writing, reading, speaking, listening, and making models.

Scientists communicate to share results, information, and opinions. Scientists often communicate about their work in journals, over the telephone, in letters, and on the Internet.

They also attend scientific meetings where they share their ideas with one another in person.

Activity

On a sheet of paper, write out clear, detailed directions for tying your shoe. Then exchange directions with a partner. Follow your partner's directions exactly. How successful were you at tying your shoe? How could your partner have communicated more clearly?

Skills Handbook ◆ 159

Communicating

Focus Have students identify the methods of communication they have used today.

Teach Ask: **How is the way you communicate with a friend similar to and different from the way scientists communicate about their work to other scientists?** (*Both may communicate using various methods, but scientists must be very detailed and precise, whereas communication between friends may be less detailed and*

precise.) Encourage students to communicate like a scientist as they carry out the activity.

Activity

Students' answers will vary but should identify a step-by-step process for tying a shoe. Help students identify communication errors such as leaving out a step, putting steps in the wrong order, or disregarding the person's handedness.

Classifying

Focus Encourage students to think of common things that are classified.

Teach Ask: **What things at home are classified?** (*Clothing might be classified in order to place it in the appropriate dresser drawer; glasses, plates, and silverware are grouped in different parts of the kitchen; screws, nuts, bolts, washers, and nails might be separated into small containers.*) **What are some things that scientists classify?** (*Scientists classify many things they study, including organisms, geological features and processes, and kinds of machines.*)

Activity

Some characteristics students might use include color, pattern of color, use of balls, and size. Students' criteria for classification should clearly divide the balls into two, and then three, distinct groups.

Making Models

Focus Ask: **What are some models you have used to study science?** (*Students might have used human anatomical models, solar system models, maps, or stream tables.*) **How have these models helped you?** (*Models can help you learn about things that are difficult to study because they are very large, very small, or highly complex.*)

Teach Be sure students understand that a model does not have to be three-dimensional. For example, a map is a model, as is a mathematical equation. Have students look at the photograph of the student modeling the causes of day and night on Earth. Ask: **What quality of each item makes this a good model?** (*The flashlight gives off light, and the ball is round and can be rotated by the student.*)

Activity

The flashlight represents the sun and the ball represents Earth.

Making Measurements

Students can refer to this part of the Skills Handbook whenever they need to review how to make measurements with SI units. You can use the activities here to teach or reinforce SI units.

Measuring in SI

Focus Review SI units with students. Begin by providing metric rulers, graduated cylinders, balances, and Celsius thermometers. Use these tools to reinforce that the meter is the unit of length, the liter is the unit of volume, the gram is the unit of mass, and the degree Celsius is the unit of temperature.

Teach Ask: **If you want to measure the length and the width of the classroom, which SI unit would you use?** *(Meter)* **Which unit would you use to measure the amount of mass in your textbook?** *(Gram)* **Which would you use to measure how much water a drinking glass holds?** *(Liter)* **When would you use the Celsius scale?** *(To measure the temperature of something)* Then use the measuring equipment to review SI prefixes. For example, ask: **What are the smallest units on the metric ruler?** *(Millimeters)* **How many millimeters are there in one centimeter?** *(10 millimeters)* **How many in 10 centimeters?** *(100 millimeters)* **How many centimeters are there in one meter?** *(100 centimeters)* **What does 1,000 meters equal?** *(One kilometer)*

Activity

Length The length of the shell is 7.8 centimeters, or 78 millimeters. If students need more practice measuring length, have them use meter sticks and metric rulers to measure various objects in the classroom.

Activity

Liquid Volume The volume of water in the graduated cylinder is 62 milliliters. If students need more practice, have them use a graduated cylinder to measure different volumes of water.

Making Measurements

By measuring, scientists can express their observations more precisely and communicate more information about what they observe.

Measuring in SI

The standard system of measurement used by scientists around the world is known as the International System of Units, which is abbreviated as SI (**Système International d'Unités,** in French). SI units are easy to use because they are based on multiples of 10. Each unit is ten times larger than the next smallest unit and one tenth the size of the next largest unit. The table lists the prefixes used to name the most common SI units.

Common SI Prefixes		
Prefix	Symbol	Meaning
kilo-	k	1,000
hecto-	h	100
deka-	da	10
deci-	d	0.1 (one tenth)
centi-	c	0.01 (one hundredth)
milli-	m	0.001 (one thousandth)

Length To measure length, or the distance between two points, the unit of measure is the **meter (m).** The distance from the floor to a doorknob is approximately one meter. Long distances, such as the distance between two cities, are measured in kilometers (km). Small lengths are measured in centimeters (cm) or millimeters (mm). Scientists use metric rulers and meter sticks to measure length.

Common Conversions	
1 km	= 1,000 m
1 m	= 100 cm
1 m	= 1,000 mm
1 cm	= 10 mm

Activity

The larger lines on the metric ruler in the picture show centimeter divisions, while the smaller, unnumbered lines show millimeter divisions. How many centimeters long is the shell? How many millimeters long is it?

Liquid Volume To measure the volume of a liquid, or the amount of space it takes up, you will use a unit of measure known as the **liter (L).** One liter is the approximate volume of a medium-size carton of milk. Smaller volumes are measured in milliliters (mL). Scientists use graduated cylinders to measure liquid volume.

Activity

The graduated cylinder in the picture is marked in milliliter divisions. Notice that the water in the cylinder has a curved surface. This curved surface is called the *meniscus.* To measure the volume, you must read the level at the lowest point of the meniscus. What is the volume of water in this graduated cylinder?

Common Conversion
1 L = 1,000 mL

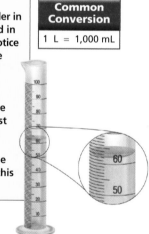

Mass To measure mass, or the amount of matter in an object, you will use a unit of measure known as the **gram (g).** One gram is approximately the mass of a paper clip. Larger masses are measured in kilograms (kg). Scientists use a balance to find the mass of an object.

Common Conversion

1 kg = 1,000 g

Activity

The mass of the potato in the picture is measured in kilograms. What is the mass of the potato? Suppose a recipe for potato salad called for one kilogram of potatoes. About how many potatoes would you need?

0.25 KG

Temperature To measure the temperature of a substance, you will use the **Celsius scale.** Temperature is measured in degrees Celsius (°C) using a Celsius thermometer. Water freezes at 0°C and boils at 100°C.

Time The unit scientists use to measure time is the **second (s).**

Activity

What is the temperature of the liquid in degrees Celsius?

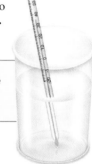

Converting SI Units

To use the SI system, you must know how to convert between units. Converting from one unit to another involves the skill of **calculating,** or using mathematical operations. Converting between SI units is similar to converting between dollars and dimes because both systems are based on multiples of ten.

Suppose you want to convert a length of 80 centimeters to meters. Follow these steps to convert between units.

1. Begin by writing down the measurement you want to convert—in this example, 80 centimeters.

2. Write a conversion factor that represents the relationship between the two units you are converting. In this example, the relationship is 1 meter = 100 centimeters. Write this conversion factor as a fraction, making sure to place the units you are converting from (centimeters, in this example) in the denominator.

3. Multiply the measurement you want to convert by the fraction. When you do this, the units in the first measurement will cancel out with the units in the denominator. Your answer will be in the units you are converting to (meters, in this example).

Example

80 centimeters = ▨ meters

$$80 \text{ centimeters} \times \frac{1 \text{ meter}}{100 \text{ centimeters}} = \frac{80 \text{ meters}}{100}$$

$$= 0.8 \text{ meters}$$

Activity

Convert between the following units.
1. 600 millimeters = ▨ meters
2. 0.35 liters = ▨ milliliters
3. 1,050 grams = ▨ kilograms

Skills Handbook ♦ 161

Activity

Mass The mass of the potato is 0.25 kilograms. You would need 4 potatoes to make one kilogram. If students need more practice, give them various objects, such as coins, paper clips, and books, to measure mass.

Activity

Temperature The temperature of the liquid is 35°C. Students who need more practice can measure the temperatures of various water samples.

Converting SI Units

Focus Review the steps for converting SI units, and work through the example with students.

Teach Ask: **How many millimeters are in 80 centimeters?** (*With the relationship 10 millimeters = 1 centimeter, students should follow the steps to calculate that 80 centimeters is equal to 800 millimeters.*) Have students do the conversion problems in the activity.

Activity

1. *600 millimeters = 0.6 meters*
2. *0.35 liters = 350 milliliters*
3. *1,050 grams = 1.05 kilograms*
If students need more practice converting SI units, have them make up conversion problems to trade with partners.

Conducting a Scientific Investigation

Students can refer to this part of the Skills Handbook whenever they need to review the steps of a scientific investigation. You can use the activities here to teach or reinforce these steps.

Posing Questions

Focus Ask: **What do you do when you want to learn about something?** (*Answers might include asking questions about it or looking for information in books or on the Internet.*) Explain that scientists go through the same process to learn about something.

Teach Tell students that the questions scientists ask may have no answers or many different answers. To answer their questions, scientists often conduct experiments. Ask: **Why is a scientific question important to a scientific investigation?** (*It helps the scientist decide if an experiment is necessary; the answer might already be known. It also helps focus the idea so that the scientist can form a hypothesis.*) **What is the scientific question in the activity on the next page?** (*Is a ball's bounce affected by the height from which it is dropped?*)

Developing a Hypothesis

Focus Emphasize that a hypothesis is one possible explanation for a set of observations. It is *not* a guess. It is often based on an inference.

Teach Ask: **On what information do scientists base their hypotheses?** (*Their observations and previous knowledge or experience*) Point out that a hypothesis does not always turn out to be correct. Ask: **When a hypothesis turns out to be incorrect, do you think the scientist wasted his or her time? Explain.** (*No. The scientist learned from the investigation and will develop another hypothesis that could prove to be correct.*)

Designing an Experiment

Focus Have a volunteer read the Experimental Procedure in the box. Invite students to identify the manipulated variable (*amount of salt*), the variables kept constant (*amount and temperature of water, location of containers*), the control (*Container 3*), and the responding variable (*time required for the water to freeze*).

Conducting a Scientific Investigation

In some ways, scientists are like detectives, piecing together clues to learn about a process or event. One way that scientists gather clues is by carrying out experiments. An experiment tests an idea in a careful, orderly manner. Although experiments do not all follow the same steps in the same order, many follow a pattern similar to the one described here.

Posing Questions

Experiments begin by asking a scientific question. A scientific question is one that can be answered by gathering evidence. For example, the question "Which freezes faster—fresh water or salt water?" is a scientific question because you can carry out an investigation and gather information to answer the question.

Developing a Hypothesis

The next step is to form a hypothesis. A **hypothesis** is a possible explanation for a set of observations or answer to a scientific question. In science, a hypothesis must be something that can be tested. A hypothesis can be worded as an *If . . . then . . .* statement. For example, a hypothesis might be *"If I add salt to fresh water, then the water will take longer to freeze."* A hypothesis worded this way serves as a rough outline of the experiment you should perform.

162 ◆ K

Teach Ask: **How might the experiment be affected if Container 1 had only 100 milliliters of water?** (*It wouldn't be an accurate comparison with the containers that have more water.*) Also make sure that students understand the importance of the control. Then, ask: **What operational definition is used in this experiment?** (*"Frozen" means the time at which a wooden stick can no longer move in a container.*)

Designing an Experiment

Next you need to plan a way to test your hypothesis. Your plan should be written out as a step-by-step procedure and should describe the observations or measurements you will make.

Two important steps involved in designing an experiment are controlling variables and forming operational definitions.

Controlling Variables In a well-designed experiment, you need to keep all variables the same except for one. A **variable** is any factor that can change in an experiment. The factor that you change is called the **manipulated variable**. In this experiment, the manipulated variable is the amount of salt added to the water. Other factors, such as the amount of water or the starting temperature, are kept constant.

The factor that changes as a result of the manipulated variable is called the **responding variable.** The responding variable is what you measure or observe to obtain your results. In this experiment, the responding variable is how long the water takes to freeze.

An experiment in which all factors except one are kept constant is called a **controlled experiment.** Most controlled experiments include a test called the control. In this experiment, Container 3 is the control. Because no salt is added to Container 3, you can compare the results from the other containers to it. Any difference in results must be due to the addition of salt alone.

Forming Operational Definitions Another important aspect of a well-designed experiment is having clear operational definitions. An **operational definition** is a statement that describes how a particular variable is to be measured or how a term is to be defined. For example, in this experiment, how will you determine if the water has frozen? You might decide to insert a stick in each container at the start of the experiment. Your operational definition of "frozen" would be the time at which the stick can no longer move.

Experimental Procedure
1. Fill 3 containers with 300 milliliters of cold tap water.
2. Add 10 grams of salt to Container 1; stir. Add 20 grams of salt to Container 2; stir. Add no salt to Container 3.
3. Place the 3 containers in a freezer.
4. Check the containers every 15 minutes. Record your observations.

Interpreting Data

The observations and measurements you make in an experiment are called **data.** At the end of an experiment, you need to analyze the data to look for any patterns or trends. Patterns often become clear if you organize your data in a data table or graph. Then think through what the data reveal. Do they support your hypothesis? Do they point out a flaw in your experiment? Do you need to collect more data?

Drawing Conclusions

A **conclusion** is a statement that sums up what you have learned from an experiment. When you draw a conclusion, you need to decide whether the data you collected support your hypothesis or not. You may need to repeat an experiment several times before you can draw any conclusions from it. Conclusions often lead you to pose new questions and plan new experiments to answer them.

Activity

Is a ball's bounce affected by the height from which it is dropped? Using the steps just described, plan a controlled experiment to investigate this problem.

Skills Handbook ◆ 163

Interpreting Data

Focus Ask: **What kind of data would you collect from the experiment with freezing salt water?** *(Time and state of the water)*

Teach Ask: **What if you forgot to record some data during an investigation?** *(You wouldn't be able to draw valid conclusions because some data are missing.)* Then, ask: **Why are data tables and graphs a good way to organize data?** *(They make it easier to record data accurately, as well as compare and analyze data.)* **What kind of data table and graph might you use for this experiment?** *(A table would have columns for each container with a row for each time interval in which the state of water is recorded. A bar graph would show the time elapsed until water froze for each container.)*

Drawing Conclusions

Focus Help students understand that a conclusion is not necessarily the end of a scientific investigation. A conclusion about one experiment may lead right into another experiment.

Teach Point out that in scientific investigations, a conclusion is a summary and explanation of the results of an experiment. For the Experimental Procedure described on this page, tell students to suppose that they obtained the following results: Container 1 froze in 45 minutes, Container 2 in 80 minutes, and Container 3 in 25 minutes. Ask: **What conclusions can you draw from this experiment?** *(Students might conclude that water takes longer to freeze as more salt is added to it. The hypothesis is supported, and the question of which freezes faster is answered—fresh water.)*

Activity

You might wish to have students work in pairs to plan the controlled experiment. Students should develop a hypothesis, such as, "If I increase the height from which a ball is dropped, then the height of its bounce will increase." They can test the hypothesis by dropping a ball from varying heights (the manipulated variable). All trials should be done with the same kind of ball and on the same surface (constants). For each trial, they should measure the height of the bounce (responding variable). After students have designed the experiment, provide rubber balls, and invite them to carry out the experiment so they can collect and interpret data and draw conclusions.

Technology Design Skills

Students can refer to this part of the Skills Handbook whenever they need to review the process of designing new technologies. You can use the activities here to teach or reinforce the steps in this process.

Identify a Need

Focus Solicit from students any situations in which they have thought that a tool, machine, or other object would be really helpful to them or others. Explain that this is the first step in the design of new products.

Teach Point out that identifying specific needs is very important to the design process. Ask: **If it was specified that the toy boat be wind-powered, how might that affect the design?** (*The boat would likely be designed with sails.*)

Research the Problem

Focus Explain that research focuses the problem so that the design is more specific.

Teach Ask: **What might happen if you didn't research the problem before designing the solution?** (*Answers include developing a design that has already been found to fail, using materials that aren't the best, or designing a solution that already exists.*) **What would you research before designing your toy boat?** (*Students might research designs and materials.*)

Design a Solution

Focus Emphasize the importance of a design team. Ask: **Why are brainstorming sessions important in product design?** (*A group will propose more new ideas than one person.*)

Teach Divide the class into teams to design the toy boat. Instruct them to brainstorm design ideas. Then, ask: **Why do you think engineers evaluate constraints after brainstorming?** (*Evaluating constraints while brainstorming often stops the flow of new ideas.*) **What design constraints do you have for your toy boat?** (*Materials must be readily available and teacher-approved. The boat must be 15 centimeters or less in length and must travel 2 meters in a straight line carrying a load of 20 pennies*)

Technology Design Skills

Engineers are people who use scientific and technological knowledge to solve practical problems. To design new products, engineers usually follow the process described here, even though they may not follow these steps in the exact order. As you read the steps, think about how you might apply them in technology labs.

Identify a Need

Before engineers begin designing a new product, they must first identify the need they are trying to meet. For example, suppose you are a member of a design team in a company that makes toys. Your team has identified a need: a toy boat that is inexpensive and easy to assemble.

Research the Problem

Engineers often begin by gathering information that will help them with their new design. This research may include finding articles in books, magazines, or on the Internet. It may also include talking to other engineers who have solved similar problems. Engineers often perform experiments related to the product they want to design.

For your toy boat, you could look at toys that are similar to the one you want to design. You might do research on the Internet. You could also test some materials to see whether they will work well in a toy boat.

Drawing for a boat design ▼

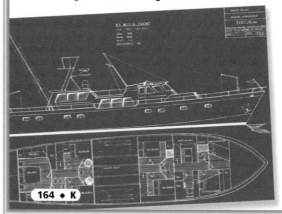

164 ◆ K

Design a Solution

Research gives engineers information that helps them design a product. When engineers design new products, they usually work in teams.

Generating Ideas Often design teams hold brainstorming meetings in which any team member can contribute ideas. **Brainstorming** is a creative process in which one team member's suggestions often spark ideas in other group members. Brainstorming can lead to new approaches to solving a design problem.

Evaluating Constraints During brainstorming, a design team will often come up with several possible designs. The team must then evaluate each one.

As part of their evaluation, engineers consider constraints. **Constraints** are factors that limit or restrict a product design. Physical characteristics, such as the properties of materials used to make your toy boat, are constraints. Money and time are also constraints. If the materials in a product cost a lot, or if the product takes a long time to make, the design may be impractical.

Making Trade-offs Design teams usually need to make trade-offs. In a **trade-off,** engineers give up one benefit of a proposed design in order to obtain another. In designing your toy boat, you will have to make trade-offs. For example, suppose one material is sturdy but not fully waterproof. Another material is more waterproof, but breakable. You may decide to give up the benefit of sturdiness in order to obtain the benefit of waterproofing.

Build and Evaluate a Prototype

Once the team has chosen a design plan, the engineers build a prototype of the product. A **prototype** is a working model used to test a design. Engineers evaluate the prototype to see whether it works well, is easy to operate, is safe to use, and holds up to repeated use.

Think of your toy boat. What would the prototype be like? Of what materials would it be made? How would you test it?

Troubleshoot and Redesign

Few prototypes work perfectly, which is why they need to be tested. Once a design team has tested a prototype, the members analyze the results and identify any problems. The team then tries to **troubleshoot,** or fix the design problems. For example, if your toy boat leaks or wobbles, the boat should be redesigned to eliminate those problems.

Communicate the Solution

A team needs to communicate the final design to the people who will manufacture and use the product. To do this, teams may use sketches, detailed drawings, computer simulations, and word descriptions.

Activity

You can use the technology design process to design and build a toy boat.

Research and Investigate

1. Visit the library or go online to research toy boats.

2. Investigate how a toy boat can be powered, including wind, rubber bands, or baking soda and vinegar.

3. Brainstorm materials, shapes, and steering for your boat.

Design and Build

4. Based on your research, design a toy boat that
   - is made of readily available materials
   - is no larger than 15 cm long and 10 cm wide
   - includes a power system, a rudder, and an area for cargo
   - travels 2 meters in a straight line carrying a load of 20 pennies

5. Sketch your design and write a step-by-step plan for building your boat. After your teacher approves your plan, build your boat.

Evaluate and Redesign

6. Test your boat, evaluate the results, and troubleshoot any problems.

7. Based on your evaluation, redesign your toy boat so it performs better.

Skills Handbook ♦ 165

Build and Evaluate a Prototype

Focus Explain that building a prototype enables engineers to test design ideas.

Teach Relate building and testing a prototype to conducting an experiment. Explain that engineers set up controlled experiments to test the prototype. Ask: **Why do you think engineers set up controlled experiments?** *(From the data, they can determine which component of the design is working and which is failing.)* **How would you test your prototype of the toy boat?** *(Answers will vary depending on the toy boat's propulsion system.)*

Troubleshoot and Redesign

Focus Make sure students know what it means to troubleshoot. If necessary, give an example. One example is a stapler that isn't working. In that case, you would check to see if it is out of staples or if the staples are jammed. Then you would fix the problem and try stapling again. If it still didn't work, you might check the position of staples and try again.

Teach Explain that engineers often are not surprised if the prototype doesn't work. Ask: **Why isn't it a failure if the prototype doesn't work?** *(Engineers learn from the problems and make changes to address the problems. This process makes the design better.)* Emphasize that prototypes are completely tested before the product is made in the factory.

Communicate the Solution

Focus Inquire whether students have ever read the instruction manual that comes with a new toy or electronic device.

Teach Emphasize the importance of good communication in the design process. Ask: **What might happen if engineers did not communicate their design ideas clearly?** *(The product might not be manufactured correctly or used properly.)*

Activity

The design possibilities are endless. Students might use small plastic containers, wood, foil, or plastic drinking cups for the boat. Materials may also include toothpicks, straws, or small wooden dowels. Brainstorm with students the different ways in which a toy boat can be propelled. The boats may be any shape, but must be no longer than 15 centimeters.

As student groups follow the steps in the design process, have them record their sources, brainstorming ideas, and prototype design in a logbook. Also give them time to troubleshoot and redesign their boats. When students turn in their boats, they should include assembly directions with a diagram, as well as instructions for use.

Creating Data Tables and Graphs

Students can refer to this part of the Skills Handbook whenever they need to review the skills required to create data tables and graphs. You can use the activities provided here to teach or reinforce these skills.

Data Tables

Focus Emphasize the importance of organizing data. Ask: **What might happen if you didn't use a data table for an experiment?** (*Possible answers include that data might not be collected or they might be forgotten.*)

Teach Have students create a data table to show how much time they spend on different activities during one week. Suggest that students first list the main activities they do every week. Then they should determine the amount of time they spend on each activity each day. Remind students to give the data table a title. A sample data table is shown below.

Bar Graphs

Focus Have students compare and contrast the data table and the bar graph on this page. Ask: **Why would you make a bar graph if the data are already organized in a table?** (*The bar graph organizes the data in a visual way that makes them easier to interpret.*)

Teach Students can use the data from the data table they created to make a bar graph that shows the amount of time they spend on different activities during a week. The vertical axis should be divided into units of time, such as hours. Remind students to label both axes and give their graph a title. A sample bar graph is shown below.

Creating Data Tables and Graphs

How can you make sense of the data in a science experiment? The first step is to organize the data to help you understand them. Data tables and graphs are helpful tools for organizing data.

Data Tables

You have gathered your materials and set up your experiment. But before you start, you need to plan a way to record what happens during the experiment. By creating a data table, you can record your observations and measurements in an orderly way.

Suppose, for example, that a scientist conducted an experiment to find out how many Calories people of different body masses burn while doing various activities. The data table shows the results.

Notice in this data table that the manipulated variable (body mass) is the heading of one column. The responding variable (for

Calories Burned in 30 Minutes			
Body Mass	Experiment 1: Bicycling	Experiment 2: Playing Basketball	Experiment 3: Watching Television
30 kg	60 Calories	120 Calories	21 Calories
40 kg	77 Calories	164 Calories	27 Calories
50 kg	95 Calories	206 Calories	33 Calories
60 kg	114 Calories	248 Calories	38 Calories

Experiment 1, the number of Calories burned while bicycling) is the heading of the next column. Additional columns were added for related experiments.

Bar Graphs

To compare how many Calories a person burns doing various activities, you could create a bar graph. A bar graph is used to display data in a number of separate, or distinct, categories. In this example, bicycling, playing basketball, and watching television are the three categories.

To create a bar graph, follow these steps.

1. On graph paper, draw a horizontal, or *x-*, axis and a vertical, or *y-*, axis.
2. Write the names of the categories to be graphed along the horizontal axis. Include an overall label for the axis as well.
3. Label the vertical axis with the name of the responding variable. Include units of measurement. Then create a scale along the axis by marking off equally spaced numbers that cover the range of the data collected.

4. For each category, draw a solid bar using the scale on the vertical axis to determine the height. Make all the bars the same width.
5. Add a title that describes the graph.

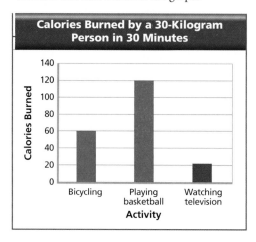

Calories Burned by a 30-Kilogram Person in 30 Minutes

Time Spent on Different Activities in a Week				
	Going to Classes	Eating Meals	Playing Soccer	Watching Television
Monday	6	2	2	0.5
Tuesday	6	1.5	1.5	1.5
Wednesday	6	2	1	2
Thursday	6	2	2	1.5
Friday	6	2	2	0.5
Saturday	0	2.5	2.5	1
Sunday	0	3	1	2

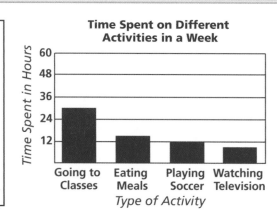

Time Spent on Different Activities in a Week

Line Graphs

To see whether a relationship exists between body mass and the number of Calories burned while bicycling, you could create a line graph. A line graph is used to display data that show how one variable (the responding variable) changes in response to another variable (the manipulated variable). You can use a line graph when your manipulated variable is **continuous,** that is, when there are other points between the ones that you tested. In this example, body mass is a continuous variable because there are other body masses between 30 and 40 kilograms (for example, 31 kilograms). Time is another example of a continuous variable.

Line graphs are powerful tools because they allow you to estimate values for conditions that you did not test in the experiment. For example, you can use the line graph to estimate that a 35-kilogram person would burn 68 Calories while bicycling.

To create a line graph, follow these steps.

1. On graph paper, draw a horizontal, or x-, axis and a vertical, or y-, axis.
2. Label the horizontal axis with the name of the manipulated variable. Label the vertical axis with the name of the responding variable. Include units of measurement.
3. Create a scale on each axis by marking off equally spaced numbers that cover the range of the data collected.
4. Plot a point on the graph for each piece of data. In the line graph above, the dotted lines show how to plot the first data point (30 kilograms and 60 Calories). Follow an imaginary vertical line extending up from the horizontal axis at the 30-kilogram mark. Then follow an imaginary horizontal line extending across from the vertical axis at the 60-Calorie mark. Plot the point where the two lines intersect.

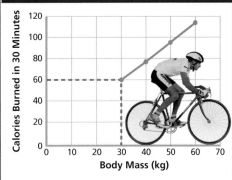

Effect of Body Mass on Calories Burned While Bicycling

5. Connect the plotted points with a solid line. (In some cases, it may be more appropriate to draw a line that shows the general trend of the plotted points. In those cases, some of the points may fall above or below the line. Also, not all graphs are linear. It may be more appropriate to draw a curve to connect the points.)
6. Add a title that identifies the variables or relationship in the graph.

Activity

Create line graphs to display the data from Experiment 2 and Experiment 3 in the data table.

Activity

You read in the newspaper that a total of 4 centimeters of rain fell in your area in June, 2.5 centimeters fell in July, and 1.5 centimeters fell in August. What type of graph would you use to display these data? Use graph paper to create the graph.

Skills Handbook ◆ 167

Line Graphs

Focus Ask: **Would a bar graph show the relationship between body mass and the number of Calories burned in 30 minutes?** *(No. Bar graphs can only show data in distinct categories.)* Explain that line graphs are used to show how one variable changes in response to another variable.

Teach Walk students through the steps involved in creating a line graph using the example illustrated on the page. For example, ask: **What is the label on the horizontal axis? On the vertical axis?** *(Body Mass (kg); Calories Burned in 30 Minutes)* **What scale is used on each axis?** *(10 kg on the x-axis and 20 Calories on the y-axis)* **What does the second data point represent?** *(77 Calories burned for a body mass of 40 kg)* **What trend or pattern does the graph show?** *(The number of Calories burned in 30 minutes of cycling increases with body mass.)*

Activity

Students should make a different graph for each experiment. Each graph should have a different x-axis scale that is appropriate for the data. See sample graphs below.

Activity

Students should conclude that a bar graph would be best for displaying the data.

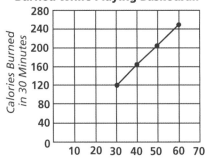

Effect of Body Mass on Calories Burned While Playing Basketball

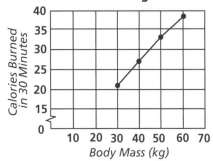

Effect of Body Mass on Calories Burned While Watching Television

K ● 167

Circle Graphs

Focus Emphasize that a circle graph must include 100 percent of the categories for the topic being graphed. For example, ask: **Could the data in the bar graph titled "Calories Burned by a 30-kilogram Person in Various Activities" (on the previous page) be shown in a circle graph? Why or why not?** *(No. It does not include all the possible ways a 30-kilogram person can burn Calories.)*

Teach Walk students through the steps for making a circle graph. If necessary, help them with the compass and the protractor. Use the protractor to illustrate that a circle has 360 degrees. Make sure students understand the mathematical calculations involved in making a circle graph.

Activity

You might have students work in pairs to complete the activity. Students' circle graphs should look like the graph below.

Ways Students Get to School

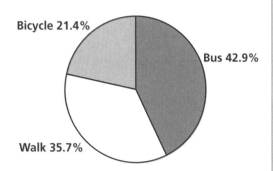

Circle Graphs

Like bar graphs, circle graphs can be used to display data in a number of separate categories. Unlike bar graphs, however, circle graphs can only be used when you have data for *all* the categories that make up a given topic. A circle graph is sometimes called a pie chart. The pie represents the entire topic, while the slices represent the individual categories. The size of a slice indicates what percentage of the whole a particular category makes up.

The data table below shows the results of a survey in which 24 teenagers were asked to identify their favorite sport. The data were then used to create the circle graph at the right.

Favorite Sports

Sport	Students
Soccer	8
Basketball	6
Bicycling	6
Swimming	4

To create a circle graph, follow these steps.

1. Use a compass to draw a circle. Mark the center with a point. Then draw a line from the center point to the top of the circle.

2. Determine the size of each "slice" by setting up a proportion where *x* equals the number of degrees in a slice. (*Note:* A circle contains 360 degrees.) For example, to find the number of degrees in the "soccer" slice, set up the following proportion:

$$\frac{\text{Students who prefer soccer}}{\text{Total number of students}} = \frac{x}{\text{Total number of degrees in a circle}}$$

$$\frac{8}{24} = \frac{x}{360}$$

Cross-multiply and solve for x.

$$24x = 8 \times 360$$
$$x = 120$$

The "soccer" slice should contain 120 degrees.

Sports That Teens Prefer

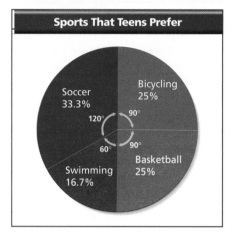

3. Use a protractor to measure the angle of the first slice, using the line you drew to the top of the circle as the 0° line. Draw a line from the center of the circle to the edge for the angle you measured.

4. Continue around the circle by measuring the size of each slice with the protractor. Start measuring from the edge of the previous slice so the wedges do not overlap. When you are done, the entire circle should be filled in.

5. Determine the percentage of the whole circle that each slice represents. To do this, divide the number of degrees in a slice by the total number of degrees in a circle (360), and multiply by 100%. For the "soccer" slice, you can find the percentage as follows:

$$\frac{120}{360} \times 100\% = 33.3\%$$

6. Use a different color for each slice. Label each slice with the category and with the percentage of the whole it represents.

7. Add a title to the circle graph.

Activity

In a class of 28 students, 12 students take the bus to school, 10 students walk, and 6 students ride their bicycles. Create a circle graph to display these data.

Math Review

Scientists use math to organize, analyze, and present data. This appendix will help you review some basic math skills.

Mean, Median, and Mode

The **mean** is the average, or the sum of the data divided by the number of data items. The middle number in a set of ordered data is called the **median**. The **mode** is the number that appears most often in a set of data.

Example

A scientist counted the number of distinct songs sung by seven different male birds and collected the data shown below.

Male Bird Songs						
Bird	A	B	C	D	E	F	G
Number of Songs	36	29	40	35	28	36	27

To determine the mean number of songs, add the total number of songs and divide by the number of data items—in this case, the number of male birds.

$$\text{Mean} = \frac{231}{7} = 33 \text{ songs}$$

To find the median number of songs, arrange the data in numerical order and find the number in the middle of the series.

27 28 29 35 36 36 40

The number in the middle is 35, so the median number of songs is 35.

The mode is the value that appears most frequently. In the data, 36 appears twice, while each other item appears only once. Therefore, 36 songs is the mode.

Practice

Find out how many minutes it takes each student in your class to get to school. Then find the mean, median, and mode for the data.

Probability

Probability is the chance that an event will occur. Probability can be expressed as a ratio, a fraction, or a percentage. For example, when you flip a coin, the probability that the coin will land heads up is 1 in 2, or $\frac{1}{2}$, or 50 percent.

The probability that an event will happen can be expressed in the following formula.

$$P(\text{event}) = \frac{\text{Number of times the event can occur}}{\text{Total number of possible events}}$$

Example

A paper bag contains 25 blue marbles, 5 green marbles, 5 orange marbles, and 15 yellow marbles. If you close your eyes and pick a marble from the bag, what is the probability that it will be yellow?

$$P(\text{yellow marbles}) = \frac{15 \text{ yellow marbles}}{50 \text{ marbles total}}$$

$$P = \frac{15}{50}, \text{ or } \frac{3}{10}, \text{ or } 30\%$$

Practice

Each side of a cube has a letter on it. Two sides have *A*, three sides have *B*, and one side has *C*. If you roll the cube, what is the probability that *A* will land on top?

Math Review

Students can refer to this part of the Skills Handbook whenever they need to review some basic math skills. You can use the activities provided here to teach or reinforce these skills.

Mean, Median, and Mode

Focus Remind students that data from an experiment might consist of hundreds or thousands of numbers. Unless analyzed, the numbers likely will not be helpful.

Teach Work through the process of determining mean, median, and mode using the example in the book. Make sure students realize that these three numbers do not always equal each other. Point out that taken together, these three numbers give more information about the data than just one of the numbers alone.

Practice

Answers will vary based on class data. The mean should equal the total number of minutes divided by the number of students. The median should equal the number in the middle after arranging the data in numerical order. The mode should equal the number of minutes that is given most frequently.

Probability

Focus Show students a coin and ask: **What is the chance that I will get tails when I flip the coin?** (*Some students might know that there is a 1 in 2, or 50 percent, chance of getting tails.*)

Teach Set up a bag of marbles like the one in the example. Allow students to practice determining the probabilities of picking marbles of different colors. Then, encourage them to actually pick marbles and compare their actual results with those results predicted by probability.

Practice

$P(A) = 2$ sides with $\frac{A}{6}$ sides total

$P = \frac{2}{6}$, or $\frac{1}{3}$, or 33%

Area

Focus Ask: **Who knows what area is?** (*Area is equal to the number of square units needed to cover a certain shape or object.*) On the board, write the formulas for the area of a rectangle and a circle.

Teach Give students various objects of different shapes. Have them measure each object and determine its area based on the measurements. Point out that the units of the answer are squared because they are multiplied together. If students are interested, you might also explain that π is equal to the ratio of the circumference of a circle to its diameter. For circles of all sizes, π is approximately equal to the number 3.14, or $\frac{22}{7}$.

Practice

The area of the circle is equal to $21\text{ m} \times 21\text{ m} \times \frac{22}{7}$, or 1,386 m².

Circumference

Focus Draw a circle on the board. Then trace the outline with your finger and explain that this is the circumference of the circle, or the distance around it.

Teach Show students that the radius is equal to the distance from the center of the circle to any point on it. Point out that the diameter of a circle is equal to two times the radius. Give students paper circles of various sizes, and have them calculate the circumference of each.

Practice

The circumference is equal to $2 \times 28\text{ m} \times \frac{22}{7}$, or 176 m.

Volume

Focus Fill a beaker with 100 milliliters of water. Ask: **What is the volume of water?** (*100 milliliters*) Explain that volume is the amount of space that something takes up. Then point out that one milliliter is equal to one cubic centimeter (cm³).

Teach Write on the board the formulas for calculating the volumes of a rectangle and a cylinder. Point out that volume is equal to the area of an object multiplied by its height. Then measure the beaker to show students the relationship between liquid volume (100 milliliters) and the number of cubic units it contains (100 cubic centimeters).

Area

The **area** of a surface is the number of square units that cover it. The front cover of your text-book has an area of about 600 cm².

Area of a Rectangle and a Square To find the area of a rectangle, multiply its length times its width. The formula for the area of a rectangle is

$$A = \ell \times w, \text{ or } A = \ell w$$

Since all four sides of a square have the same length, the area of a square is the length of one side multiplied by itself, or squared.

$$A = s \times s, \text{ or } A = s^2$$

Example

A scientist is studying the plants in a field that measures 75 m × 45 m. What is the area of the field?

$$A = \ell \times w$$
$$A = 75\text{ m} \times 45\text{ m}$$
$$A = 3,375\text{ m}^2$$

Area of a Circle The formula for the area of a circle is

$$A = \pi \times r \times r, \text{ or } A = \pi r^2$$

The length of the radius is represented by r, and the value of π is approximately $\frac{22}{7}$.

Example

Find the area of a circle with a radius of 14 cm.

$$A = \pi r^2$$
$$A = 14 \times 14 \times \frac{22}{7}$$
$$A = 616\text{ cm}^2$$

Practice

Find the area of a circle that has a radius of 21 m.

Circumference

The distance around a circle is called the circumference. The formula for finding the circumference of a circle is

$$C = 2 \times \pi \times r, \text{ or } C = 2\pi r$$

Example

The radius of a circle is 35 cm. What is its circumference?

$$C = 2\pi r$$
$$C = 2 \times 35 \times \frac{22}{7}$$
$$C = 220\text{ cm}$$

Practice

What is the circumference of a circle with a radius of 28 m?

Volume

The volume of an object is the number of cubic units it contains. The volume of a wastebasket, for example, might be about 26,000 cm³.

Volume of a Rectangular Object To find the volume of a rectangular object, multiply the object's length times its width times its height.

$$V = \ell \times w \times h, \text{ or } V = \ell wh$$

Example

Find the volume of a box with length 24 cm, width 12 cm, and height 9 cm.

$$V = \ell wh$$
$$V = 24\text{ cm} \times 12\text{ cm} \times 9\text{ cm}$$
$$V = 2,592\text{ cm}^3$$

Practice

What is the volume of a rectangular object with length 17 cm, width 11 cm, and height 6 cm?

Practice

The volume of the rectangular object is equal to $17\text{ cm} \times 11\text{ cm} \times 6\text{ cm}$, or 1,122 cm³.

Fractions

A **fraction** is a way to express a part of a whole. In the fraction $\frac{4}{7}$, 4 is the numerator and 7 is the denominator.

Adding and Subtracting Fractions
To add or subtract two or more fractions that have a common denominator, first add or subtract the numerators. Then write the sum or difference over the common denominator.

To find the sum or difference of fractions with different denominators, first find the least common multiple of the denominators. This is known as the least common denominator. Then convert each fraction to equivalent fractions with the least common denominator. Add or subtract the numerators. Then write the sum or difference over the common denominator.

> **Example**
>
> $\frac{5}{6} - \frac{3}{4} = \frac{10}{12} - \frac{9}{12} = \frac{10 - 9}{12} = \frac{1}{12}$

Multiplying Fractions
To multiply two fractions, first multiply the two numerators, then multiply the two denominators.

> **Example**
>
> $\frac{5}{6} \times \frac{2}{3} = \frac{5 \times 2}{6 \times 3} = \frac{10}{18} = \frac{5}{9}$

Dividing Fractions
Dividing by a fraction is the same as multiplying by its reciprocal. Reciprocals are numbers whose numerators and denominators have been switched. To divide one fraction by another, first invert the fraction you are dividing by—in other words, turn it upside down. Then multiply the two fractions.

> **Example**
>
> $\frac{2}{5} \div \frac{7}{8} = \frac{2}{5} \times \frac{8}{7} = \frac{2 \times 8}{5 \times 7} = \frac{16}{35}$

> **Practice**
>
> Solve the following: $\frac{3}{7} \div \frac{4}{5}$.

Decimals

Fractions whose denominators are 10, 100, or some other power of 10 are often expressed as decimals. For example, the fraction $\frac{9}{10}$ can be expressed as the decimal 0.9, and the fraction $\frac{7}{100}$ can be written as 0.07.

Adding and Subtracting With Decimals
To add or subtract decimals, line up the decimal points before you carry out the operation.

> **Example**
>
> | 27.4 | 278.635 |
> |---|---|
> | + 6.19 | − 191.4 |
> | 33.59 | 87.235 |

Multiplying With Decimals
When you multiply two numbers with decimals, the number of decimal places in the product is equal to the total number of decimal places in each number being multiplied.

> **Example**
>
> 46.2 (one decimal place)
> × 2.37 (two decimal places)
> 109.494 (three decimal places)

Dividing With Decimals
To divide a decimal by a whole number, put the decimal point in the quotient above the decimal point in the dividend.

> **Example**
>
> $15.5 \div 5$
>
> $\frac{3.1}{5 \overline{)15.5}}$

To divide a decimal by a decimal, you need to rewrite the divisor as a whole number. Do this by multiplying both the divisor and dividend by the same multiple of 10.

> **Example**
>
> $1.68 \div 4.2 = 16.8 \div 42$
>
> $\frac{0.4}{42 \overline{)16.8}}$

> **Practice**
>
> Multiply 6.21 by 8.5.

Fractions

Focus Draw a circle on the board, and divide it into eight equal sections. Shade in one of the sections, and explain that one out of eight, or one eighth, of the sections is shaded. Also use the circle to show that four eighths is the same as one half.

Teach Write the fraction $\frac{3}{4}$ on the board. Ask: **What is the numerator?** *(Three)* **What is the denominator?** *(Four)* Emphasize that when adding and subtracting fractions, the denominators of the two fractions must be the same. If necessary, review how to find the least common denominator. Remind students that when multiplying and dividing, the denominators do not have to be the same.

> **Practice**
>
> $\frac{3}{7} \div \frac{4}{5} = \frac{3}{7} \times \frac{5}{4} = \frac{15}{28}$

Decimals

Focus Write the number *129.835* on the board. Ask: **What number is in the ones position?** *(9)* **The tenths position?** *(8)* **The hundredths position?** *(3)* Make sure students know that 0.8 is equal to $\frac{8}{10}$ and 0.03 is equal to $\frac{3}{100}$.

Teach Use the examples in the book to review addition, subtraction, multiplication, and division with decimals. Make up a worksheet of similar problems to give students additional practice. Also show students how a fraction is converted to a decimal by dividing the numerator by the denominator. For example, $\frac{1}{2}$ is equal to 0.5.

> **Practice**
>
> $6.21 \times 8.5 = 52.785$

Ratio and Proportion

Focus Differentiate a ratio from a fraction. Remind students that a fraction tells how many parts of the whole. In contrast, a ratio compares two different numbers. For example, $\frac{12}{22}$, or $\frac{6}{11}$, of a class are girls. But the ratio of boys to girls in the class is 10 to 12, or $\frac{5}{6}$.

Teach Use the example in the book to explain how to use a proportion to find an unknown quantity. Provide students with additional practice problems, if needed.

Practice

$6 \times 49 = 7x$

$294 = 7x$

$294 \div 7 = x$

$x = 42$

Percentage

Focus On the board, write $50\% = \frac{50}{100}$. Explain that a percentage is a ratio that compares a number to 100.

Teach Point out that when calculating percentages, you are usually using numbers other than 100. In this case, you set up a proportion. Go over the example in the book. Emphasize that the number representing the total goes on the bottom of the ratio, as does the 100%.

Practice

Students should set up the proportion

$\frac{42 \text{ marbles}}{300 \text{ marbles}} = \frac{x\%}{100\%}$

$42 \times 100 = 300x$

$4200 = 300x$

$4200 \div 300 = 14\%$

Ratio and Proportion

A **ratio** compares two numbers by division. For example, suppose a scientist counts 800 wolves and 1,200 moose on an island. The ratio of wolves to moose can be written as a fraction, $\frac{800}{1,200}$, which can be reduced to $\frac{2}{3}$. The same ratio can also be expressed as 2 to 3 or 2 : 3.

A **proportion** is a mathematical sentence saying that two ratios are equivalent. For example, a proportion could state that $\frac{800 \text{ wolves}}{1,200 \text{ moose}} = \frac{2 \text{ wolves}}{3 \text{ moose}}$. You can sometimes set up a proportion to determine or estimate an unknown quantity. For example, suppose a scientist counts 25 beetles in an area of 10 square meters. The scientist wants to estimate the number of beetles in 100 square meters.

Example

1. Express the relationship between beetles and area as a ratio: $\frac{25}{10}$, simplified to $\frac{5}{2}$.

2. Set up a proportion, with x representing the number of beetles. The proportion can be stated as $\frac{5}{2} = \frac{x}{100}$.

3. Begin by cross-multiplying. In other words, multiply each fraction's numerator by the other fraction's denominator.

   $5 \times 100 = 2 \times x$, or $500 = 2x$

4. To find the value of x, divide both sides by 2. The result is 250, or 250 beetles in 100 square meters.

Practice

Find the value of x in the following proportion: $\frac{6}{7} = \frac{x}{49}$.

Percentage

A **percentage** is a ratio that compares a number to 100. For example, there are 37 granite rocks in a collection that consists of 100 rocks. The ratio $\frac{37}{100}$ can be written as 37%. Granite rocks make up 37% of the rock collection.

You can calculate percentages of numbers other than 100 by setting up a proportion.

Example

Rain falls on 9 days out of 30 in June. What percentage of the days in June were rainy?

$\frac{9 \text{ days}}{30 \text{ days}} = \frac{d\%}{100\%}$

To find the value of d, begin by cross-multiplying, as for any proportion:

$9 \times 100 = 30 \times d$ $d = \frac{900}{30}$ $d = 30$

Practice

There are 300 marbles in a jar, and 42 of those marbles are blue. What percentage of the marbles are blue?

Significant Figures

The **precision** of a measurement depends on the instrument you use to take the measurement. For example, if the smallest unit on the ruler is millimeters, then the most precise measurement you can make will be in millimeters.

The sum or difference of measurements can only be as precise as the least precise measurement being added or subtracted. Round your answer so that it has the same number of digits after the decimal as the least precise measurement. Round up if the last digit is 5 or more, and round down if the last digit is 4 or less.

Example

Subtract a temperature of 5.2°C from the temperature 75.46°C.

75.46 − 5.2 = 70.26

5.2 has the fewest digits after the decimal, so it is the least precise measurement. Since the last digit of the answer is 6, round up to 3. The most precise difference between the measurements is 70.3°C.

Practice

Add 26.4 m to 8.37 m. Round your answer according to the precision of the measurements.

Significant figures are the number of nonzero digits in a measurement. Zeroes between nonzero digits are also significant. For example, the measurements 12,500 L, 0.125 cm, and 2.05 kg all have three significant figures. When you multiply and divide measurements, the one with the fewest significant figures determines the number of significant figures in your answer.

Example

Multiply 110 g by 5.75 g.

110 × 5.75 = 632.5

Because 110 has only two significant figures, round the answer to 630 g.

Scientific Notation

A **factor** is a number that divides into another number with no remainder. In the example, the number 3 is used as a factor four times.

An **exponent** tells how many times a number is used as a factor. For example, $3 \times 3 \times 3 \times 3$ can be written as 3^4. The exponent 4 indicates that the number 3 is used as a factor four times. Another way of expressing this is to say that 81 is equal to 3 to the fourth power.

Example

$$3^4 = 3 \times 3 \times 3 \times 3 = 81$$

Scientific notation uses exponents and powers of ten to write very large or very small numbers in shorter form. When you write a number in scientific notation, you write the number as two factors. The first factor is any number between 1 and 10. The second factor is a power of 10, such as 10^3 or 10^6.

Example

The average distance between the planet Mercury and the sun is 58,000,000 km. To write the first factor in scientific notation, insert a decimal point in the original number so that you have a number between 1 and 10. In the case of 58,000,000, the number is 5.8.

To determine the power of 10, count the number of places that the decimal point moved. In this case, it moved 7 places.

58,000,000 km = 5.8 × 10^7 km

Practice

Express 6,590,000 in scientific notation.

Significant Figures

Focus Measure the length of a paper clip using two different rulers. Use one ruler that is less precise than the other. Compare the two measurements. Ask: **Which measurement is more precise?** (*The ruler with the smallest units will give the more precise measurement.*)

Teach Give students the opportunity to take measurements of an object using tools with different precision. Encourage students to add and subtract their measurements, making sure that they round the answers to reflect the precision of the instruments. Go over the example for significant digits. Check for understanding by asking: **How many significant digits are in the number 324,000?** (*Three*) **In the number 5,901?** (*Four*) **In the number 0.706?** (*Three*) If students need additional practice, create a worksheet with problems in multiplying and dividing numbers with various significant digits.

Practice

26.4 m + 8.37 m = 34.77 m
This answer should be rounded to 34.8 m because the least precise measurement has only one digit after the decimal. This number is rounded up to 8 because the last digit is more than 5.

Scientific Notation

Focus Write a very large number on the board, such as 100 million, using all the zeros. Then, write the number using scientific notation. Ask: **Why do you think scientists prefer to write very large numbers using scientific notation?** (*Possible answers include that it is easier to do calculations, convert units, and make comparisons with other numbers.*)

Teach Go over the examples, and ask: **In the second example, which numbers are the factors?** (*5.8 and 10^7*) **Which number is the exponent?** (*^{7}*) Explain that very small numbers have a negative exponent because the decimal point is moved to the right to produce the first factor. For example, 0.00000628 is equal to 6.28×10^{-6}.

Practice

$6,590,000 = 6.59 \times 10^6$

Reading Comprehension Skills

Students can refer to this part of the Skills Handbook whenever they need to review a reading skill. You can use the activities provided here to teach or reinforce these skills.

Learning From Science Textbooks

Reading in a content area presents challenges different from those encountered when reading fiction. Science texts often have more new vocabulary and more unfamiliar concepts that place greater emphasis on inferential reasoning. Students who can apply reading skills and information-organizing strategies will be more successful in reading and understanding a science textbook.

Activity

Turn with students to the first page of any section. Walk through the Reading Preview with students, showing them the Key Concepts that provide a guiding set of questions that students can answer from the text. Next, point out the Key Terms list, which highlights the science vocabulary. Last, have students find the Target Reading Skill with graphic organizer. Make the connection for students to the help in this Skills Handbook.

All in One Teaching Resources

• Target Reading Skills Handbook

Building Vocabulary

Focus Explain to students that knowing the definitions of key concept words can help them understand what they read.

Teach List on the board strategies to learn the definitions of new terms. Also solicit from students strategies that work for them —drawing a picture for the term, acting it out, or using it in conversation. Challenge students to choose a new strategy to learn the Key Terms in your next section.

Using Prior Knowledge

Focus Explain to students that using prior knowledge helps connect what they already know to what they are about to read.

Teach Point out that prior knowledge might not be accurate because memories have faded or perspectives have changed. Encourage students to ask questions

Reading Comprehension Skills

Your textbook is an important source of science information. As you read your science textbook, you will find that the book has been written to assist you in understanding the science concepts.

Learning From Science Textbooks

As you study science in school, you will learn science concepts in a variety of ways. Sometimes you will do interesting activities and experiments to explore science ideas. To fully understand what you observe in experiments and activities, you will need to read your science textbook. To help you read, some of the important ideas are highlighted so that you can easily recognize what they are. In addition, a target reading skill in each section will help you understand what you read.

By using the target reading skills, you will improve your reading comprehension—that is, you will improve your ability to understand what you read. As you learn science, you will build knowledge that will help you understand even more of what you read. This knowledge will help you learn about all the topics presented in this textbook.

And—guess what?—these reading skills can be useful whenever you are reading. Reading to learn is important for your entire life. You have an opportunity to begin that process now.

The target reading skills that will improve your reading comprehension are described below.

Building Vocabulary

To understand the science concepts taught in this textbook, you need to remember the meanings of the Key Terms. One strategy consists of writing the definitions of these terms in your own words. You can also practice using the terms in sentences and make lists of words or phrases you associate with each term.

Using Prior Knowledge

Your prior knowledge is what you already know before you begin to read about a topic. Building on what you already know gives you a head start on learning new information. Before you begin a new assignment, think about what you know. You might page through your reading assignment, looking at the headings and the visuals to spark your memory. You can list what you know in the graphic organizer provided in the section opener. Then, as you read, consider questions like the ones below to connect what you learn to what you already know.

• How does what you learn relate to what you know?

• How did something you already know help you learn something new?

• Did your original ideas agree with what you have just learned? If not, how would you revise your original ideas?

Asking Questions

Asking yourself questions is an excellent way to focus on and remember new information in your textbook. You can learn how to ask good questions.

One way is to turn the text headings into questions. Then your questions can guide you to identify and remember the important information as you read. Look at these examples:

Heading: Using Seismographic Data
Question: How are seismographic data used?
Heading: Kinds of Faults
Question: What are the kinds of faults?

to resolve discrepancies between their prior knowledge and what they have learned.

Asking Questions

Focus Demonstrate to students how to change a text heading into a question to help them anticipate the concepts, facts, and events they will read about.

Teach Encourage students to use this reading skill for the next section they read. Instruct them to turn the text headings into questions. Also challenge students to write at least four *what, how, why, who, when,* or *where* questions. Then, have students evaluate the skill. Ask: **Did asking questions about the text help you focus on the reading and remember what you read?** (*Answers will vary, but encourage honesty.*) If this reading skill didn't help, challenge them to assess why not.

You do not have to limit your questions to the text headings. Ask questions about anything that you need to clarify or that will help you understand the content. *What* and *how* are probably the most common question words, but you may also ask *why, who, when,* or *where* questions. Here is an example:

Properties of Waves

Question	Answer
What is amplitude?	Amplitude is . . .

Previewing Visuals

Visuals are photographs, graphs, tables, diagrams, and illustrations. Visuals, such as this diagram of a normal fault, contain important information. Look at visuals and their captions before you read. This will help you prepare for what you will be reading about.

Often you will be asked what you want to learn about a visual. For example, after you look at the normal fault diagram, you might ask: What is the movement along a normal fault? Questions about visuals give you a purpose for reading—to answer your questions. Previewing visuals also helps you see what you already know.

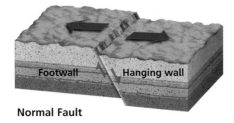

Footwall   Hanging wall

Normal Fault

Outlining

An outline shows the relationship between main ideas and supporting ideas. An outline has a formal structure. You write the main ideas, called topics, next to Roman numerals. The supporting ideas, sometimes called subtopics, are written under the main ideas and labeled A, B, C, and so on. An outline looks like this:

Technology and Society

I. Technology through history

II. The impact of technology on society

   A.

   B.

When you have completed an outline like this, you can see at a glance the structure of the section. You can use this outline as a study tool.

Identifying Main Ideas

When you are reading, it is important to try to understand the ideas and concepts that are in a passage. As you read science material, you will recognize that each paragraph has a lot of information and detail. Good readers try to identify the most important—or biggest—idea in every paragraph or section. That's the main idea. The other information in the paragraph supports or further explains the main idea.

Sometimes main ideas are stated directly. In this book, some main ideas are identified for you as key concepts. These are printed in bold-face type. However, you must identify other main ideas yourself. In order to do this, you must identify all the ideas within a paragraph or section. Then ask yourself which idea is big enough to include all the other ideas.

Skills Handbook ◆ 175

Previewing Visuals

Focus Explain to students that looking at the visuals before reading will help them activate prior knowledge and predict what they are about to read.

Teach Assign a section for students to preview the visuals. First, instruct them to write a sentence describing what the section will be about. Then, encourage them to write one or two questions for each visual to give purpose to their reading. Also have them list any prior knowledge about the subject.

Outlining

Focus Explain that using an outline format helps organize information by main topic, subtopic, and details.

Teach Choose a section in the book, and demonstrate how to make an outline for it. Make sure students understand the structure of the outline by asking: **Is this a topic or a subtopic? Where does this information go in the outline? Would I write this heading next to a Roman numeral or a capital letter?** *(Answers depend on the section being outlined.)* Also show them how to indent and add details to the outline using numerals and lowercase letters.

Identifying Main Ideas

Focus Explain that identifying main ideas and details helps sort the facts from the information into groups. Each group can have a main topic, subtopics, and details.

Teach Tell students that paragraphs are often written so that the main idea is in the first or second sentence, or in the last sentence. Assign students a page in the book. Instruct them to write the main idea for each paragraph on that page. If students have difficulty finding the main idea, suggest that they list all of the ideas given in the paragraph, and then choose the idea that is big enough to include all the others.

Comparing and Contrasting

Focus Explain that comparing and contrasting information shows how concepts, facts, and events are similar or different. The results of the comparison can have importance.

Teach Point out that Venn diagrams work best when comparing two things. To compare more than two things, students should use a compare/contrast table. Have students make a Venn diagram or compare/contrast table using two or more different sports or other activities, such as playing musical instruments. Emphasize that students should select characteristics that highlight the similarities and differences in the activities.

Sequencing

Focus Tell students that organizing information from beginning to end will help them understand a step-by-step process.

Teach Encourage students to create a flowchart to show the things they did this morning to get ready for school. Remind students that a flowchart should show the correct order in which events occur. *(A typical flowchart might include: got up ➤ took a shower ➤ got dressed ➤ ate breakfast ➤ brushed teeth ➤ gathered books and homework ➤ put on jacket.)* Then explain that a cycle diagram shows a sequence of events that is continuous. Challenge students to create a cycle diagram that shows how the weather changes with the seasons where they live. *(Most cycle diagrams will include four steps, one for each season.)*

Comparing and Contrasting

When you compare and contrast, you examine the similarities and differences between things. You can compare and contrast in a Venn diagram or in a table. Your completed diagram or table shows you how the items are alike and how they are different.

Venn Diagram A Venn diagram consists of two overlapping circles. In the space where the circles overlap, you write the characteristics that the two items have in common. In one of the circles outside the area of overlap, you write the differing features or characteristics of one of the items. In the other circle outside the area of overlap, you write the differing characteristics of the other item.

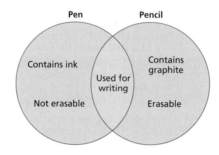

Table In a compare/contrast table, you list the items to be compared across the top of the table. Then list the characteristics or features to be compared in the left column. Complete the table by filling in information about each characteristic or feature.

Blood Vessel	Function	Structure of Wall
Artery	Carries blood away from heart	
Capillary		
Vein		

Sequencing

A sequence is the order in which a series of events occurs. Recognizing and remembering the sequence of events is important to understanding many processes in science. Sometimes the text uses words like *first, next, during,* and *after* to signal a sequence. A flowchart or a cycle diagram can help you visualize a sequence.

Flowchart To make a flowchart, write a brief description of each step or event in a box. Place the boxes in order, with the first event at the top of the page. Then draw an arrow to connect each step or event to the next.

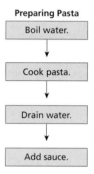

Cycle Diagram A cycle diagram shows a sequence that is continuous, or cyclical. A continuous sequence does not have an end because when the final event is over, the first event begins again. To create a cycle diagram, write the starting event in a box placed at the top of a page in the center. Then, moving in a clockwise direction around an imaginary circle, write each event in a box in its proper sequence. Draw arrows that connect each event to the one that occurs next, forming a continuous circle.

Identifying Supporting Evidence

A hypothesis is a possible explanation for observations made by scientists or an answer to a scientific question. A hypothesis is tested over and over again. The tests may produce evidence that supports the hypothesis. When enough supporting evidence is collected, a hypothesis may become a theory.

Identifying the supporting evidence for a hypothesis or theory can help you understand the hypothesis or theory. Evidence consists of facts—information whose accuracy can be confirmed by testing or observation.

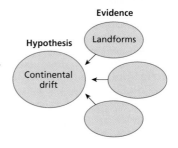

Relating Cause and Effect

Identifying causes and effects helps you understand relationships among events. A cause makes something happen. An effect is what happens. When you recognize that one event causes another, you are relating cause and effect. Words like *cause, because, effect, affect,* and *result* often signal a cause or an effect.

Sometimes an effect can have more than one cause, or a cause can produce several effects. For example, car exhaust and smoke from industrial plants are two causes of air pollution. Some effects of air pollution include breathing difficulties for some people, death of plants along some highways, and damage to some building surfaces.

Science involves many cause-and-effect relationships. Seeing and understanding these relationships helps you understand science processes.

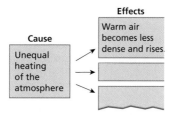

Concept Mapping

Concept maps are useful tools for organizing information on any topic. A concept map begins with a main idea or core concept and shows how the idea can be subdivided into related subconcepts or smaller ideas. In this way, relationships between concepts become clearer and easier to understand.

You construct a concept map by placing concepts (usually nouns) in ovals and connecting them with linking words. The biggest concept or idea is placed in an oval at the top of the map. Related concepts are arranged in ovals below the big idea. The linking words are often verbs and verb phrases and are written on the lines that connect the ovals.

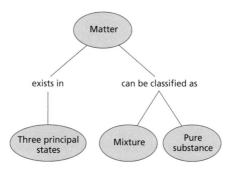

Identifying Supporting Evidence

Focus Explain to students that identifying the supporting evidence will help them to understand the relationship between the facts and the hypothesis.

Teach Remind students that a hypothesis is neither right nor wrong, but it is either supported or not supported by the evidence from testing or observation. If evidence is found that does not support a hypothesis, the hypothesis can be changed to accommodate the new evidence, or it can be dropped.

Relating Cause and Effect

Focus Explain to students that cause is the reason for what happens. The effect is what happens in response to the cause. Relating cause and effect helps students relate the reason for what happens to what happens as a result.

Teach Emphasize that not all events that occur together have a cause-and-effect relationship. For example, tell students that you went to the grocery store and your car stalled. Ask: **Is there a cause-and-effect relationship in this situation? Explain.** (*No. Going to the grocery store could not cause a car to stall. There must be another cause to make the car stall.*)

Concept Mapping

Focus Elicit from students how a map shows the relationship of one geographic area to another. Connect this idea to how a concept map shows the relationship between terms and concepts.

Teach Challenge students to make a concept map with at least three levels of concepts to organize information about types of transportation. All students should start with the phrase *Types of transportation* at the top of the concept map. After that point, their concepts may vary. (*For example, some students might place* private transportation *and* public transportation *at the next level, while other students might choose* human-powered *and* gas-powered.) Make sure students connect the concepts with linking words.

K ● 177

- Complete student edition
- Video and audio
- Simulations and activities
- Section and chapter activities

Laboratory Safety

Laboratory safety is an essential element of a successful science class. Students need to understand exactly what is safe and unsafe behavior and what the rationale is behind each safety rule.

All in One Teaching Resources

- Laboratory Safety Teacher Notes
- Laboratory Safety Rules
- Laboratory Safety Symbols
- Laboratory Safety Contract

General Precautions

- Post safety rules in the classroom, and review them regularly with students before beginning every science activity.
- Familiarize yourself with the safety procedures for each activity before introducing it to your students.
- For open-ended activities like Chapter Projects, have students submit their procedures or design plans in writing and check them for safety considerations.
- Always act as an exemplary role model by displaying safe behavior.
- Know how to use safety equipment, such as fire extinguishers and fire blankets, and always have it accessible.
- Have students practice leaving the classroom quickly and orderly to prepare them for emergencies.
- Explain to students how to use the intercom or other available means of communication to get help during an emergency.
- Never leave students unattended while they are engaged in science activities.
- Provide enough space for students to safely carry out science activities.
- Instruct students to report all accidents and injuries to you immediately.

Safety Symbols

These symbols warn of possible dangers in the laboratory and remind you to work carefully.

 Safety Goggles Wear safety goggles to protect your eyes in any activity involving chemicals, flames or heating, or glassware.

 Lab Apron Wear a laboratory apron to protect your skin and clothing from damage.

 Breakage Handle breakable materials, such as glassware, with care. Do not touch broken glassware.

 Heat-Resistant Gloves Use an oven mitt or other hand protection when handling hot materials such as hot plates or hot glassware.

 Plastic Gloves Wear disposable plastic gloves when working with harmful chemicals and organisms. Keep your hands away from your face, and dispose of the gloves according to your teacher's instructions.

 Heating Use a clamp or tongs to pick up hot glassware. Do not touch hot objects with your bare hands.

 Flames Before you work with flames, tie back loose hair and clothing. Follow instructions from your teacher about lighting and extinguishing flames.

 No Flames When using flammable materials, make sure there are no flames, sparks, or other exposed heat sources present.

 Corrosive Chemical Avoid getting acid or other corrosive chemicals on your skin or clothing or in your eyes. Do not inhale the vapors. Wash your hands after the activity.

 Poison Do not let any poisonous chemical come into contact with your skin, and do not inhale its vapors. Wash your hands when you are finished with the activity.

 Fumes Work in a ventilated area when harmful vapors may be involved. Avoid inhaling vapors directly. Only test an odor when directed to do so by your teacher, and use a wafting motion to direct the vapor toward your nose.

 Sharp Object Scissors, scalpels, knives, needles, pins, and tacks can cut your skin. Always direct a sharp edge or point away from yourself and others.

 Animal Safety Treat live or preserved animals or animal parts with care to avoid harming the animals or yourself. Wash your hands when you are finished with the activity.

 Plant Safety Handle plants only as directed by your teacher. If you are allergic to certain plants, tell your teacher; do not do an activity involving those plants. Avoid touching harmful plants such as poison ivy. Wash your hands when you are finished with the activity.

 Electric Shock To avoid electric shock, never use electrical equipment around water, or when the equipment is wet or your hands are wet. Be sure cords are untangled and cannot trip anyone. Unplug equipment not in use.

 Physical Safety When an experiment involves physical activity, avoid injuring yourself or others. Alert your teacher if there is any reason you should not participate.

 Disposal Dispose of chemicals and other laboratory materials safely. Follow the instructions from your teacher.

 Hand Washing Wash your hands thoroughly when finished with the activity. Use antibacterial soap and warm water. Rinse well.

⚠ **General Safety Awareness** When this symbol appears, follow the instructions provided. When you are asked to develop your own procedure in a lab, have your teacher approve your plan before you go further.

End-of-Experiment Rules

- Always have students use warm water and soap for washing their hands.

Heating and Fire Safety

- No flammable substances should be in use around hot plates, light bulbs, or open flames.
- Test tubes should be heated only in water baths.

- Students should be permitted to strike matches to light candles or burners *only* with strict supervision. When possible, you should light the flames, especially when working with younger students.
- Be sure to have proper ventilation when fumes are produced during a procedure.
- All electrical equipment used in the lab should have GFI (Ground Fault Interrupter) switches.

Science Safety Rules

General Precautions

Follow all instructions. Never perform activities without the approval and supervision of your teacher. Do not engage in horseplay. Never eat or drink in the laboratory. Keep work areas clean and uncluttered.

Dress Code

Wear safety goggles whenever you work with chemicals, glassware, heat sources such as burners, or any substance that might get into your eyes. If you wear contact lenses, notify your teacher.

Wear a lab apron or coat whenever you work with corrosive chemicals or substances that can stain. Wear disposable plastic gloves when working with organisms and harmful chemicals. Tie back long hair. Remove or tie back any article of clothing or jewelry that can hang down and touch chemicals, flames, or equipment. Roll up long sleeves. Never wear open shoes or sandals.

First Aid

Report all accidents, injuries, or fires to your teacher, no matter how minor. Be aware of the location of the first-aid kit, emergency equipment such as the fire extinguisher and fire blanket, and the nearest telephone. Know whom to contact in an emergency.

Heating and Fire Safety

Keep all combustible materials away from flames. When heating a substance in a test tube, make sure that the mouth of the tube is not pointed at you or anyone else. Never heat a liquid in a closed container. Use an oven mitt to pick up a container that has been heated.

Using Chemicals Safely

Never put your face near the mouth of a container that holds chemicals. Never touch, taste, or smell a chemical unless your teacher tells you to.

Use only those chemicals needed in the activity. Keep all containers closed when chemicals are not being used. Pour all chemicals over the sink or a container, not over your work surface. Dispose of excess chemicals as instructed by your teacher.

Be extra careful when working with acids or bases. When mixing an acid and water, always pour the water into the container first and then add the acid to the water. Never pour water into an acid. Wash chemical spills and splashes immediately with plenty of water.

Using Glassware Safely

If glassware is broken or chipped, notify your teacher immediately. Never handle broken or chipped glass with your bare hands.

Never force glass tubing or thermometers into a rubber stopper or rubber tubing. Have your teacher insert the glass tubing or thermometer if required for an activity.

Using Sharp Instruments

Handle sharp instruments with extreme care. Never cut material toward you; cut away from you.

Animal and Plant Safety

Never perform experiments that cause pain, discomfort, or harm to animals. Only handle animals if absolutely necessary. If you know that you are allergic to certain plants, molds, or animals, tell your teacher before doing an activity in which these are used. Wash your hands thoroughly after any activity involving animals, animal parts, plants, plant parts, or soil.

During field work, wear long pants, long sleeves, socks, and closed shoes. Avoid poisonous plants and fungi as well as plants with thorns.

End-of-Experiment Rules

Unplug all electrical equipment. Clean up your work area. Dispose of waste materials as instructed by your teacher. Wash your hands after every experiment.

Appendix A ◆ 179

Handling Organisms Safely

- In an activity where students are directed to taste something, be sure to store the material in clean, *nonscience* containers. Distribute the material to students in *new* plastic or paper dispensables, which should be discarded after the tasting. Tasting or eating should never be done in a lab classroom.

- When growing bacterial cultures, use only disposable petri dishes. After streaking, the dishes should be sealed and not opened again by students. After the lab, students should return the unopened dishes to you.

- Two methods are recommended for the safe disposal of bacterial cultures. *First method:* Autoclave the petri dishes and discard them without opening. *Second method:* If no autoclave is available, carefully open the dishes (never have a student do this), pour full-strength bleach into the dishes, and let them stand for a day. Then pour the bleach from the petri dishes down a drain, and flush the drain with lots of water. Tape the petri dishes back together, and place them in a sealed plastic bag. Wrap the plastic bag with a brown paper bag or newspaper, and tape securely. Throw the sealed package in the trash. Thoroughly disinfect the work area with bleach.

- To grow mold, use a new, sealable plastic bag that is two to three times larger than the material to be placed inside. Seal the bag and tape it shut. After the bag is sealed, students should not open it. To dispose of the bag and mold culture, make a small cut near an edge of the bag, and cook the bag in a microwave oven on a high setting for at least one minute. Discard the bag according to local ordinance, usually in the trash.

- Students should wear disposable nitrile, latex, or food-handling gloves when handling live animals or nonliving specimens.

Using Glassware Safely

- Use plastic containers, graduated cylinders, and beakers whenever possible. If using glass, students should wear safety goggles.
- Use only nonmercury thermometers with anti-roll protectors.

Using Chemicals Safely

- When students use both chemicals and microscopes in one activity, microscopes should be in a separate part of the room from the chemicals so that when students remove their goggles to use the microscopes, their eyes are not at risk.

The laboratory balance is an important tool in scientific investigations. You can use a balance to determine the masses of materials that you study or experiment with in the laboratory.

Different kinds of balances are used in the laboratory. One kind of balance is the triple-beam balance. The balance that you may use in your science class is probably similar to the balance illustrated in this Appendix. To use the balance properly, you should learn the name, location, and function of each part of the balance you are using. What kind of balance do you have in your science class?

The Triple-Beam Balance

The triple-beam balance is a single-pan balance with three beams calibrated in grams. The back, or 100-gram, beam is divided into ten units of 10 grams each. The middle, or 500-gram, beam is divided into five units of 100 grams each. The front, or 10-gram, beam is divided into ten major units of 1 gram each. Each of these units is further divided into units of 0.1 gram. What is the largest mass you could find with a triple-beam balance?

The following procedure can be used to find the mass of an object with a triple-beam balance:

1. Place the object on the pan.

2. Move the rider on the middle beam notch by notch until the horizontal pointer drops below zero. Move the rider back one notch.

3. Move the rider on the back beam notch by notch until the pointer again drops below zero. Move the rider back one notch.

4. Slowly slide the rider along the front beam until the pointer stops at the zero point.

5. The mass of the object is equal to the sum of the readings on the three beams.

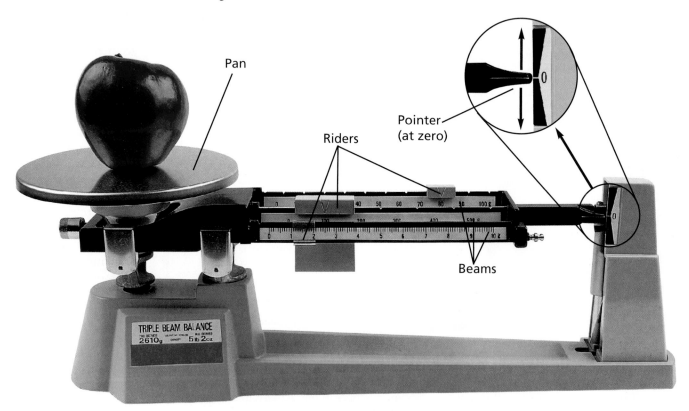

Triple-Beam Balance

Name	Symbol	Atomic Number	Atomic Mass[†]
Actinium	Ac	89	(227)
Aluminum	Al	13	26.982
Americium	Am	95	(243)
Antimony	Sb	51	121.75
Argon	Ar	18	39.948
Arsenic	As	33	74.922
Astatine	At	85	(210)
Barium	Ba	56	137.33
Berkelium	Bk	97	(247)
Beryllium	Be	4	9.0122
Bismuth	Bi	83	208.98
Bohrium	Bh	107	(264)
Boron	B	5	10.81
Bromine	Br	35	79.904
Cadmium	Cd	48	112.41
Calcium	Ca	20	40.08
Californium	Cf	98	(251)
Carbon	C	6	12.011
Cerium	Ce	58	140.12
Cesium	Cs	55	132.91
Chlorine	Cl	17	35.453
Chromium	Cr	24	51.996
Cobalt	Co	27	58.933
Copper	Cu	29	63.546
Curium	Cm	96	(247)
Darmstadtium	Ds	110	(269)
Dubnium	Db	105	(262)
Dysprosium	Dy	66	162.50
Einsteinium	Es	99	(252)
Erbium	Er	68	167.26
Europium	Eu	63	151.96
Fermium	Fm	100	(257)
Fluorine	F	9	18.998
Francium	Fr	87	(223)
Gadolinium	Gd	64	157.25
Gallium	Ga	31	69.72
Germanium	Ge	32	72.59
Gold	Au	79	196.97
Hafnium	Hf	72	178.49
Hassium	Hs	108	(265)
Helium	He	2	4.0026
Holmium	Ho	67	164.93
Hydrogen	H	1	1.0079
Indium	In	49	114.82
Iodine	I	53	126.90
Iridium	Ir	77	192.22
Iron	Fe	26	55.847
Krypton	Kr	36	83.80
Lanthanum	La	57	138.91
Lawrencium	Lr	103	(262)
Lead	Pb	82	207.2
Lithium	Li	3	6.941
Lutetium	Lu	71	174.97
Magnesium	Mg	12	24.305
Manganese	Mn	25	54.938
Meitnerium	Mt	109	(268)
Mendelevium	Md	101	(258)

Name	Symbol	Atomic Number	Atomic Mass[†]
Mercury	Hg	80	200.59
Molybdenum	Mo	42	95.94
Neodymium	Nd	60	144.24
Neon	Ne	10	20.179
Neptunium	Np	93	(237)
Nickel	Ni	28	58.71
Niobium	Nb	41	92.906
Nitrogen	N	7	14.007
Nobelium	No	102	(259)
Osmium	Os	76	190.2
Oxygen	O	8	15.999
Palladium	Pd	46	106.4
Phosphorus	P	15	30.974
Platinum	Pt	78	195.09
Plutonium	Pu	94	(244)
Polonium	Po	84	(209)
Potassium	K	19	39.098
Praseodymium	Pr	59	140.91
Promethium	Pm	61	(145)
Protactinium	Pa	91	231.04
Radium	Ra	88	(226)
Radon	Rn	86	(222)
Rhenium	Re	75	186.21
Rhodium	Rh	45	102.91
Rubidium	Rb	37	85.468
Ruthenium	Ru	44	101.07
Rutherfordium	Rf	104	(261)
Samarium	Sm	62	150.4
Scandium	Sc	21	44.956
Seaborgium	Sg	106	(263)
Selenium	Se	34	78.96
Silicon	Si	14	28.086
Silver	Ag	47	107.87
Sodium	Na	11	22.990
Strontium	Sr	38	87.62
Sulfur	S	16	32.06
Tantalum	Ta	73	180.95
Technetium	Tc	43	(98)
Tellurium	Te	52	127.60
Terbium	Tb	65	158.93
Thallium	Tl	81	204.37
Thorium	Th	90	232.04
Thulium	Tm	69	168.93
Tin	Sn	50	118.69
Titanium	Ti	22	47.90
Tungsten	W	74	183.85
Ununbium	Uub	112	(277)
Ununquadium	Uuq	114	*
Unununium	Uuu	111	(272)
Uranium	U	92	238.03
Vanadium	V	23	50.941
Xenon	Xe	54	131.30
Ytterbium	Yb	70	173.04
Yttrium	Y	39	88.906
Zinc	Zn	30	65.38
Zirconium	Zr	40	91.22

[†]Numbers in parentheses give the mass number of the most stable isotope.

*Newly discovered

Key

C	Solid
Br	Liquid
H	Gas
Tc	Not found in nature

1

1
H
Hydrogen
1.0079

	1	**2**									
			3	**4**	**5**	**6**	**7**	**8**	**9**		

2
3 **Li** Lithium 6.941
4 **Be** Beryllium 9.0122

3
11 **Na** Sodium 22.990
12 **Mg** Magnesium 24.305

4
19 **K** Potassium 39.098
20 **Ca** Calcium 40.08
21 **Sc** Scandium 44.956
22 **Ti** Titanium 47.90
23 **V** Vanadium 50.941
24 **Cr** Chromium 51.996
25 **Mn** Manganese 54.938
26 **Fe** Iron 55.847
27 **Co** Cobalt 58.933

5
37 **Rb** Rubidium 85.468
38 **Sr** Strontium 87.62
39 **Y** Yttrium 88.906
40 **Zr** Zirconium 91.22
41 **Nb** Niobium 92.906
42 **Mo** Molybdenum 95.94
43 **Tc** Technetium (98)
44 **Ru** Ruthenium 101.07
45 **Rh** Rhodium 102.91

6
55 **Cs** Cesium 132.91
56 **Ba** Barium 137.33
71 **Lu** Lutetium 174.97
72 **Hf** Hafnium 178.49
73 **Ta** Tantalum 180.95
74 **W** Tungsten 183.85
75 **Re** Rhenium 186.21
76 **Os** Osmium 190.2
77 **Ir** Iridium 192.22

7
87 **Fr** Francium (223)
88 **Ra** Radium (226)
103 **Lr** Lawrencium (262)
104 **Rf** Rutherfordium (261)
105 **Db** Dubnium (262)
106 **Sg** Seaborgium (263)
107 **Bh** Bohrium (264)
108 **Hs** Hassium (265)
109 **Mt** Meitnerium (268)

Lanthanides

57 **La** Lanthanum 138.91	58 **Ce** Cerium 140.12	59 **Pr** Praseodymium 140.91	60 **Nd** Neodymium 144.24	61 **Pm** Promethium (145)	62 **Sm** Samarium 150.4

Actinides

89 **Ac** Actinium (227)	90 **Th** Thorium 232.04	91 **Pa** Protactinium 231.04	92 **U** Uranium 238.03	93 **Np** Neptunium (237)	94 **Pu** Plutonium (244)

Key

Metal

Metalloid

Nonmetal

Properties not established

					18
					2 **He** Helium 4.0026

13	**14**	**15**	**16**	**17**	
5 **B** Boron 10.81	6 **C** Carbon 12.011	7 **N** Nitrogen 14.007	8 **O** Oxygen 15.999	9 **F** Fluorine 18.998	10 **Ne** Neon 20.179
13 **Al** Aluminum 26.982	14 **Si** Silicon 28.086	15 **P** Phosphorus 30.974	16 **S** Sulfur 32.06	17 **Cl** Chlorine 35.453	18 **Ar** Argon 39.948

10	**11**	**12**						
28 **Ni** Nickel 58.71	29 **Cu** Copper 63.546	30 **Zn** Zinc 65.38	31 **Ga** Gallium 69.72	32 **Ge** Germanium 72.59	33 **As** Arsenic 74.922	34 **Se** Selenium 78.96	35 **Br** Bromine 79.904	36 **Kr** Krypton 83.80
46 **Pd** Palladium 106.4	47 **Ag** Silver 107.87	48 **Cd** Cadmium 112.41	49 **In** Indium 114.82	50 **Sn** Tin 118.69	51 **Sb** Antimony 121.75	52 **Te** Tellurium 127.60	53 **I** Iodine 126.90	54 **Xe** Xenon 131.30
78 **Pt** Platinum 195.09	79 **Au** Gold 196.97	80 **Hg** Mercury 200.59	81 **Tl** Thallium 204.37	82 **Pb** Lead 207.2	83 **Bi** Bismuth 208.98	84 **Po** Polonium (209)	85 **At** Astatine (210)	86 **Rn** Radon (222)
110 **Ds** Darmstadtium (269)	111 ***Uuu** Unununium (272)	112 ***Uub** Ununbium (277)		114 ***Uuq** Ununquadium				

*Name not officially assigned
(Atomic masses in parentheses are those of the most stable isotope.)

63 **Eu** Europium 151.96	64 **Gd** Gadolinium 157.25	65 **Tb** Terbium 158.93	66 **Dy** Dysprosium 162.50	67 **Ho** Holmium 164.93	68 **Er** Erbium 167.26	69 **Tm** Thulium 168.93	70 **Yb** Ytterbium 173.04

95 **Am** Americium (243)	96 **Cm** Curium (247)	97 **Bk** Berkelium (247)	98 **Cf** Californium (251)	99 **Es** Einsteinium (252)	100 **Fm** Fermium (257)	101 **Md** Mendelevium (258)	102 **No** Nobelium (259)

English and Spanish Glossary

A

alkali metal An element in Group 1 of the periodic table. (p. 90)
metal alcalino Elemento en el Grupo 1 de la tabla periódica.

alkaline earth metal An element in Group 2 of the periodic table. (p. 91)
metal alcalinotérreo Elemento en el Grupo 2 de la tabla periódica.

alloy A mixture of two or more elements, one of which is a metal. (pp. 92, 130)
aleación Mezcla de dos o más elementos, uno de los cuales es el metal.

alpha particle A type of nuclear radiation consisting of two protons and two neutrons. (p. 141)
partícula alfa Tipo de radiación nuclear que consiste de dos protones y dos neutrones.

amorphous solid A solid made up of particles that are not arranged in a regular pattern. (p. 44)
sólido amorfo Sólido constituido por partículas que no están dispuestas en un patrón regular.

atom The basic particle from which all elements are made. (p. 11)
átomo Partícula básica de la que están formados todos los elementos.

atomic mass The average mass of all the isotopes of an element. (p. 81)
masa atómica Promedio de la masa de todos los isótopos de un elemento.

atomic number The number of protons in the nucleus of an atom. (p. 78)
número atómico Número de protones en el núcleo de un átomo.

B

beta particle A fast-moving electron that is given off as nuclear radiation. (p. 141)
partícula beta Electrón de rápido movimiento que se produce como radiación nuclear.

boiling The process that occurs when vaporization takes place inside a liquid as well as on the surface. (p. 51)
ebullición Proceso que se da cuando la vaporización se efectúa dentro de un líquido, además de en la superficie.

boiling point The temperature at which a substance changes from a liquid to a gas; the same as the condensation point, or temperature at which a gas changes to a liquid. (p. 51)
punto de ebullición Temperatura a la que una sustancia cambia de líquido a gas; es lo mismo que el punto de condensación (la temperatura a la que un gas se vuelve líquido).

Boyle's law A principle that describes the relationship between the pressure and volume of a gas at constant temperature. (p. 58)
ley de Boyle Principio que describe la relación entre la presión y el volumen de un gas a temperatura constante.

C

ceramic A hard, crystalline solid made by heating clay and other mineral materials to high temperatures. (p. 135)
cerámica Sólido cristalino duro hecho al calentar a altas temperaturas arcilla y otros materiales minerales.

Charles's law A principle that describes the relationship between the temperature and volume of a gas at constant pressure. (p. 60)
ley de Charles Principio que describe la relación entre la temperatura y el volumen de un gas a presión constante.

chemical bond The force that holds two atoms together. (p. 11)
enlace químico Fuerza que mantiene juntos a dos átomos.

chemical change A change in which one or more substances combine or break apart to form new substances. (p. 24)
cambio químico Cambio en el cual una o más sustancias se combinan o se rompen para formar nuevas sustancias.

chemical energy A form of potential energy that is stored in chemical bonds between atoms. (p. 32)
energía química Forma de energía potencial almacenada en los enlaces químicos entre átomos.

chemical formula A formula that gives the elements in a compound and the ratio of atoms. (p. 12)
fórmula química Fórmula que da los elementos en un compuesto y la razón de los átomos.

chemical property A characteristic of a pure substance that describes its ability to change into a different substance. (p. 9)
propiedad química Característica de una sustancia pura que describe su capacidad para cambiar a una sustancia diferente.

chemical symbol A one- or two-letter representation of an element. (p. 83)
símbolo químico Representación con una o dos letras de un elemento.

chemistry The study of the properties of matter and how matter changes. (p. 7)
química Estudio de las propiedades de la materia y de cómo cambia.

composite A combination of two or more substances that creates a new material with different properties. (p. 122)
compuesto Combinación de dos o más sustancias que crea un nuevo material con propiedades diferentes.

compound A pure substance made of two or more elements chemically combined. (p. 12)
compuesto Sustancia pura formada por dos o más elementos combinados químicamente.

condensation The change of state from a gas to a liquid. (p. 52)
condensación Cambio del estado gaseoso a líquido.

conductivity The ability of an object to transfer heat or electricity to another object. (p. 89)
conductividad Capacidad de un objeto para transferir calor o electricidad a otro objeto.

corrosion The gradual wearing away of a metal element due to a chemical reaction. (p. 89)
corrosión Desgaste gradual de un elemento metal debido a una reacción química.

crystalline solid A solid that is made up of crystals in which particles are arranged in a regular, repeating pattern. (p. 44)
sólido cristalino Sólido constituido por cristales en los que las partículas están dispuestas en un patrón regular repetitivo.

 D

density The measurement of how much mass of a substance is contained in a given volume. (p. 19)
densidad Medida de cuánta masa de una sustancia hay contenida en un volumen dado.

diatomic molecule A molecule consisting of two atoms. (p. 101)
molécula diatómica Molécula que tiene dos átomos.

directly proportional A term used to describe the relationship between two variables whose graph is a straight line passing through the point (0, 0). (p. 64)
directamente proporcional Término empleado para describir la relación entre dos variables cuya gráfica forma una línea recta que pasa por el punto (0, 0).

ductile A term used to describe a material that can be pulled out into a long wire. (p. 88)
dúctil Término usado para describir un material que se puede estirar hasta convertirlo en un alambre largo.

E

electrical energy The energy of electrically charged particles moving from one place to another. (p. 32)
energía eléctrica Energía de las partículas cargadas eléctricamente cuando se mueven de un lugar a otro.

electrode A metal strip that conducts electricity. (p. 32)
electrodo Tira de metal que conduce la electricidad.

electromagnetic energy A form of energy that travels through space as waves. (p. 32)
energía electromagnética Forma de energía que viaja a través del espacio en forma de ondas.

electron A tiny, negatively charged particle that moves around the nucleus of an atom. (p. 75)
electrón Partícula diminuta cargada negativamente, que se mueve alrededor del núcleo de un átomo.

element A pure substance that cannot be broken down into other substances by chemical or physical means. (p. 10)
elemento Sustancia pura que no se puede descomponer en otras sustancias por medios químicos o físicos.

endothermic change A change in which energy is taken in. (p. 26)
cambio endotérmico Cambio en el que se absorbe energía.

energy The ability to do work or cause change. (p. 26)
energía Capacidad de realizar trabajo o causar un cambio.

evaporation The process that occurs when vaporization takes place only on the surface of a liquid. (p. 50)
evaporación Proceso que se da cuando la vaporización se efectúa únicamente en la superficie de un líquido.

exothermic change A change in which energy is given off. (p. 26)
cambio exotérmico Cambio en el que se libera energía.

fluid Any substance that can flow. (p. 45)
fluid Cualquier sustancia que puede fluir.

freezing The change in state from a liquid to a solid. (p. 50)
congelación Cambio del estado líquido al sólido.

gamma radiation A type of nuclear radiation made of high-energy waves. (p. 141)
radiación gamma Tipo de radiación nuclear hecha de ondas de alta energía.

gas A state of matter with no definite shape or volume. (p. 47)
gas Estado de la materia sin forma ni volumen definidos.

glass A clear, solid material with no crystal structure, created by heating sand to a very high temperature. (p. 137)
vidrio Material sólido y transparente que no tiene estructura de cristal, creado al calentar arena a temperaturas muy altas.

graph A diagram that shows how two variables are related. (p. 62)
gráfica Diagrama que muestra la relación entre dos variables.

group Elements in the same vertical column of the periodic table; also called family. (p. 87)
grupo Elementos en la misma columna vertical de la tabla periódica; también llamado familia

half-life The length of time needed for half of the atoms of a sample of a radioactive isotope to decay. (p. 143)
vida media Tiempo que necesita la mitad de los átomos de una muestra de isótopo radiactivo para desintegrarse.

halogen An element found in Group 17 of the periodic table. (p. 103)
halógeno Elemento que se encuentra en el Grupo 17 de la tabla periódica.

heterogeneous mixture A mixture in which pure substances are unevenly distributed throughout the mixture. (p. 13)
mezcla heterogénea Mezcla en la cual las sustancias puras están distribuidas desigualmente.

homogeneous mixture A mixture in which substances are evenly distributed throughout the mixture. (p. 13)
mezcla homogénea Mezcla en la cual las sustancias químicas están distribuidas uniformemente.

International System of Units The system of units (SI) used by scientists to measure the properties of matter. (p. 17)
Sistema Internacional de Unidades Sistema de unidades usado por los científicos para medir las propiedades de la materia.

isotope An atom with the same number of protons and a different number of neutrons from other atoms of the same element. (p. 78)
isótopo Átomo con el mismo número de protones y un número diferente de neutrones que otros átomos del mismo elemento.

kinetic energy The energy of matter in motion. (p. 31)
energía cinética Energía de la materia en movimiento.

law of conservation of mass The principle that the total amount of matter is neither created nor destroyed during any chemical or physical change. (p. 25)
ley de conservación de masa Principio que enuncia que la cantidad de materia total no se crea ni se destruye durante cambios químicos o físicos.

liquid A state of matter that has no definite shape but has a definite volume. (p. 45)
líquido Estado de la materia que no tiene forma definida pero sí volumen definido.

malleable A term used to describe material that can be pounded into shapes. (p. 88)
maleable Término usado para describir el material al que se le puede dar forma.

mass A measure of how much matter is in an object. (p. 17)
masa Medida de cuánta materia hay en un objeto.

mass number The sum of protons and neutrons in the nucleus of an atom. (p. 78)
número de masa Suma de protones y neutrones en el núcleo de un átomo.

matter Anything that has mass and occupies space. (p. 6)
materia Cualquier cosa que tiene masa y ocupa un espacio.

melting The change in state from a solid to a liquid. (p. 49)
fusión Cambio del estado sólido a líquido.

melting point The temperature at which a substance changes from a solid to a liquid; the same as the freezing point, or temperature at which a liquid changes to a solid. (p. 49)
punto de fusión Temperatura a la que una sustancia cambia de estado sólido a líquido; es lo mismo que el punto de congelación (la temperatura a la que un líquido se vuelve sólido).

metal A class of elements characterized by physical properties that include shininess, malleability, ductility, and conductivity. (p. 88)
metal Clase de elementos caracterizados por las propiedades físicas que incluye brillo, maleabilidad, ductilidad y conductividad.

metalloid An element that has some characteristics of both metals and nonmetals. (p. 105)
metaloide Elemento que tiene algunas características de metales y de no metales.

mixture Two or more substances that are mixed together but not chemically combined. (p. 13)
mezcla Dos o más sustancias que están mezcladas, pero que no están combinadas químicamente.

model In science, a diagram, a mental picture, a mathematical statement, or an object that helps explain ideas about the natural world. (p. 79)
modelo En ciencias, un diagrama, una imagen mental, un enunciado matemático o un objeto que ayuda a explicar ideas sobre el mundo natural.

molecule A particle made of two or more atoms bonded together. (p. 11)
molécula Partícula formada de dos o más átomos unidos.

monomer One of the smaller molecules from which polymers are built. (p. 119)
monómero Una de las moléculas más pequeñas que componen un polímero.

nebula The cloudlike region of gases left over in the remains of a shrinking, sun-sized star. (p. 110)
nebulosa Región de gases parecida a una nube que queda como resto de una estrella del tamaño del sol en proceso de reducción.

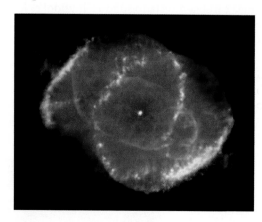

neutron A small particle in the nucleus of the atom, with no electrical charge. (p. 75)
neutrón Partícula pequeña en el núcleo del átomo, que no tiene carga eléctrica.

noble gas An element in Group 18 of the periodic table. (p. 104)
gas noble Elemento del Grupo 18 de la tabla periódica.

nonmetal An element that lacks most of the properties of a metal. (p. 99)
no metal Elemento que carece de la mayoría de las propiedades de un metal.

nuclear fusion The process in which two atomic nuclei combine to form a larger nucleus, forming a heavier element and releasing huge amounts of energy. (p. 109)
fusión nuclear Proceso en el cual dos núcleos atómicos se combinan para formar un núcleo mayor; forman un elemento más pesado y liberan grandes cantidades de energía.

nuclear reaction A reaction involving the particles in the nucleus of an atom that can change one element into another element. (p. 140)
reacción nuclear Reacción que involucra a las partículas en el núcleo de un átomo que puede transformar un elemento a otro.

nucleus The central core of an atom containing protons and usually neutrons. (p. 75)
núcleo Parte central del átomo que contiene protones y normalmente neutrones.

optical fiber A threadlike piece of glass (or plastic) that can be used for transmitting messages in the form of light. (p. 138)
fibra óptica Pieza de vidrio (o plástico) parecido a hilo que se puede usar para transmitir mensajes en forma de luz.

origin The (0, 0) point on a line graph. (p. 64)
origen Punto (0, 0) en una gráfica lineal.

particle accelerator A machine that moves atomic nuclei at higher and higher speeds until they crash into one another, sometimes forming heavier elements. (p. 94)
acelerador de partículas Máquina que mueve los núcleos atómicos a velocidades cada vez más altas hasta que chocan entre ellas, a veces forman elementos más pesados.

period A horizontal row of elements in the periodic table. (p. 86)
período Fila horizontal de los elementos en la tabla periódica.

periodic table A chart of the elements showing the repeating pattern of their properties. (p. 82)
tabla periódica Tabla de los elementos que muestra el patrón repetido de sus propiedades.

physical change A change in a substance that does not change its identity. (p. 23)
cambio físico Cambio en una sustancia que no cambia su identidad.

physical property A characteristic of a pure substance that can be observed without changing it into another substance. (p. 8)
propiedad física Característica de una sustancia pura que se puede observar sin convertirla en otra sustancia.

plasma A gas-like state of matter consisting of a mixture of free electrons and atoms that are stripped of their electrons. (p. 109)
plasma Estado de la materia similar al gas que consiste en la mezcla de electrones libres y átomos que son desprovistos de sus electrones.

plastic A synthetic polymer that can be molded or shaped. (p. 121)
plástico Polímero sintético que se puede moldear o se le puede dar forma.

polymer A large, complex molecule built from smaller molecules joined together in a repeating pattern. (p. 118)
polímero Molécula grande y compleja formada por moléculas más pequeñas que se unen en un patrón que se repite.

potential energy The energy an object has because of its position; also the internal stored energy of an object, such as energy stored in chemical bonds. (p. 31)
energía potencial Energía que tiene un objeto por su posición; también es la energía interna almacenada de un objeto, como la energía almacenada en los enlaces químicos.

pressure The force pushing on a surface divided by the area of that surface. (p. 57)
presión Fuerza que actúa contra una superficie, dividida entre el área de esa superficie.

proton A small, positively charged particle in the nucleus of the atom. (p. 75)
protón Partícula pequeña cargada positivamente, que se encuentra en el núcleo del átomo.

radioactive dating The process of determining the age of an object using the half-life of one or more radioactive isotopes. (p. 143)
datación radiactiva Proceso para determinar la edad de un objeto usando la vida media de uno o más isótopos radiactivos.

radioactive decay The process in which the atomic nuclei of unstable isotopes release fast-moving particles and energy. (p. 140)
desintegración radiactiva Proceso por el cual los núcleos atómicos de isótopos inestables liberan partículas de rápido movimiento y gran cantidad de energía.

radioactivity The spontaneous emission of radiation by an unstable atomic nucleus. (p. 140)
radioactividad Emisión espontánea de radiación por un núcleo atómico inestable.

reactivity The ease and speed with which an element combines, or reacts, with other elements and compounds. (p. 89)
reactividad Facilidad y rapidez con las que un elemento se combina, o reacciona, con otros elementos y compuestos.

semiconductor A substance that can conduct electricity under some conditions. (p. 105)
semiconductor Sustancia que puede conducir electricidad bajo algunas condiciones.

solid A state of matter that has a definite shape and a definite volume. (p. 43)
sólido Estado de la materia con forma y volumen definidos.

solution An example of a homogeneous mixture; forms when substances dissolve. (p. 13)
solución Ejemplo de una mezcla homogénea; se forma cuando las sustancias se disuelven.

sublimation The change in state from a solid directly to a gas without passing through the liquid state. (p. 53)
sublimación Cambio del estado sólido directamente a gas, sin pasar por el estado líquido.

substance A single kind of matter that is pure and has a specific set of properties. (p. 7)
sustancia Tipo único de materia que es pura y tiene un conjunto de propiedades específicas.

supernova An explosion of a massive star. (p. 111)
supernova Explosión de una estrella gigantesca.

surface tension The result of an inward pull among the molecules of a liquid that brings the molecules on the surface closer together; causes the surface to act as if it has a thin skin. (p. 46)
tensión superficial Resultado de la atracción hacia el centro entre las moléculas de un líquido, que hace que las moléculas de la superficie se junten más, y la superficie actúe como si tuviera una piel delgada.

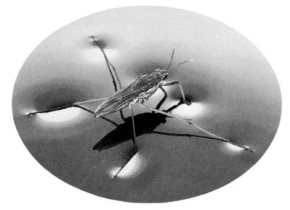

 T

temperature A measure of the average energy of motion of the particles of a substance. (p. 26)
temperatura Medida de la energía de movimiento de las partículas de una sustancia.

thermal energy The total energy of all the particles of an object. (p. 26)
energía térmica Energía total de las partículas de un objeto.

tracer A radioactive isotope that can be followed through the steps of a chemical reaction or industrial process. (p. 144)
trazador Isótopo radiactivo que se puede seguir mediante los pasos de una reacción química o proceso industrial.

transition metal One of the elements in Groups 3 through 12 of the periodic table. (p. 92)
metal de transición Uno de los elementos en los Grupos 3 a 12 de la tabla periódica.

 V

vaporization The change of state from a liquid to a gas. (p. 50)
vaporización Cambio del estado de líquido a gas.

vary inversely A term used to describe the relationship between two variables whose graph forms a curve that slopes downward. (p. 65)
variar inversamente Término empleado para describir la relación entre dos variables cuya gráfica forma una curva con pendiente hacia abajo.

viscosity A liquid's resistance to flowing. (p. 46)
viscosidad Resistencia a fluir que presenta un líquido.

volume The amount of space that matter occupies. (p. 18)
volumen Cantidad de espacio que ocupa la materia.

 W

weight A measure of the force of gravity on an object. (p. 17)
peso Medida de la fuerza de gravedad sobre un objeto.

Page numbers for key terms are printed in **boldface** type.
Page numbers for illustrations, maps, and charts are printed in *italics*.

Index

Index

Page numbers for key terms are printed in **boldface** type.
Page numbers for illustrations, maps, and charts are printed in *italics*.

Index

Page numbers for key terms are printed in **boldface** type.
Page numbers for illustrations, maps, and charts are printed in *italics*.

Index

Page numbers for key terms are printed in **boldface** type.
Page numbers for illustrations, maps, and charts are printed in *italics*.

Acknowledgments

Acknowledgment for page 155: "Rune of Riches" by Florence Converse from *Sung Under the Silver Umbrella: Poems for Young Children.* Copyright © 1937 by The Macmillan Company. Reprinted by permission of the Association for Childhood Education International.

Staff Credits

Scott Andrews, Jennifer Angel, Laura Baselice, Carolyn Belanger, Barbara A. Bertell, Suzanne Biron, Peggy Bliss, Stephanie Bradley, James Brady, Anne M. Bray, Kerry Cashman, Jonathan Cheney, Joshua D. Clapper, Lisa J. Clark, Bob Craton, Patricia Cully, Patricia M. Dambry, Kathy Dempsey, Emily Ellen, Thomas Ferreira, Jonathan Fisher, Patricia Fromkin, Paul Gagnon, Robert Graham, Ellen Granter, Barbara Hollingdale, Etta Jacobs, Linda Johnson, Anne Jones, John Judge, Kevin Keane, Kelly Kelliher, Toby Klang, Russ Lappa, Carolyn Lock, Rebecca Loveys, Constance J. McCarty, Carolyn B. McGuire, Ranida Touranont McKneally, Anne McLaughlin, Eve Melnechuk, Tania Mlawer, Janet Morris, Francine Neumann, Marie Opera, Jill Ort, Joan Paley, Dorothy Preston, Rashid Ross, Siri Schwartzman, Laurel Smith, Emily Soltanoff, Jennifer A. Teece, Diane Walsh, Amanda M. Watters, Merce Wilczek, Amy Winchester, Char Lyn Yeakley. **Additional Credits** Tara Allamilla, Terence Hegarty, Louise Gachet, Andrea Golden, Stephanie Rogers, Kim Schmidt, Joan Tobin.

Illustration

All art development by Morgan Cain and Associates.

Photography

Photo Research Sue McDermott
Cover image top, Thom Lang/Corbis; **bottom,** Arnold Fisher/Photo Researchers, Inc.

Page vi t, Brand X Pictures/Getty Images, Inc.; **vi bl,** Richard Megna/Fundamental Photographs; **vi bm,** Charles D. Winters/Photo Researchers, Inc.; **vi br,** Layne Kennedy/Corbis; **vii,** Richard Haynes; **viii,** Richard Haynes; **x inset,** Courtesy of Dr. Rathin Datta; **x,** Charlie Waite/Getty Images, Inc.; **1 both,** Courtesy of Dr. Rathin Datta; **2b,** Lisa Blumenfeld/Getty Images, Inc.; **2t,** Laszlo Selly/Getty Images, Inc.; **3tl,** Photo courtesy of Cargill Dow LLC; **3ml,** Photodisc/Getty Images, Inc.; **3bl,** Royalty-Free/Corbis; **3tr,** Photodisc/Getty Images, Inc.; **3br,** Courtesy of Dr. Rathin Datta; **3 car,** Alamy Images; **3 Rathin,** Courtesy of Dr. Rathin Datta.

Chapter 1

Pages 4–5, (c) Lawrence Migdale/PIX; **5 inset,** Richard Haynes; **6b,** Russ Lappa; **6t,** Richard Haynes; **7,** Russ Lappa; **8bl,** Norbert Wu/DRK Photo; **8r,** Richard Haynes; **8t,** Ted Kinsman/Photo Researchers, Inc.; **9l,** Walter Hodges/Getty Images, Inc.; **9m,** Mary Ellen Bartley/PictureArts/Corbis; **9r,** Layne Kennedy/Corbis; **10bl,** MVR Photo; **10r,** Corbis; **10tl,** Mahaux Photography/Getty Images, Inc.; **11,** Tim Ridley/Dorling Kindersley; **12tl,** Andrew Lambert Photography/SPL/Photo Researchers, Inc.; **12tr,** Ed Degginger/Color-Pic, Inc.; **12b,** Grant V. Faint/Getty Images, Inc.; **13b,** graficart.net/Alamy Images; **13t,** Michael Newman/PhotoEdit; **14 all,** Richard Haynes; **15 all,** Richard Haynes; **16 both,** Richard Haynes; **17l,** Russ Lappa; **17r,** Richard Haynes; **18,** Russ Lappa; **20,** Dorling Kindersley; **22,** Frans Lemmens/Getty Images, Inc.; **23bl,** Tony Freeman/PhotoEdit; **23br,** Photo Researchers, Inc.; **23t,** Richard Megna/Fundamental Photographs; **24,** Art Montes de Oca; **25,** Brand X pictures/Getty Images, Inc.; **26b,** Snaevarr Gudmundsson/Nordic Photos/Alamy Images; **26t,** Victoria Pearson/Getty Images, Inc.; **28–29,** Digital Vision/Getty Images, Inc.; **30,** Russ Lappa; **31l,** Richard R. Hansen/Photo Researchers, Inc.; **31r,** Mark Richards/PhotoEdit; **32,** Russ Lappa; **33,** Adam Jones/Photographer's Choice/Getty Images, Inc.; **34,** Richard Haynes; **35,** Richard Haynes; **36,** Corbis.

Chapter 2

Pages 40–41, Steve Bloom; **41 inset,** Richard Haynes; **42b,** LWA-Dann Tardif/Corbis; **42t,** Richard Haynes; **43,** James A. Sugar/Corbis; **44b,** Patrick J. LaCroix/Getty Images, Inc.; **44t,** S. Stammer/Photo Researchers Inc.; **45 all,** Richard Haynes; **46b,** Herman Eisenbeiss /Photo Researchers, Inc.; **46t,** Breck Kent/Earth Scenes; **48b,** Hubert Camille/Getty Images, Inc.; **48t,** Richard Haynes; **49l,** Breck P. Kent/Earth Scenes; **49m,** Chuck O'Rear/Corbis; **49r,** Leslie Harris/Index Stock; **50 both,** Richard Haynes; **51 both,** Dorling Kindersley/Science Museum; **52,** Tony Freeman/PhotoEdit; **53,** Charles D. Winters/Photo Researchers Inc.; **54,** Russ Lappa; **55,** Carl & Ann Purcell/Corbis; **56b,** MVR Photo; **56t,** Richard Hutchings/Corbis; **57 both,** Richard Haynes; **58,** Richard Haynes; **60 all,** Dorling Kindersley; **61,** Eye Ubiquitous/Corbis; **66,** Russ Lappa; **67,** Richard Haynes; **68b,** Eye Ubiquitous/Corbis; **68t,** S. Stammer/Photo Researchers, Inc.

Chapter 3

Pages 72–73, Greg Elms/Lonely Planet Images; **73 inset,** Richard Haynes; **74 both,** 1998, The Art Institute of Chicago; **76l,** Royalty-Free/Corbis; **76r,** Russ Lappa; **77l,** Dorling Kindersley; **77m,** Dorling Kindersley; **77r,** Frank Cezus/FPG International; **79,** courtesy of the National Institute of Science and Technology; **80b,** Richard Haynes; **80t,** Russ Lappa; **81bl,** Richard Megna/Fundamental Photographs; **81br,** Richard Megna/Fundamental Photographs; **81m,** Robert Mathena/Fundamental Photographs; **81t,** Philip Coblentz/Alamy Images; **83,** Photodisc/Getty Images, Inc.; **87,** Richard Megna/Fundamental Photos; **88,** Richard Haynes; **89b,** Cameron Davidson/Getty Images, Inc.; **89m,** Jeffrey L. Rotman/Corbis; **89t,** Dorling Kindersley; **90l,** Richard Megna/Fundamental Photographs; **90m,** Dorling Kindersley; **90r,** Eyewire/Getty Images, Inc.; **91,** Jeff Greenberg/PhotoEdit; **93b,** Richard Haynes; **93ml,** Christie's Images; **93mr,** Russ Lappa; **93t,** Richard Haynes; **94,** NASA/Johnson Space Center; **95l,** Stephen Marks/Getty Images, Inc.; **95r,** David Parker/Photo Researchers, Inc.; **96b,** Russ Lappa; **96t,** Richard Haynes; **97 both,** Richard Haynes; **98,** Kathy Bushue/Getty Images, Inc.; **99bl,** Lawrence Migdale/Science Source/Photo Researchers Inc.; **99br,** Dennis McDonald/PhotoEdit; **99t,** Bettmann/Corbis; **100b,** Charles D. Winters/Photo Researchers Inc.; **100t,** Grant Heilman Photography, Inc.; **101 inset,** Michael Newman/PhotoEdit; **101l,** David Porter/Index Stock; **101r,** Joseph Devenney/Getty Images, Inc.; **102l,** Novovitch/Liaison International; **102r,** Pete Oxford/Minden Pictures; **103l,** Mary Kate Denny/PhotoEdit; **103r,** Richard Megna/Fundamental Photographs; **104b,** A & L Sinibaldi/Getty Images, Inc.; **104t,** Michael Dalton/Fundamental Photographs; **105,** Andrew Syred/SPL/Photo Researchers Inc.; **107,** Grant V. Faint/Getty Images, Inc.; **108–09,** NASA; **109,** Celestron International; **110,** J.P. Harrington & K.J. Borkowski/NASA; **111,** NC: Science VU/ESO/Visuals Unlimited; **112,** Richard Megna/Fundamental Photographs.

Chapter 4

Pages 116–17, Paul Chesley/Getty Images, Inc.; **117 inset,** Jon Chomitz; **118,** John Terence Turner; **119,** Russ Lappa; **120l,** Joe McDonald/Corbis; **120m,** Royalty-Free/Corbis; **120r,** Larry Ulrich/DRK Photo; **121,** Superstock; **122l,** Corbis-Bettmann; **122m,** Chris Rogers/Corbis; **122r,** Terry Wild Studio/Uniphoto; **123l,** David Young-Wolfe/PhotoEdit; **123m,** Jeffry W. Myers/Corbis; **123r,** Courtesy of Dow Corporation; **124l,** Ariel Skelley/Corbis; **124r,** David Stoecklein/Corbis; **125,** Fred Habegger/Grant Heilman Photography; **126,** Daemmrich/Uniphoto; **127,** Richard Haynes; **128,** Richard Haynes; **129b,** Richard Megna/Fundamental Photographs; **129t,** 2004 Richard Megna/Fundamental Photographs; **130b,** Photodisc; **130t,** Russ Lappa; **131l,** Diana Calder/The Stock Market; **131r,** Royalty-Free/Corbis; **133bl,** Marc Pokempner/Corbis; **133bm,** Richard Haynes; **133br,** Dorling Kindersley; **133t,** William Hopkins; **134,** Chris Sorensen; **135,** M. Borchi White Star/Photo Researchers Inc.; **136l,** Dan McCoy/Rainbow; **136r,** Jacky Chapman/Alamy Images; **137,** James L. Amos/Peter Arnold; **138,** Ted Horowitz/Corbis; **139,** Jan Van Der Straet/Granger Collection; **140b,** Bettmann/Corbis; **140t,** Paul Silverman/Fundamental Photographs; **143,** T.A. Wiewandt/DRK Photo; **145b,** Reuters NewMedia Inc./Corbis; **145t,** RVI Medical Physics, Newcastle/Simon, Fraser/Science Photo Library; **146,** Robert Patrick/Corbis Sygma; **147,** Richard Megna/Fundamental Photographs; **148bl,** Photodisc/Getty Images, Inc.; **148br,** Robert Patrick/Corbis Sygma; **148t,** Superstock; **152b,** Colin Keates/Dorling Kindersley; **152–53,** Bob Burch/Index Stock Imagery; **153b,** The British Museum/Dorling Kindersley; **153m,** Kim Jae-Hwan/AFP/Corbis; **153t,** Rosenfeld Imaged Ltd/Rainbow; **154–55,** Ali Murat Atay/Atlas Geographic; **155,** Index Stock Imagery; **156t,** Winfield I. Parks/National Geographic Image Collection; **156b,** Photodisc/Getty Images, Inc.; **157b,** C.M. Dixon; **157t,** Royalty-Free/Corbis; **158,** Tony Freeman/PhotoEdit; **159b,** Russ Lappa; **159m,** Richard Haynes; **159t,** Russ Lappa; **160,** Richard Haynes; **162,** Richard Haynes; **164,** Morton Beebe/Corbis; **165,** Richard Haynes; **167b,** Richard Haynes; **167t,** Dorling Kinderlsey; **169,** Image Stop/Phototake; **172,** Richard Haynes; **179,** Richard Haynes; **180,** Richard Haynes; **184,** Dan McCoy/Rainbow; **185,** Tony Freeman/PhotoEdit; **186,** Snaevarr Gudmundsson/Nordic Photos/Alamy Images; **187,** Andrew Syred/SPL/Photo Researchers Inc.; **188b,** Tony Freeman/PhotoEdit **188t,** J.P. Harrington & K.J. Borkowski/NASA; **189,** Charles D. Winters/Photo Researchers, Inc.; **190,** Herman Eisenbeiss/Photo Researchers, Inc.